D1163148

Alternating Current
FUNDAMENTALS

PRENTICE-HALL
TECHNICAL-INDUSTRIAL-VOCATIONAL SERIES

Alternating Current FUNDAMENTALS

By

Joseph J. DeFrance, B.S.,E.E.

Head of Department of Electrical Technology
New York City Community College

Second Edition

PRENTICE-HALL, INC.

Englewood Cliffs, N. J., 1957

Library of Congress Catalog Card Number: 57-6243

PRINTED IN THE UNITED STATES OF AMERICA

02309

Preface to Second Edition

SINCE THE PUBLICATION of the first edition (which was written specifically for the electronics field) many requests were received for the addition of material that would make this text equally applicable to students in the "power" field. With this aim in mind—and without detracting from the original electronics goal—several chapters were expanded and new chapters were added to include:

1. Additional problems with power applications
2. Measurement of power—wattmeter
3. Reactive volt-amperes
4. Three-phase systems (balanced)
5. Power in three-phase systems
6. Unbalanced three-phase loads

This text is the outgrowth of courses given by the author at the United States Coast Guard Training Station at Groton, Conn., and presently being taught at the New York City Community College. The author has maintained the same conversational style that proved so successful in the first volume, the second edition of *Direct Current Fundamentals.*

Before a machinist or a carpenter is assigned to work in the production of an intricate finished product, he must learn what tools are used in his trade, when to use each to best advantage, and how to use them skillfully. Similarly, before a technician can apply himself to intelligent study, analysis, and maintenance of actual electrical and electronic circuits, he too must master the "tools of his trade." The alternating current fundamentals to be covered in this text together with the direct current fundamentals of the previous volume are the tools that the electronic technician will need.

Pre-requisite to the understanding of this volume is a good foundation in direct current principles, including inductance and capacitance (as covered in *Direct Current Fundamentals*). In addition, the student must have a good background in the principles of algebra and a basic knowledge of the elementary trigonometric functions. It is recommended that if *Direct Current Fundamentals* (or its equivalent) is used as a first course, a mathematics course covering the above phases, plus use of slide rule be included at the same time as preparation for *Alternating Current Fundamentals*.

The text is intended for use at the "technical institute" level—above high school. Engineering students will also find this book of value, in that it clearly presents the basic concepts so often lost in a maze of advanced mathematics.

The review problems at the end of each chapter serve a dual purpose—to summarize, in challenging form, the highlights of each chapter, and at the same time to check on the student's mastery of the chapter's contents.

The author wishes to acknowledge gratefully the assistance of Mr. Irving Kosow, Head of the Department of Electrical Technology at the Staten Island Community College, for his helpful suggestions for revision of this text and his review of the new chapters on three phase circuits.

JOSEPH J. DEFRANCE

Contents

CHAPTER 1

Introduction to Alternating Currents

WHEN ELECTRIC UTILITIES first started commercial distribution, the power supplied was primarily for lighting and the distribution system was a two-wire direct current (D.C.) system. The first problem they encountered was the choice of a suitable line voltage. They were faced with two conflicting considerations.

1. The higher the line voltage, the lower the current required to meet any given load demand. For example, assuming a load of 100 kw, if a 10-volt distribution system were used, the current required to meet this load would be

$$I = \frac{P}{E} = \frac{100{,}000}{10} = 10{,}000 \text{ amps}$$

On the other hand if the line voltage were raised to 1000 volts, the current required for the same load would drop to 100 amperes. Since the generator itself has resistance and the distribution lines between the generating station and the consumers have resistance, when current is delivered to the load, there will be voltage drops (IR) and power losses (I^2R). The higher the line voltage, the lower the current and therefore the lower the line drop and line losses, for any given load. High currents present another problem in that larger size feeders must be used and the installation and maintenance costs of the distribution system would be increased. From an economic point of view, the power company would prefer to use as high a line voltage as possible.

2. The second consideration in selecting the line voltage for the distribution system is safety. High voltages can endanger the lives of the consumers! From a safety point of view, the lower the line voltage the better.

Obviously some compromise was necessary between these two conflicting factors. And so, 120 volts was selected. It was not too dangerous and since the lighting load in those early years was quite small, the feeder currents and line losses were within tolerable limits.

Three-wire distribution system. The demand for electric power grew, and with the adoption of electric motors for industrial applications, it was no longer practical to meet the added power demand with a 120-volt distribution system. This led to the development of a three-wire distribution system (Fig. 1-1). Heavy industrial loads were supplied with 240 volts D.C. to reduce the current

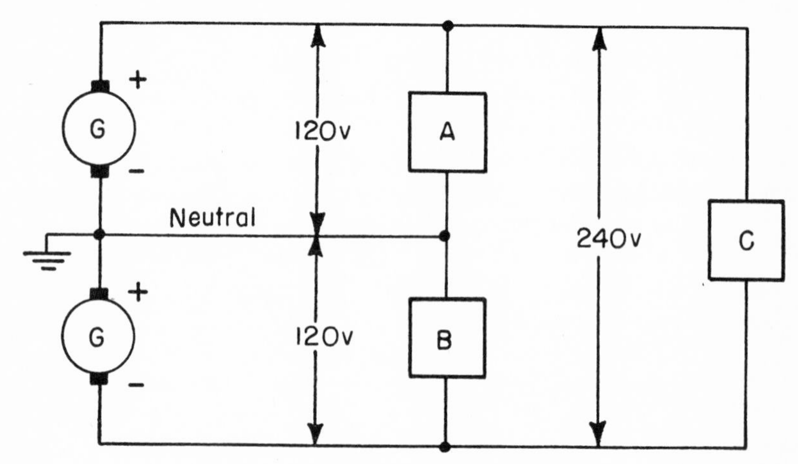

Fig. 1-1. Three-wire distribution system.

requirements, while lighting loads and residential loads were maintained at 120 volts. In Fig. 1-1, *A* and *B* represent lighting loads and *C* represents industrial machinery loads. It is interesting to note that if the lighting loads represented at *A* and *B* were perfectly balanced no current would flow in the neutral wire and it could be removed. However, in practice, perfect balance is impossible and the neutral wire does carry some current.

A.C. distribution systems. The above system proved to be only a temporary solution. More and more homes were electrified and in addition to lighting, electrical appliances came into use. Meanwhile industry, quick to realize the advantage of electric motors in stepping up production, also joined the bandwagon. The demand for electric power zoomed. How could this increased demand be satisfied and line currents still be kept within reason? Higher distribution voltages would solve the problem—but then what about safety? If high *distribution* voltage could be coupled with lower voltage at the consumer area, both aspects of the problem would be solved. This very desirable feature could be achieved by using an alternating current (A.C.) distribution system. With an A.C. supply, a device called a *transformer** can be used at the generating station to step up (increase) the generator voltage before feeding the transmission power lines. Then at the local consumer area another transformer can be used to step down (decrease) the voltage to safe values.

There was one fly in the ointment that prevented early adoption of the A.C. distribution system. Efficient motors with suitable characteristics were not available for operation on A.C. So conversion to A.C. distribution system had to wait till the induction motor was developed. From then on no new D.C. installations were made and gradually most of the earlier D.C. consumers have been converted to A.C. operation. In addition, with improvement in equipment design the actual generated voltage has been steadily increased and distribution voltages are still climbing.

By 1956 the highest generated voltage in the Consolidated Edison Company of New York stations was 13,800 volts and the distribution voltage was 138,000! In 1958 they expect to put into operation generators rated at 20,000 volts. Meanwhile, experimental distribution systems have been in operation at a voltage of 300,000 volts.

It is fantastic to realize the growth of the electric power industries since Thomas Edison first transmitted power for his electric light bulb. The total capacity of the electric utilities in the United States in 1955 was 116,328,000 kw. The Consolidated Edison Company of New York alone has a capacity of 3,690,000 kw and is planning to add two additional generators each rated at 335,000 kw to meet immediate future needs. Their long range plans include construction of additional plants and use of atomic energy for the primary source of power in place of coal or water power.

---

* Transformer action is not possible in D.C. circuits, since it depends on the voltage induced by varying magnetic fields (see Chapter 18, *Direct Current Fundamentals*, 2nd ed., by the author. Englewood Cliffs, N.J.: Prentice-Hall, Inc., 1955.)

The distribution system in use is almost entirely A.C. 60-cycles, three-phase, 4-wire.* The amount of D.C. distribution is less than 5 per cent and decreasing. In this connection it is interesting to note that all power generated by the power companies is A.C., and where they are obligated to maintain D.C. service they convert the A.C. to D.C. by electronic or rotating rectifiers.

Since ninety five per cent of the power delivered to consumers is A.C. it should be obvious why study of A.C. fundamentals and the behavior of circuit elements (resistors, inductors, and capacitors) on A.C. is necessary. This may set off another train of thought. Yes—study of A.C. is advisable for those interested in power, but how does it fit in if one's major interest is electronics? To explain this let us discuss in a general way a field of electronics, with which you are all familiar, and show how A.C. principles fit in with radio.

In a broad sense radio communications can be considered as a means of transmitting intelligent sounds to a large group of listeners over a wide area without interference from other sounds, intelligent or otherwise. A brief discussion of sound and its characteristics will follow. However, if the student has not already covered this subject in a physics course, any good book on physics is recommended for details.

Sound. Any sound that is created, whether it is speech, music, ringing of a bell, or just noise creates pressure changes in the air around the source of the sound. Normal air pressure is approximately 15 pounds per square inch. Sounds will cause the air pressure alternately to rise above normal, drop back to normal, drop below normal and again return to normal. This *cycle* or series of variation of air pressure changes is repeated over and over again as long as the sound continues. We can represent this by the pressure versus time curve shown in Fig. 1-2.

The louder the sound, the greater the change in pressure or the greater the amplitude of the sound wave. As the pressure of the air surrounding the sound source changes, it reacts on the air just beyond—pushing it, or allowing it to expand. So, the air pressure just beyond also rises above and falls below normal in accordance with the vibrations of the sound source. This effect is transmitted to air farther and farther away. In this manner pressure variations

* See Chapter 12.

travel outward from the sound source in all directions. Sound is transmitted through the air. When these varying air pressure waves strike a listener's ear, through the mechanism of the ear, nervous system, and brain—these pressure changes register as sounds.

Sound waves travel through the air at a speed of approximately 1100 feet per second. (This speed is affected by the temperature and barometric pressure of the air.) If the listener is located some distance from the sound source it will take time for the sound to reach him. The truth of this statement should be obvious. Have you ever watched a baseball game from the bleachers? You see

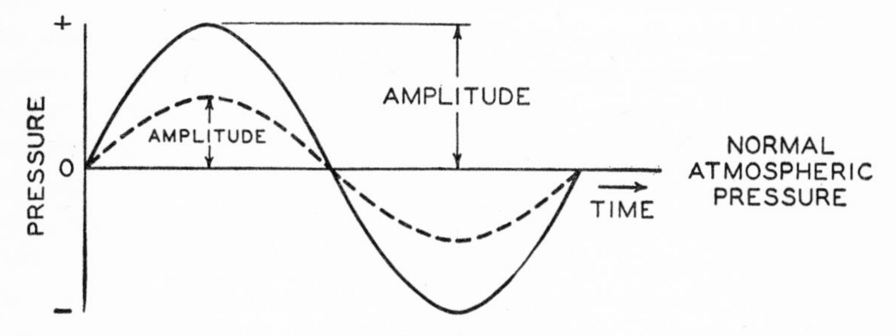

Fig. 1-2. Sound waves.

the batter hit the ball. A short time later you hear the crack of the bat. Another example is lightning followed later by thunder.

If a sound source creates 100 'cycles' of air pressure variations in 1 second, the sound is said to have a *frequency* of 100 cycles per second (cps). Such a sound would be recognized as a note of low pitch. A high-pitched sound, such as a whistle, might produce 10,000 cycles of pressure variations in one second. Its frequency would be 10,000 cps. The *audio frequency* range is from 20 to 20,000 cps. The term audio frequency is used to designate frequencies that can be heard (audible) directly by the human ear. Sounds below 20 cps are also audible, but they are heard as separate sounds (such as the staccato tappings of a woodpecker) rather than a continuous tone. Sound waves above 15,000 cps may not be audible to some people. Probably very few, if any, humans can hear 20,000 cps.

Musical instruments produce frequencies as low as 20 cycles ('per second' is often omitted, as being understood), and up to as high as 15,000 cycles. Yet if the frequencies below 50 and above 8000 cycles were lost, the sound would lose little of its quality. In fact, if only the frequencies between 100 and 5000 cycles were heard, musical instruments could be recognized and the quality, although not true, would still be acceptable. Real high-pitched sounds would of course be lost. For speech, the most important frequencies lie between 200 and 3000 cycles. However, speech does contain frequencies as low as 100 and as high as 10,000 cycles.

Obviously, the simplest way to transmit intelligent sounds (music or speech) to a group of listeners is to gather them into an auditorium or open space. Equally obvious is the fact that only a few people would hear these sounds. Special acoustically designed auditoriums, larger orchestras, or careful selection of speakers with loud, carrying voices would help, but the coverage would still be relatively low. For speech, a megaphone would help. In this way sounds that would normally be lost in back of the speaker are directed out to the audience, increasing the speech energy in the forward direction.

Audio amplifier systems. If we could amplify the sounds before transmitting them to the audience, we could reach larger groups of people. This can be done electronically by use of microphones, amplifiers, and loudspeakers. Such a system is shown in Fig. 1-3.

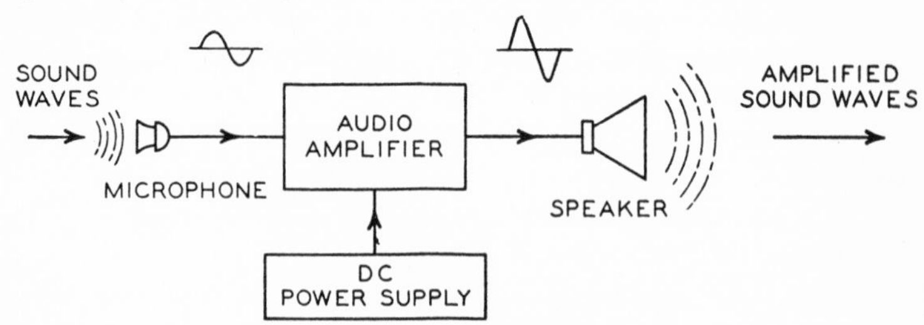

Fig. 1-3. Audio amplifier systems.

The microphone picks up the pressure-variation sound waves from the sound source and converts them into a varying electrical potential (or current). These potentials have the same frequencies as the frequencies produced by the original sound source, but they are very weak. The amplifier, by means of vacuum tube circuits, takes energy from the D.C. power supply and builds up the energy of these 'signals.' The amplified electrical signals are then fed to a loudspeaker that converts the variations in the potential of the electrical signals back into air pressure variations or sounds. The sounds coming from the loudspeaker will have the same characteristics as the original sounds. But now they are very much louder. In order to reproduce all sounds faithfully, each component of the amplifier system must be capable of passing all audio frequencies with equal efficiency. An ideal high-fidelity system should amplify all frequencies from 20 to 20,000 cycles without discrimination.

By use of such amplifier systems, the number of listeners that can be reached is greatly increased. Even so, the size of audience and the distance covered by amplifier systems is still quite restricted. You have heard public address systems, so you know their range limitations. To increase range by increasing the power of the amplifier beyond certain limits would make the sound levels, near the speaker, too loud to be comfortable.

Principle of radio communication. Suppose we could convert these sound waves into some other type of waves that could be transmitted through the air, and then, at many remote listening locations, reconvert these new waves back into sound waves! This would be a means of transmitting sound intelligence to a widely scattered audience. In this way the sound could not be heard except at the special listening points, and we would avoid the extremely loud sound levels near the original sound source. The problem is: what type of wave can travel through the air and be made to transmit sound?

If you have previously studied magnetism,* you must have learned that:

1. A wire carrying current produced a magnetic field.
2. Magnetic fields reached out into space.
3. Magnetic fields were energy fields.
4. If a conductor were located in a varying magnetic field, a voltage was induced in the conductor.
5. The greater the rate of cutting, the greater the induced voltage.

There it is, five simple steps—can you see what is coming? A microphone will convert sound waves into electrical potentials or currents. An audio amplifier will increase the energy of these electrical signals. With sufficient amplification, we can build these

---

* See Chapter 14, *Direct Current Fundamentals*.

signals up into very large currents varying in magnitude at the same frequency as the original sound source. Now these currents can be made to flow through a wire (transmitting antenna). The magnetic field around this wire will reach far out into space. The magnetic field strength will vary exactly with the variation in signal current and sound pressure. We have transmitted intelligence into space.

In this discussion, the electromagnetic waves transmitted were varying directly within the audio-frequency range. This results in a serious disadvantage.

If several different programs were being transmitted at the same time, the air would be filled with electromagnetic waves from different sound sources, all in the same frequency range of 20 to 20,000 cycles. The listener would hear all of these programs at the same time—bedlam!

Simple radio transmitter. The solution to the above problem is to transmit the electromagnetic waves at frequencies much higher than the audio frequencies themselves. This higher frequency is called the CARRIER frequency of the transmitting station. By assigning a different carrier frequency to each station, each program would then have its own private 'channel.' The listener can then select the channel he wishes to hear. This eliminates the bedlam of sounds produced when transmitting the audio-frequency waves directly.

Figure 1-4 shows, in block form, the basic equipment necessary for a radio transmitter.

Let us review the purpose of each unit.

1. *Oscillator:* This unit generates the much needed radio-frequency carrier wave. The oscillator circuit must have some means for 'tuning' it to the desired carrier frequency. (You will recall that each transmitting station should use a different channel or carrier frequency).

2. *R.F. Amplifier:* The output of any practical oscillator is rather weak. We must build up the energy in the carrier wave if we wish the electromagnetic field of the transmitter to reach far out into space. The purpose of the R.F. amplifier is to increase the energy or amplitude of the R.F. carrier to the required level.

3. *Microphone:* Converts sound (air pressure) waves into electrical waves of the same (audio) frequencies.

4. *Audio Amplifier:* Increases the energy or amplitude of the audio-frequency waves.

5. *Modulator:* Raises the audio intelligence to the desired high frequency. This process is known as *modulation*. Strong, modulated carrier-frequency currents are developed in the output of this stage.

6. *Transmitting Antenna:* Carries the strongly modulated carrier-frequency currents and allows the electromagnetic field around itself to reach out or *radiate* into space.

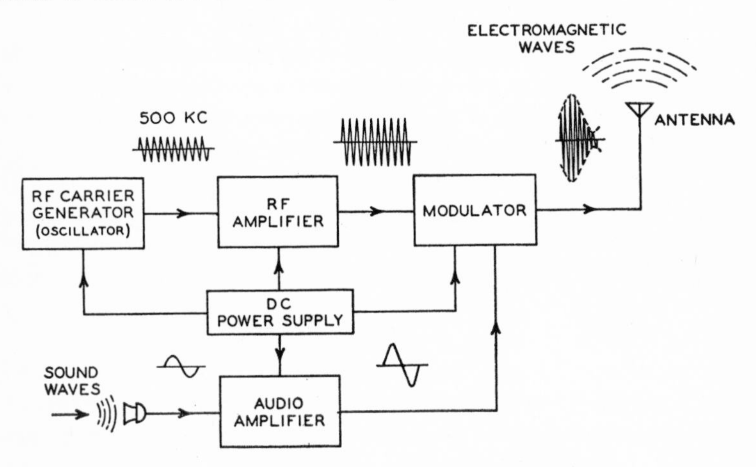

Fig. 1-4. Block diagram of a radio transmitter.

7. *D.C. Power Supplies:* In the various units of the transmitter, signals are generated or amplified by vacuum tube circuits. The energy needed for these functions is supplied by the D.C. power supplies. In general, power supplies are operated from A.C. house supply. They take energy from the A.C. line and convert it to A.C. or D.C. of proper voltage as required by the vacuum tubes. The vacuum tubes, in turn, take energy from the power supply and convert this energy into increased signal energy.

Simple radio receiver. Now that we have produced this modulated carrier wave and have sent it out into space as an electromagnetic wave, what are we going to do with it? Luckily it is not a 'Frankenstein'; we can control it and use it. However, it does require special equipment—a receiving system.

What must this receiver accomplish?

1. It must intercept these electromagnetic waves and convert them into varying electrical potentials. This is done by the receiving antenna. The antenna should be located in free space, where it can be cut by the electromagnetic waves of any transmitting stations in the area. The induced voltage in the antenna will have the same shape as the modulated carrier. Of which transmitting station? It will develop induced voltages for *all transmitting stations* within reach. But this sounds like bedlam again! No—each induced voltage will be of a different frequency, corresponding to the frequencies of the carriers from the various transmitters.

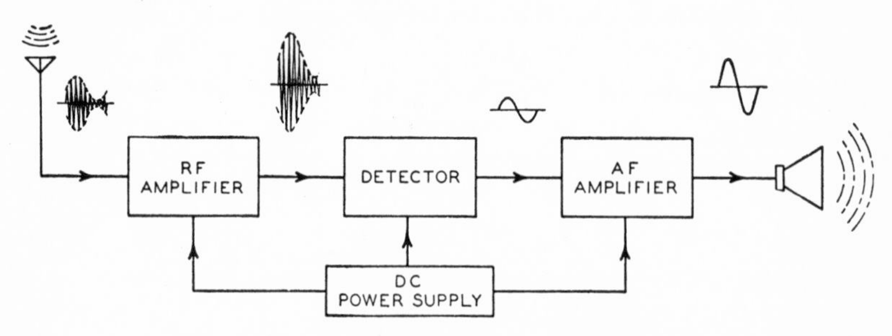

Fig. 1-5. Receiver block diagram.

2. The receiver must be able to select one carrier frequency at a time and reject all other carrier frequencies. This is done by the *radio-frequency tuner and amplifier.* By means of capacitors and inductors, the tuner can be made to select only one frequency. If either the capacitance or the inductance is variable, the frequency selected can be changed. Amplification is necessary in the tuner because the induced voltage in the antenna is very low. The signal strength must be built up to higher amplitudes. Since the signals are radio frequencies, this section of the receiver is called the *radio-frequency amplifier.*

3. The next step is to get rid of the carrier frequency and retain only the audio components of the modulated wave. This is done by the DETECTOR.

4. Now we have audio frequencies again, but they are too weak to drive a loudspeaker and produce sufficient volume. An audio-frequency amplifier will build up these audio signals to the required amplitude and energy.

5. Finally, a loudspeaker is used to convert these amplified audio-frequency electrical waves back into sound.

6. Again, a D.C. power supply is needed to supply the tubes in the above circuits with the energy that they will need to accomplish their specific purposes.

A block diagram of a receiver is shown in Fig. 1-5.

Radio frequency bands. In transmitting radio waves, we have shown that the carrier frequency used must be higher than audio frequencies. The transmitter used as an illustration had a carrier frequency of 500 kc. What other frequencies are used for electronic work? The radio frequency spectrum has been divided into 5 bands depending on the characteristics of these frequencies. These bands are shown in Table 1.

TABLE 1

Band	Frequency	Range		Power Required
		Day	Night	
Low Frequency (L.F.)	30–300 kc	Long	Long	Very high
Medium Frequency (M.F.)	300–3000 kc	Medium	Long	High to medium
High Frequency (H.F.)	3–30 mc	Short	Medium to long	Medium
Very High Frequency (V.H.F.)	30–300 mc	Short	Short	Low
Ultra High Frequency (U.H.F.)	300–3000 mc	Short	Short	Low

Radio frequencies extend beyond the limit of 3000 megacycles (mc) shown in the table. Electronic equipment is already operating at frequencies around 30,000 mc, and development work is being done at even higher frequencies. The radio frequency spectrum extends as high as 500,000 mc, although little is known about the characteristics of these 'super-high' frequencies.

We have discussed two types of waves and have given their frequency range (air pressure or sound waves—20 to 20,000 cycles, and electromagnetic or radio waves—30 kc to 500,000 mc). Notice that the radio waves start just about where the sound waves leave off. You may have heard of SUPERSONIC waves. These are sound waves just above the human audibility range. They occupy the region between audible sound waves and radio waves.

From the preceding, it is not surprising to learn that there are other types of waves occupying the region above radio waves. To make the wave-spectrum picture complete, these waves will be listed with their approximate frequencies:

1. *Heat waves*—from 5×10^{13} cycles to 1.5×10^{14} cycles.
2. *Light waves* (from infrared to ultraviolet)—from 1.5×10^{14} cycles to 1×10^{15} cycles.
3. *X-rays*—from 5×10^{16} cycles to 1.5×10^{20} cycles.

You may have noticed that there still are 'holes' in this frequency spectrum. At present little is known about waves in these regions.

Review Problems

1. (a) What is the advantage of high voltage in a distribution system?
(b) What is the advantage of low voltage?

2. Why was the three-wire D.C. distribution system preferable to the simple two-wire system?

3. (a) Explain briefly the advantage of an A.C. distribution system over D.C.
(b) What device makes this advantage possible?

4. (a) What type of distribution system is in common use today?
(b) What maximum distribution voltage is being planned?

5. (a) What is a sound wave?
(b) Describe how sound is transmitted through the air.

6. (a) What is the difference between a low-frequency and high-frequency sound? Give an example of each.
(b) What determines the amplitude of a sound wave?

7. (a) What is the frequency range of sound waves?
(b) What is the minimum frequency band for acceptable musical reproduction?
(c) What is the frequency band for high-fidelity reproduction?

8. Name the components of an audio amplifier system and give the function of each component.

9. What are the advantages of radio communication over direct sound communication?

10. (a) What is meant by carrier frequency?

(b) Why is it necessary to use a carrier frequency for radio communication?

11. Name the components of a simple radio transmitter and describe briefly the purpose of each component.

12. Name the components of a simple receiver and state briefly the function of each component.

13. What frequency bands are normally used for radio frequency transmission?

CHAPTER 2

Characteristics of Sine Waves

ELECTRICAL AND ELECTRONIC COURSES usually start with a study of direct currents.* Why? Electronic devices contain many D.C. circuits; vacuum tubes are operated with D.C. potentials; the energy gained by an R.F. or A.F. signal when it is amplified comes from a D.C. supply. In the preceding chapter we saw that the signals themselves are not D.C.—they vary in amplitude. They are classified as some form of alternating current. So now, in order that we may understand electronic circuits, we must first study alternating currents (A.C.) and the behavior of circuit components on A.C. The simplest type of A.C. wave is the SINE WAVE.

Generation of sine waves. If a conductor is rotated in a magnetic field, the conductor cuts the lines of force and a voltage is induced in the wire. But we know that the induced voltage varies with the rate of cutting and that the polarity of the induced voltage depends on the direction of cutting. Even though the speed of rotation is constant, the rate of cutting and the direction of cutting at any instant will depend on the position of the conductor. Figure 2-1 shows eight positions of a conductor as it is rotated in a magnetic field.

Position 1: The conductor is starting to move up. At this instant it is moving parallel to the magnetic field. Rate of cutting is zero, and the induced voltage is zero.

Position 2: The conductor is moving up. At this instant it has rotated through 45 degrees. It is now cutting the magnetic field, but it is cutting at a 45-degree angle. The rate of cutting has increased, but it has not reached a maximum. A voltage will be induced in the wire. This voltage is not at its maximum value; it is still rising. Since the conductor is moving up, the polarity of the induced electromotive force (emf) is such as to make the far end of the conductor positive and the near end negative. Check this polarity by means of Lenz's law or Fleming's hand rule.

Position 3: The conductor has now rotated through 90 degrees and is moving perpendicular to the field. The rate of cutting is maximum. The induced voltage is also at its maximum value. Since the conductor is still

* *Direct Current Fundamentals.*

moving up, the polarity, as before, will make the far end of the conductor positive and the near end negative.

Position 4: The conductor has rotated through 135 degrees. It is again cutting at a 45-degree angle. The rate of cutting has dropped and is dropping further. The induced voltage will be the same as for position 2, but now it is decreasing. Since the conductor is still moving up, the polarity has not changed.

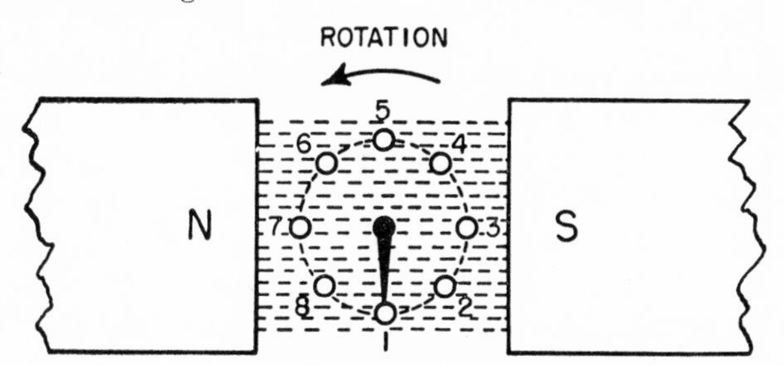

Fig. 2-1. Variation of speed of cutting with conductor position.

Position 5: The conductor has turned through 180 degrees. It is moving parallel to the lines of force—rate of cutting is zero; induced voltage is zero. The conductor is now starting to move down through the magnetic field.

Position 6: The angle through which the conductor has rotated is 225 degrees. Again the wire is cutting the field at an angle of 45 degrees. The induced voltage will have the same magnitude as in position 2. But this time the wire is moving down through the magnetic field. The polarity has reversed—the far end of the wire is now negative.

Position 7: The conductor has rotated through 270 degrees. It is cutting directly across the lines of force. The rate of cutting is maximum; the induced voltage is maximum. (Compare this with position 3.) Since the wire is moving down through the field, its far end is negative.

Position 8: The conductor has rotated through 315 degrees and is cutting the field at a 45-degree angle. The value of induced voltage is the same as for position 2. The speed of cutting is dropping; the induced voltage is also dropping. Since the conductor is still moving down, the polarity of the induced voltage will make the far end of the conductor negative.

Position 1: The coil has completed one revolution. It is again moving parallel to the lines of force. The induced voltage will be zero.

With each succeeding revolution, the process just described in detail will take place: The induced voltage will vary in magnitude from zero to some maximum value; back to zero; reverse in polarity and rise to maximum value; back to zero; reverse in polarity; and repeat this sequence of events over and over again.

You may have noticed that:

1. Between zero and 90-degree rotation, the voltage is rising to its maximum value.
2. At 90 degrees the voltage is a maximum.
3. Between 90 and 180 degrees, the voltage is dropping back to zero.
4. At 180 degrees the voltage is again zero.
5. Between 180- and 270-degrees rotation the voltage is again rising to a maximum.
6. At 270 degrees the voltage is again a maximum.
7. Between 270 and 360 degrees the voltage is again dropping back to zero.
8. At 360 (zero) degrees the voltage is once more zero.
9. Between zero and 180 degrees the potential of the far end of the conductor is positive.
10. Between 180 and 360 degrees the potential of the far end of the conductor is negative.

But this variation in potential is exactly the same relation as the variation of the sine of an angle between zero and 360 degrees! Check these sine values with a trigonometric table. In other words the voltage induced in a conductor at any instant during its rotation is some portion of its maximum value, depending on the sine of the angle through which the coil has rotated. From this we can write the equation for the instantaneous voltage (e) induced in the conductor:

$$e = E_{max} \sin \theta$$

where θ is the angle through which the coil has rotated. Since this is the equation of a sine curve, the potential developed in the conductor is referred to as a *sine wave*.

In commercial generators one conductor alone would not develop sufficiently high voltages. Since the magnitude of induced voltages depends on the number of turns that are being cut by the magnetic field, generators use coils of many turns instead of a single conductor. This method of generating alternating currents is used for power work (machinery, lighting, etc.) where the frequency is comparatively low (60 cycles). In electronic applications where the frequencies are much higher, sine waves are generated by vacuum tube circuits called *oscillators.* Carrier frequencies used by transmitting stations are sine waves.

Plotting of sine waves. There are two methods by which we can plot the curve for the sine wave of induced voltage. They are best illustrated by an example.

EXAMPLE 1

A generator develops 100 volts as its maximum value. Plot the curve for the instantaneous value of induced voltage versus degrees of rotation.

SOLUTION A: Trigonometric Plot.

Using the equation $e = E_{max} \sin \theta$, calculate the value of e for several values of the angle θ. The more points used, the more accurate the plot. Let us use 30-degree intervals.

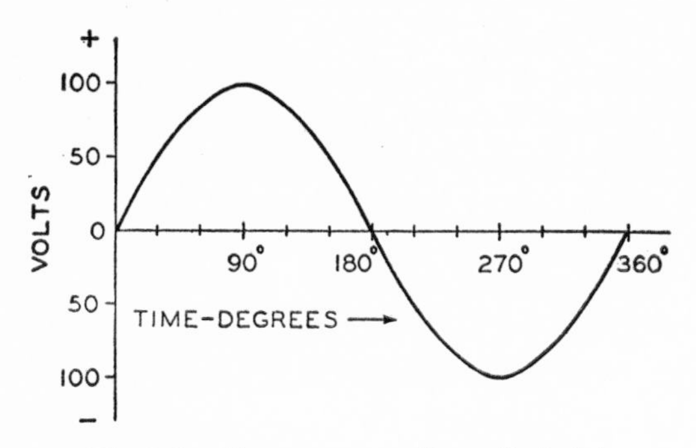

Fig. 2-2. Sine wave—mathematical plot.

θ	0	30	60	90	120	150	180
$\sin \theta$	0.00	0.500	0.866	1.00	0.866	0.500	0.00
e	0.00	50.0	86.6	100	86.6	50.0	0.00

θ	210	240	270	300	330	360
$\sin \theta$	−0.500	−0.866	−1.00	−0.866	−0.500	0.00
e	−50.0	−86.6	−100	−86.6	−50.0	0.00

SOLUTION B: Radius Vector Method.

This is a graphical solution. Pick a scale suitable to the size of paper you will use for the plot. As in all graphical solutions, the larger the scale, the more accurate the plot. Using the value of E_{max} as a radius, draw a circle. Since our plot is to be for 30-degree intervals, draw radii every 30 degrees. The vertical projection of these radii is equal to the sine value for the respective angles. Since the radius itself is E_{max}, each vertical projection is equal to $E_{max} \sin \theta$ or e!

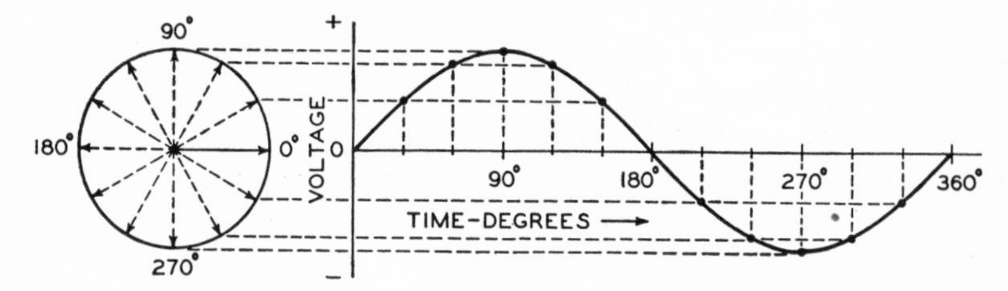

Fig. 2-3. Sine wave—graphical plot.

Cycle. With every revolution of a coil in a magnetic field, the induced-voltage wave goes through the series of variations shown in Figs. 2-2 and 2-3. Since it is a repetitive or periodic function, one complete series of events (the wave shape corresponding to one revolution) is called a CYCLE. Figure 2-4 shows three cycles of a sine wave.

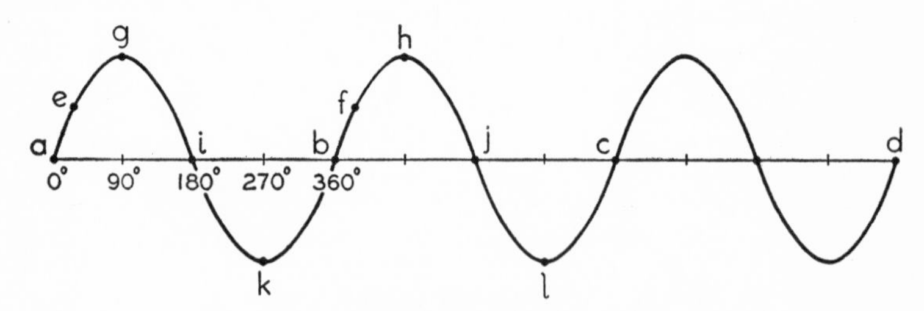

Fig. 2-4. Sine wave—showing cycles.

It is obvious from our definition of a cycle that distances *a-b*, *b-c*, and *c-d* each represent one cycle; also that *a-c* is two cycles, and *a-d* is three cycles. A cycle does not have to start at zero degrees and end at 360 degrees. A cycle can be measured from any point in 1 revolution of the coil to the corresponding point in the next revolution. For example: *g-h* is 1 cycle (90-degree point to 90-degree point); *i-j* is 1 cycle (180-degree point to 180-degree point); similarly, *k-l* is 1 cycle and *e-f* is 1 cycle!

How many cycles does *g-k* represent? Since it is 90 to 270 degrees of the same revolution, it is only $\frac{1}{2}$ cycle. How about *a-h*? One complete cycle from *a-b* plus $\frac{1}{4}$ cycle from *b-h*, or a total of $1\frac{1}{4}$ cycles. Similarly, *a-l* would be $1\frac{3}{4}$ cycles, and *i-d* would be $2\frac{1}{2}$ cycles.

Frequency and angular velocity. The frequency of any wave is a measure of how many cycles are produced in 1 second. For example, in the two pole machine of Fig. 2-1, if the generating coil made 1 revolution in 1 second, and since it produces 1 cycle in 1 revolution, the frequency of the sine wave would be 1 cycle per second. If the speed of rotation were 100 revolutions per second the frequency would be 100 cycles per second. What would be the frequency of the sine wave produced, if the speed of rotation were 1200 revolutions *per minute?* 1200 rpm would mean 20 revolutions *per second*, or 20 cycles per second.

It is obvious that frequency is directly related to speed of rotation, or the angular velocity of the rotating coil. There are a number of ways of expressing angular velocity. You have already seen one way: revolutions per second (rps) or revolutions per minute (rpm). In its basic form, angular velocity is a measure of the angle through which the coil has rotated per unit time. Angular velocity can therefore be expressed in degrees per second, or preferably in radians per second. When measured in radians per second, angular velocity is denoted by the Greek letter omega (ω).

You may be wondering, "What is a radian?" To explain this we have to go back to some simple geometry. Figure 2-5(a) shows

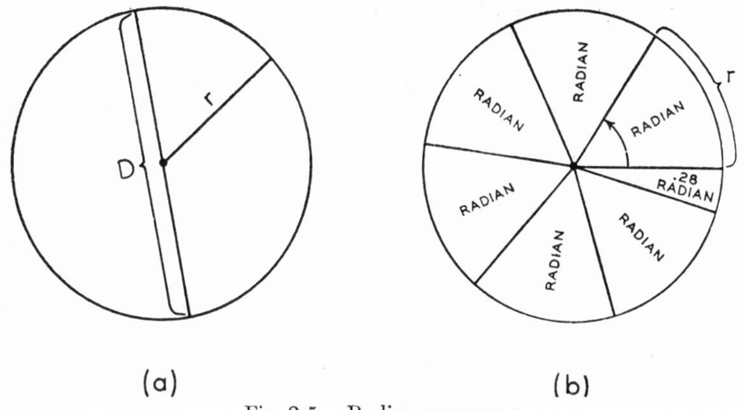

Fig. 2-5. Radian measure.

a circle with radius *r* and diameter *D*. If we use the diameter as a flexible measuring tape we would find that the circumference of the circle (C) is a little longer than three times the diameter, the exact value being 3.14159+ times the diameter. This ratio (approximately 3.14) is true for any circle. For convenience, this ratio, since it is constant, is assigned the symbol π (pi). Expressing the above relationship by formula we get:

$$C = \pi D$$

or in terms of the radius

$$C = 2\pi r$$

Now let us divide the circumference into arcs equal in length to the radius, and join the ends of each arc to the center of the circle. The angle subtended at the center of the circle by an arc equal in length to the radius is called a *radian*. Since the circumference of the circle equals $2\pi r$, there must be 2π radians (or approximately 6.28 radians) in a circle. But we know that there are 360 degrees in a circle. Therefore 2π radians equals 360 degrees; π radians equals 180 degrees; and 1 radian equals $180/\pi$, or approximately 57.3 degrees.

EXAMPLE 2

Change 1.5 radians into degrees.

SOLUTION

1. A radian = $180/\pi$ degrees, or radians $\times \dfrac{180}{\pi}$ = degrees.

2. 1.5 radians $= \dfrac{1.5 \times 180}{\pi} = 86°$.

EXAMPLE 3

A coil has rotated through 210 degrees. What is this angle in radians?

SOLUTION

1. The numerical answer in radians must be smaller.

2. Radians = degrees $\times \dfrac{\pi}{180} = \dfrac{210\pi}{180}$ = 3.67 radians.

Now let us get back to angular velocity. What is the relation between angular velocity and frequency? If a coil is generating a sine wave of 60 cps, it must be making 60 rps. Since each revolution is 2π radians, the angular velocity is:

$$\omega = 2\pi \times 60 = 377 \text{ radians per second}$$

Since frequency and revolutions per second are equal, angular velocity is directly proportional to frequency, or

$$\omega = 2\pi f$$

You might be wondering, how do frequency and angular velocity apply to a sine wave? Previously we developed the equation for the voltage at any instant as $e = E_{max} \sin \theta$, where θ was the angle through which the coil has turned at any instant. The angle θ must depend on the angular velocity of the coil and the time that the coil has been rotating (t).

$$\theta = \omega t$$

An example will best tie this all together.

Example 4

An A.C. generator produces a sine wave having a frequency of 60 cycles and a maximum value of 100 v. What is the voltage developed at 0.005 second?

Solution

1. $\omega = 2\pi f = 2\pi \times 60 = 377$ radians per sec.
2. $\theta = \omega t = 377 \times 0.005 = 1.89$ radians.
3. $\theta = 57.3 \times 1.89 = 108$ degrees and $\sin \theta = 0.951$.
4. $e = E_{max} \sin \theta = 100 \times 0.951 = 95.1$ v.

From the above discussion, particularly since we have shown that $\theta = \omega t$, the equation of instantaneous voltage for a sine wave can now be written as:

$$e = E_{max} \sin \omega t$$

This form of the equation is more commonly used since it expresses frequency ($\omega = 2\pi f$) and time.

In Figs. 2-2 and 2-3 we plotted the equation for the instantaneous voltage of a sine wave ($e = E_{max} \sin \theta$). The plot was for voltage versus angle of rotation. Since time (in seconds) was not involved in the equation, such a plot would represent a sine wave of any frequency. Based on our new equation ($e = E_{max} \sin \omega t$), we can now plot a sine wave as voltage versus *time*. As an illustration let us plot a sine wave having a frequency of 10 cps. The time for 1 cycle will be $1/f$ or 0.1 second. A half-cycle (180 degrees) would require 0.05 second; a quarter-cycle (90 degrees) would take 0.025 second. A plot for this sine wave is shown in Fig. 2-6.

What is the advantage in plotting sine waves against time instead of degrees? Plotted in degrees, 1 cycle would be 360 degrees, regardless of frequency. It would be impossible to show the relation between two or more sine waves of different frequency! On the other hand, look at Fig. 2-6. The solid curve was the 10 cps sine wave. Now notice the dotted curve. It completes 1 cycle in 0.05 second. Its frequency is 20 cps. Sine waves of any other frequency could be plotted on the same axis for com-

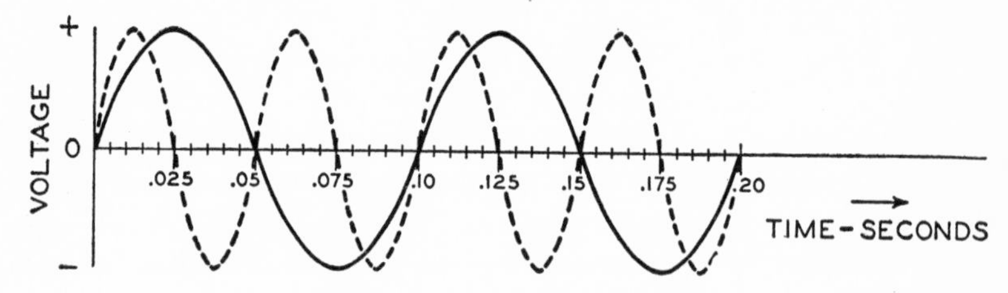

Fig. 2-6. Sine waves of 10 and 20 cycles per second.

parison. Since such comparisons are necessary, sine waves are generally plotted with time as the horizontal axis.

When referring to the frequency of any sine wave, the unit is cycles per second. However, as we did in our review of sound, the 'per second' is dropped and frequency is usually referred to as 50 cycles, 1000 cycles, 10,000 cycles, etc., the 'per second' being understood.

Sine wave values. All A.C. calculations are based on sine waves. In our discussion so far we have only mentioned voltage; however, the resultant currents that flow and the power that is expended is also sine wave in nature. There are four values of these sine waves that are of particular importance. We have already discussed two.

1. *Instantaneous Value:* The voltage, in an A.C. circuit is continuously changing. The value at any instant is represented by the lower-case letter (e) and is given by the equation of its curve (for example, $e = E_{max} \sin \omega t$). This value varies from zero to a maximum with time, depending on frequency (remember that $\omega = 2\pi f$). But since the voltage is continuously changing, the current flowing through the circuit and the power dissipated in the circuit must

also vary correspondingly. The instantaneous values of current and power are also represented by lower-case letters (i, p) and are obtained from their equations:

$$i = I_{max} \sin \omega t$$

or

$$p = P_{max} \sin \omega t$$

2. *Maximum Value:* For two brief instants in each cycle the sine wave reaches a maximum value. This value is represented by a capital letter and the subscript 'max' (E_{max}, I_{max}, P_{max}). It is often also referred to as the PEAK value. The two terms have identical meanings and are interchangeable.

3. *Average Value:* Since the instantaneous value of a sine wave is constantly changing, and since the maximum value occurs only twice in each cycle, it is often desirable to know what is the average value of a sine wave. As for any average, this value can be found by adding the individual values and dividing by the number of individual values. In the case of a sine wave, the individual values are the instantaneous values. But there are an infinite number of instantaneous values in 1 cycle of a sine wave! How many should be used? The more values averaged, the more accurate the final answer. The average of the instantaneous values taken every 10 degrees should be sufficient (every 15 or 30 degrees would require less work, but would not be as accurate).

If the average for a full cycle were taken, the answer would be zero. This is mathematically correct since the two half-cycles are identical, but the values for the second half-cycle are all negative, and the total sum of the instantaneous values would be zero. This answer seems to contradict statements made in other texts, where the average value is given as 0.636 of the maximum value. Such an interpretation is really a special case applicable to pure sine waves only. It was developed before complex waves were fully understood and does not consider the true meaning of 'average value.' The origin of this *conventional* average value of a sine wave is as follows: An electric current will do work regardless of the direction of the electron flow through the circuit. The negative half-cycle of a sine wave does just as much work as the positive half-cycle. For this reason, when speaking of the 'average' value of a *sine wave,* it is generally understood to mean the average value *regardless of the sign or direction of the voltage or current.* Since each half-cycle is identical, the average value of the positive or negative half-cycle will be the same. So—when finding this *conventional average value,* only half the cycle need be considered. *This special treatment can be used only when dealing with sine waves.* The importance of this statement will be seen when studying wave shapes other than sinusoidal, because the direction of current or the polarity of voltage cannot be ignored. Under such conditions remember: The actual mathematical average value of a sine wave for the full cycle is zero. Now let us apply this idea of conventional average value to a problem.

EXAMPLE 5

Find the average value of a sine wave of voltage, whose maximum value is 100 v.

SOLUTION

There are two methods possible:

(a) Plot the curve to any desired scale. Then measure the instantaneous values for every so many degrees (10, 15, or 20) or—

(b) Calculate the instantaneous values from the equation $e = 100 \sin \theta$.

The latter method will be used, and values will be taken every 10 degrees.

Degrees	$\sin \theta$	e	e^2
10	0.1736	17.4	303
20	0.3420	34.2	1179
30	0.5000	50.0	2500
40	0.6428	64.3	4135
50	0.7660	76.6	5867
60	0.8660	86.6	7500
70	0.9397	94.0	8836
80	0.9848	98.5	9722
90	1.0000	100.0	10000
100	0.9848	98.5	9722
110	0.9397	94.0	8836
120	0.8660	86.6	7500
130	0.7660	76.6	5867
140	0.6428	64.3	4135
150	0.5000	50.0	2500
160	0.3420	34.2	1179
170	0.1736	17.4	303
180	0.000	0.0	0
Sum..................................		1143.2	90084

NOTE: Disregard the last column (e^2); this will be used later.

Since we have a total of 18 values of e, the average value is equal to $1143.2/18 = 63.6$ v.

In this problem, the average value is 63.6% of the maximum value.

Had we started with a sine wave having a maximum value of 10 volts, the average value would have been 6.36 volts, or again 63.6% of E_{max}. This is not a coincidence. This relation is true for all sine waves regardless of amplitude and regardless of frequency.

$$\text{average value} = 0.636 \times \text{maximum value}$$

Average values are represented by capital letters with subscript 'av' (E_{av}, I_{av}, P_{av}).

Now that the relation between average and maximum values has been established, it is a simple matter to find the average value of any sine wave.

EXAMPLE 6

Find the average value of a sine wave of current having a maximum value of 15 amperes (amps).

SOLUTION

$$I_{av} = 0.636 I_{max} = 0.636 \times 15 = 9.54 \text{ amps.}$$

This same relation can be used to find the maximum value when the average value is known.

$$\text{maximum value} = \frac{\text{average value}}{0.636}$$

Inadvertently you may sometimes divide by 0.636 instead of multiplying (or vice-versa) in converting from one value to the other. The error should be immediately obvious, because you will end up with a maximum value that is SMALLER than the average value. This is impossible, and failure to correct such errors is inexcusable.

4. *Effective or rms Value:* In any given D.C. circuit, the voltage and current are constant. The power dissipated in the resistance of the circuit can be calculated from E^2/R or I^2R. What single value of E and I should be used for a similar A.C. circuit? Instantaneous and maximum values are definitely not the proper values. If we use the average value to find the power dissipated, the answer obtained is LESS than the actual power consumption. Looking at the power equations again, we notice that the power dissipated

as heat depends on the *square* of the voltage or current. To get the same heating effect as with D.C., the value of E and I chosen for an A.C. circuit should be obtained from the square of the instantaneous values. The procedure is similar to that used in Example 5 (page 24). For convenience we will use the same data.

EXAMPLE 7

Find the effective value of a sine wave of voltage whose maximum value is 100 v.

SOLUTION

(a) Find the instantaneous values of voltage for every 10 degrees for a half-cycle (Columns 1, 2, and 3, Example 5, page 24).

(b) Square each of these instantaneous values (Column 4, page 24).

(c) Find the sum of these squared values (90,084 from page 24).

(d) Find the average or 'mean' of these squared values. (Since there are 18 values in all, the average squared value is 90,084 ÷ 18, or 5003.)

(e) Find the square root of this average (or mean squared value):

$$\sqrt{5003} = 70.7 \text{ v}$$

A sine wave voltage of 100-v maximum would produce the same heating effect in a circuit as a steady voltage (D.C.) of 70.7 v. The 70.7 v is therefore called the EFFECTIVE VOLTAGE. From the method by which this value was found (square root of the mean of the squared values), this term is also called the ROOT MEAN SQUARE (rms) VALUE. Effective (rms) values are represented by capital letters without subscript (E, I).

In the above example, the effective value was found to be 70.7% of the maximum value. This relation is true for all sine waves regardless of maximum value and regardless of frequency.

$$\text{effective value} = 0.707 \times \text{maximum value}$$

EXAMPLE 8

House voltage for lighting purposes has an rms value of 115 v. What is the peak value?

SOLUTION

$$E_{max} = \frac{E}{0.707} = \frac{115}{0.707} = 163 \text{ v}$$

Sometimes the equation for maximum voltage is given as $E_{max} = 1.414E$. This is the same thing, i.e., $1/0.707 = 1.414$! It is easier to remember only one constant (0.707). Whether to divide or multiply by 0.707, use your common sense. Remember that the maximum value must be larger than the effective value.

In general, ammeters and voltmeters for use in A.C. circuits are calibrated to read effective values. Instruments are also specially made to indicate peak values or sometimes average values. However, unless otherwise specified, current and voltage values for A.C. circuits should be understood to be effective (rms) values. The importance of understanding this relationship between the rms and maximum values of a sine wave cannot be overemphasized, because although equipment for use on A.C. is commonly rated in rms values, the equipment must be capable of withstanding the full peak value.

Since there is a fixed relation between the maximum and effective values, and also between the maximum and average values, it follows that there must also be a fixed relation between effective and average values. The effective value is higher than the average value (70.7% as compared to 63.6%). The relation between them is the ratio of these constants:

$$70.7 \div 63.6 \quad \text{or} \quad 1.11 \quad \text{or:}$$
$$\text{effective value} = 1.11 \times \text{average value.}$$

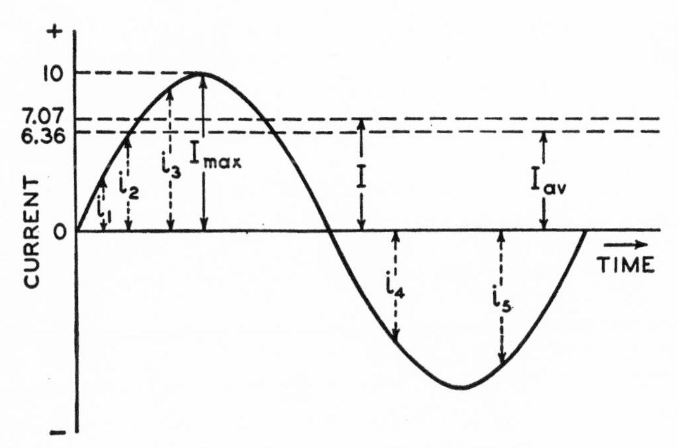

Fig. 2-7. Sine wave values of current.

By use of this last relation, we can change directly from average to rms values (or vice-versa). However, it is not necessary to remember this constant. It can be evaluated at any time, or such a solution can always be made in two steps—from average to maximum and from maximum back to effective (or vice versa).

The relation between all A.C. values is shown clearly in Fig. 2-7.

Review Problems

1. Explain briefly why the instantaneous voltages induced in a coil rotating in a uniform magnetic field generate a sine wave.

2. A sine wave of current reaches a maximum value of 8 amps.

(a) What is the equation of this curve?

(b) Using 30-degree intervals, tabulate values and plot curve of current versus degrees of rotation (trigonometric method).

3. Plot the curve of Problem 2, using the rotating-radius vector method.

4. Make the following conversions:

(a) 26 degrees to radians.
(b) 172 degrees to radians.
(c) 0.83 radian to degrees.
(d) 2.3 radians to degrees.
(e) π radians to degrees.

5. Sketch $1\frac{1}{2}$ cycles of a sine wave. Mark each zero and maximum points with successive letters (*a*, *b*, *c*, etc.). Using these letters, specify distances on the curve corresponding to:

(a) Three one-cycle intervals.
(b) Three half-cycle intervals.

6. The output of a generator is a 300-cycle sine wave. Find the angular velocity for this wave in (a) radians per second and (b) degrees per second.

7. Repeat Problem 6 for a sine wave of 60 cycles.

8. What is the frequency of each of the following waves, if it completes:

(a) One cycle in 0.1 sec.
(b) One half-cycle in 0.02 sec.
(c) Three cycles in 0.06 sec.
(d) One quarter-cycle in 0.0001 sec.

9. A generator is producing a sine wave of voltage of 200 cycles and a maximum value of 40 v.

(a) Write the equation for the instantaneous value of this voltage.
(b) Find the instantaneous value of this voltage at 0.003 sec.

10. A generator is producing a 60-cycle 120-v (rms) sine wave.

(a) Write the equation for the instantaneous value of this voltage.
(b) Find the instantaneous value of this voltage at 0.012 sec.

11. The maximum value of a sine wave voltage is 320 v. Find:
(a) rms value. (b) Average value.

12. The maximum value of a sine-wave current is 12.6 amps. Find:
(a) Average value. (b) rms value.

13. The average value of a sine-wave voltage is 220 v. Find:
(a) rms value. (b) Maximum value.

14. The effective value of a sine-wave current is 60 ma. Find the average value and maximum value of this current.

15. A capacitor rated at 8 μf, 350 v is connected in an A.C. circuit. An A.C. voltmeter in the circuit indicates 300 v. Yet in a short time, the capacitor breaks down. Explain.

CHAPTER 3

Relations between Sine Waves

IN THE PREVIOUS CHAPTER we discussed the characteristics of sine waves, considering only one sine wave at a time. But under actual operating conditions many sine waves may be present simultaneously in a piece of electronic equipment. For example refer back to the simple transmitter of Fig. 1-4 (page 8). The modulator section is receiving R.F. and audio sine waves simultaneously. In addition, the sound waves entering the microphone and the audio waves entering and leaving the audio amplifier may be several waves of different frequency. A single speech sound or a single sound from a musical instrument is a combination of several frequencies as will be shown in the next section. It is therefore important that the relation between sine waves is clearly understood.

Harmonics. When middle C is sounded on a piano, that string produces a FUNDAMENTAL, or lowest frequency, sound wave of 256 cycles. In addition, the vibrating string also produces vibrations (overtones) of two, three, and four times the fundamental frequency. It is the presence of these overtones, in varying percentages, that causes a note on the piano to sound different from the same note on a violin or any other instrument.

In electronic work, multiples of the fundamental frequency are called HARMONICS instead of overtones. Oscillators designed to produce a certain fundamental frequency will often also produce harmonics of this fundamental. At times these harmonics are desirable. A typical case is when we wish to double or triple the frequency of the output voltage (as in frequency doublers or triplers used in F.M. transmitters) we merely 'tune' the connecting circuit to the second or third harmonic of the fundamental frequency. At other times harmonics are undesirable and they must be eliminated or suppressed. For example the audio amplifier shown in Fig. 1-2 (page 4), if improperly operated, may generate second or third harmonics of the input signal. Since these harmonics were not in the original input it is a form of distortion.

For purposes of analysis, harmonics are classified depending on their relation to the fundamental frequency. The SECOND harmonic has a frequency *twice* the fundamental. The frequency of the third harmonic is three times the fundamental frequency. The fifth harmonic is five times the fundamental frequency, etc. The relation between a fundamental, its second, and its third harmonics are shown in Fig. 3-1.

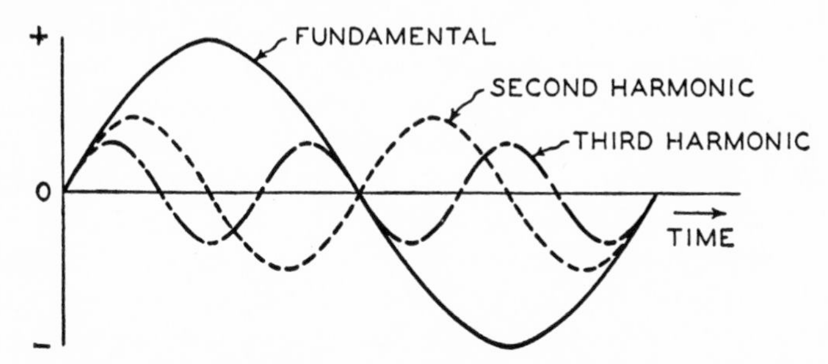

Fig. 3-1. Relation of second and third harmonics to the fundamental.

The harmonics are shown at lower amplitudes than the fundamental to make the diagram easier to follow. However, it is true that harmonics are weaker than the fundamental for which the unit was designed. In general, the higher the order of the harmonic, the lower its amplitude. But this is not always true. For example, in many cases the third harmonic (odd) may be stronger than the second harmonic (even).

Since harmonics are multiples of the fundamental frequency, their equation must be of the same form as any sine wave. If the angular velocity of a sine wave is given by $\omega = 2\pi f$, then for its second harmonic the angular velocity is 2ω; for third harmonic, 3ω, etc. The equations for such waves are:

Fundamental:	$e_1 = E_{1_{max}} \sin \omega t$
Second harmonic:	$e_2 = E_{2_{max}} \sin 2\omega t$
Third harmonic:	$e_3 = E_{3_{max}} \sin 3\omega t$
Seventh harmonic:	$e_7 = E_{7_{max}} \sin 7\omega t$

Phase and time relations. Let us consider two coils mounted on the same shaft, in parallel planes and rotating in equal magnetic fields. Since they are on a common shaft, they will rotate at the same speed and produce equal-frequency sine waves. Since the coils are parallel, the instantaneous voltage from each coil will be in step at all times. That is, they both have zero voltages and maximum voltages at the same instant, and they both reverse at the

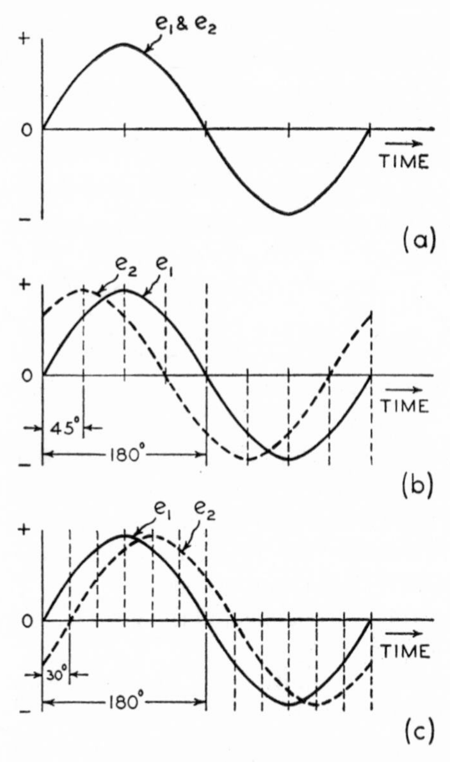

Fig. 3-2. Sine-wave phase relations: (a) In phase. (b) e_2 leading by 45°. (c) e_2 lagging by 30°.

same instant. These waves are said to be IN PHASE (Fig. 3-2a). The equation for each of these waves is: $e = E_{max} \sin \omega t$.

Now suppose the axis of coil 2 were shifted counter-clockwise, 45 degrees ahead of coil 1. (The shaft is rotating counter-clockwise.) Coil 2 will go through its cyclic points 45 degrees ($\frac{1}{8}$ cycle) ahead of coil 1. The voltage generated by coil 2 (e_2) LEADS the voltage from coil 1 (e_1) by 45 degrees. This is shown in Fig. 3-2b. Looking at the diagram, it might seem that e_1 is leading—it seems ahead of e_2. But remember these curves are plotted against time. The maximum point (and any other point) on e_1 curve occurs farther to the right—or later! Therefore, e_2 is leading. Notice that while e_1 is zero and starting positively, e_2 is positive. This is the easiest way to recognize a leading wave—it has a finite positive value when the other wave is just starting to go positive. If the equation for coil 1 is expressed as $e_1 = E_{max} \sin \omega t$, the equation for e_2 must advance the angle of rotation by 45 degrees, or

$$e_2 = E_{max} \sin (\omega t + 45°)$$

where ωt is expressed in degrees. If ωt is in radians, then since 360 degrees equals 2π radians, 45 degrees must equal $\pi/4$ radians, or

$$e_2 = E_{max} \sin \left(\omega t + \frac{\pi}{4}\right)$$

Now let us reverse the coil placement. Coil 2 is moved back, clockwise, till it is 30 degrees behind coil 1. From our discussion above, it is obvious that the voltage from coil 2 now LAGS coil 1 by 30 degrees. This is shown in Fig. 3-2c. Again a sure determination of a lagging wave is that it is still negative while the other curve is at zero *and going positive*. As before, if the equation for coil 1 is $e_1 = E_{max} \sin \omega t$, the equation for coil 2 must retard the angle of rotation by 30 degrees, or

for angles in degrees,

$$e_2 = E_{max} \sin (\omega t - 30°)$$

for angles in radians,

$$e_2 = E_{max} \sin \left(\omega t - \frac{\pi}{6}\right)$$

In general the equation for a sine wave that is leading or lagging another sine wave can be expressed by adding or subtracting some angle ϕ to the ωt value, or

$$e = E_{max} \sin (\omega t \pm \phi)$$

There are several special cases worthy of further analysis. These will be considered in turn.

1. When the angle of lead or lag (ϕ) is exactly 90 degrees: Assume e_2 is leading e_1 by 90 degrees. Using the general equation, $e_2 = E_{max} \sin (\omega t + 90°)$. But from trigonometry, the sine of $(\theta + 90°)$

$= \cos \theta$, or the $\sin (\omega t + 90°) = \cos \omega t$. The equation for e_2 is a cosine curve: $e_2 = E_{max} \cos \omega t$. Figure 3-3a shows the plot for these curves.

From the plot (Fig. 3-3a), it is obvious that when e_1 is zero, e_2 is positive maximum, and that when e_1 is positive maximum, e_2 is zero. This is the same relation as exists between the sine and cosine of any angle—sine is zero when cosine is maximum, and vice-versa. This again shows that e_2 is a cosine curve.

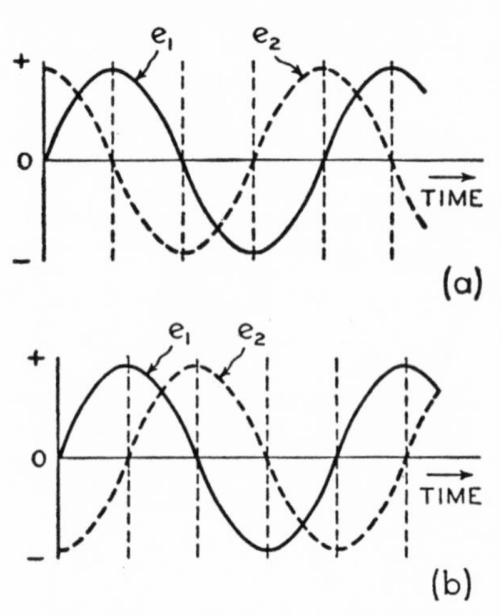

Fig. 3-3. Cosine curves for e_2: (a) e_2 leading by 90° (positive cosine curve). (b) e_2 lagging by 90° (negative cosine curve).

In Fig. 3-3b, the voltage e_2 is shown lagging by 90 degrees. Obviously the plot for e_2 is again a cosine curve. But notice this time that e_2 is at a *negative* maximum when e_1 is zero. Compare e_2 from this plot and e_2 of the previous plot (3-3a); e_2 lagging, is at all instants opposite in polarity to e_2 leading. This reversal of polarity can be expressed by formula. The equation of a curve *lagging* by 90 degrees is

$$e_2 = -E_{max} \cos \omega t.$$

2. The second special case is when the two voltages are 180 degrees apart. Such a curve is shown in Fig. 3-4. Several facts are apparent from the diagram.

(a) Both curves reach zero and maximum values at the same instant; they are both sine curves.

(b) Voltage e_2 is at all instants opposite in polarity to e_1. Therefore,

$$e_1 = E_{\max} \sin \omega t$$
$$e_2 = -E_{\max} \sin \omega t$$

(c) The curve for e_2 leading or lagging by 180 degrees would be the same curve! Therefore, it cannot be classified as leading or lagging, but merely 180 degrees out of phase.

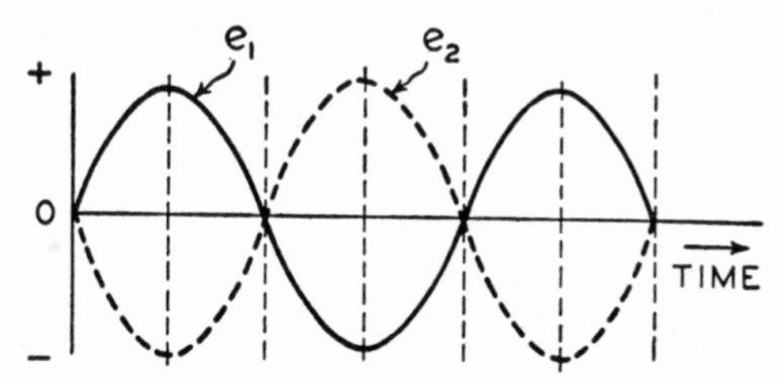

Fig. 3-4. Sine waves, 180° out of phase.

The equation for any curve 180 degrees out of phase with the reference curve could be written as $E_{\max} \sin (\omega t \pm 180°)$, but more specifically it is given by:

$$e_2 = -E_{\max} \sin \omega t$$

3. If a curve is leading by more than 180 degrees (for example 250 degrees), it can be considered as lagging by 110 degrees. Any angle of lead (ϕ) greater than 180 degrees can be considered as an

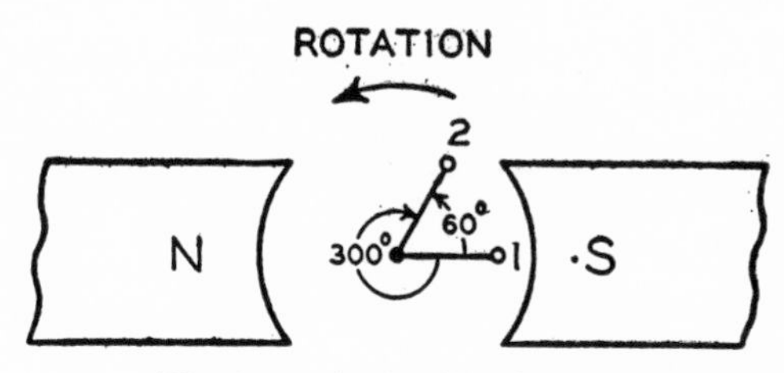

Fig. 3-5. Angle of lead or lag.

angle of lag equal to $(360° - \phi)$. Similarly any angle of lag (ϕ) greater than 180 degrees is more logically considered as an angle of lead equal to $(360° - \phi)$.

This should be apparent from our previous discussion on two curves 180 degrees apart. The 180-degree point marks the dividing line between lead and lag. It can also be explained from our basic generator principle. Figure 3-5 shows two conductors rotating in a magnetic field, on the same shaft but displaced by a fixed angle. Coil 2 may be considered as 300 degrees behind coil 1, its voltage lagging e_1 by 300 degrees; OR coil 2 may be considered as 60 degrees ahead of coil 1, and e_2 leading e_1 by 60 degrees. Obviously, it is preferable to consider the smaller angle—e_2 leading e_1 by 60 degrees.

Phase relations—different frequencies. So far we have been considering two coils rotating on the same shaft. The rotational speeds were the same and the voltages developed in each coil had to be of the same frequency. As the coils were displaced on the shaft, we noticed a difference in phase between the two voltage waves. Whatever this phase angle was, it remained constant for cycle after cycle of the generators.

What would happen to phase relations if the coils were not on the same shaft, and one coil were rotating just the slightest amount faster? Suppose coil 2 were rotating faster. Its frequency would be slightly higher. Assume that the coils start out parallel to each other—their induced voltages in phase. Coil 2 would finish its first cycle and would have started its second cycle by the time coil 1 completed one cycle. At this point coil 2 is leading by some angle. With each successive cycle this angle of lead will keep increasing. At some instant these waves will be 90 degrees out of phase; later they will be 180 degrees out, etc. Finally, at some time they will be in phase again, when coil 2 has gained one full cycle on coil 1. These phase relations will be repeated over and over again.

The phase relation between two waves of different frequency is continuously shifting. The greater the difference in frequency, the faster the phase relation between the waves will change. Due to this continuous change in phase angle, phase relations between waves of different frequency have little meaning except when the waves are harmonically related.

Earlier in this chapter we showed curves of a fundamental and its second and third harmonics (Fig. 3-1). Although the phase relation throughout one cycle of the fundamental is changing, notice that both harmonics start in phase with the fundamental and are back in phase at the end of the cycle. This applies to any harmonic. Whatever the phase relation is between fundamental and harmonic at the start of one cycle of the fundamental, that same phase relation will exist at the start of each successive fundamental cycle. *It is therefore common practice to state the STARTING phase angle as the phase relation between harmonically related waves.*

Check this for yourself. Sketch a few fundamental curves and some harmonic. You will notice, further, that all odd harmonics are also in phase with the fundamental at the start of the half-cycle of the fundamental. Also, at this half-cycle point all even harmonics are 180 degrees out of phase with the fundamental! You will find later that these relations between harmonics and fundamentals are important when considering amplifier circuits and distortion.

You might be wondering why so much time has been devoted to phase relations. Of what value is it? Any change in phasing between signals (phase shift) is another form of distortion. For example, in television, phase relations are of extreme importance. Any change in phasing will cause blurring of picture detail. In order to study the causes and cures for these undesirable phase shifts, we must understand the meaning and representation of phase relations.

Addition of sine waves—resultant. In Fig. 1-4 (page 8) we see that two signals—the R.F. and the A.F. signal—are applied to the modulator section. The 'effective signal' must be due to the sum of the applied signals. There are many such cases where more than one voltage or current are combined in electronic equipment. For example, as in D.C. circuits, voltages in a series circuit are additive, and currents in a parallel circuit are also additive. But we are now dealing with sine waves. Let us see how these additions are performed in A.C.

From D.C. theory we know that voltages in series circuits and currents in parallel circuits are additive. The same is true in A.C. circuits. But since the voltages and currents in A.C. circuits are sine waves, it will be necessary to add sine waves. The method is simple enough. Plot each sine wave (amplitude versus time). At several points along the time axis, measure the instantaneous value of each sine wave and add them to get the total instantaneous value. The more points at which this is done, the more accurate the final result. Plot these total instantaneous values and join these points. This curve is the RESULTANT wave shape. This method will be illustrated in the following diagrams.

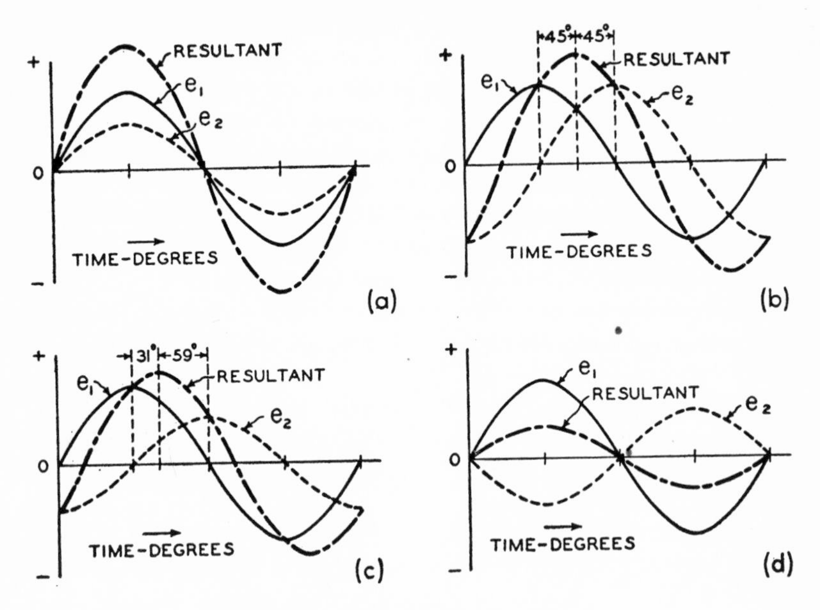

Fig. 3-6. Addition of sine waves—same frequency.

(a) Unequal amplitudes—in phase:

$$e_1 = 10 \sin \omega t$$
$$e_2 = 6 \sin \omega t$$
$$e_R = 16 \sin \omega t$$

(b) Equal amplitudes—90° out of phase:

$$e_1 = 10 \sin \omega t$$
$$e_2 = 10 \sin (\omega t - 90°) = -10 \cos \omega t$$
$$e_R = 14.1 \sin (\omega t - 45°)$$

(c) Unequal amplitudes—90° out of phase:

$$e_1 = 10 \sin \omega t$$
$$e_2 = 6 \sin (\omega t - 90°) = -6 \cos \omega t$$
$$e_R = 11.7 \sin (\omega t - 31°)$$

(d) Unequal amplitudes—180° out of phase:

$$e_1 = 10 \sin \omega t$$
$$e_2 = -6 \sin \omega t$$
$$e_R = 4 \sin \omega t$$

From Fig. 3-6, the following points should be noted.

1. The resultants are of the same frequency as the original waves.

2. When the sine waves are in phase, the resultant is also in phase.

3. When the sine waves are out of phase and of equal amplitude, the resultant has a phase shift half way between the original waves.

4. When the sine waves are out of phase but of unequal amplitude, the resultant phase angle will be in between the two original waves but will be closer to the wave of larger amplitude.

This point-by-point addition of sine waves can be applied equally well to curves of any frequency. Figure 3-7 shows the addition of

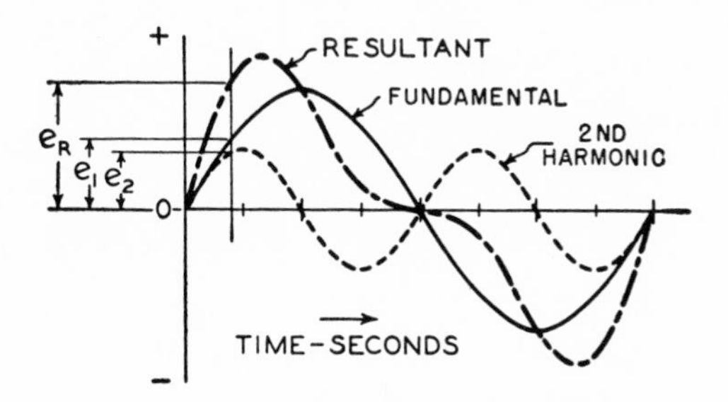

Fig. 3-7. Addition of sine waves—harmonic frequencies.

a fundamental with its second harmonic. The resultant wave is obviously not a sine wave. These wave shapes will be discussed further in the next chapter. The method for adding sine waves is however still the same.

Vector representation. From study of mathematics (or physics) you should know that a vector quantity is a quantity having both *magnitude* and *direction.* For example, a force has a push or pull in pounds, and a direction or angle at which it acts. Vector quantities are conveniently represented graphically by an arrow, whose length (to a convenient scale) represents the magnitude and whose direction represents the direction or angle in which the force acts.

Vectors are used quite commonly in A.C. circuits to represent currents or voltages, or in graphical solutions of A.C. problems. The length of the arrow represents the magnitude of the voltage or current. Since they are of fixed length, vectors do *not* represent instantaneous values. Generally, they are used to represent effective values. However, vectors can just as readily be used to represent maximum or average values. The direction of the vector arrow can also be used to represent phase angle. The horizontal direction, to the right, is the reference direction (phase angle equals zero). Phase angles are then measured *counter-clockwise* from this reference line. Where a current and a voltage are being represented in the same diagram, different scales can be used for each. However, all voltages (or all currents) *in the same diagram* must be drawn to the same scale. This system of representation is shown in the following example.

EXAMPLE 1

Show by vector diagrams the following A.C. values:

(a) $E_1 = 100$ v, $E_2 = 40$ v, in phase.
(b) $E_1 = 20$ v, leading E_2 of 16 v by 30°.
(c) $E = 80$ v, $I = 4$ amps, I leading E by 90°.
(d) $I_1 = 5$ amps, lagging I_2 of 3 amps by 45°.

SOLUTION:

See vector diagram on following page.

SOLUTION

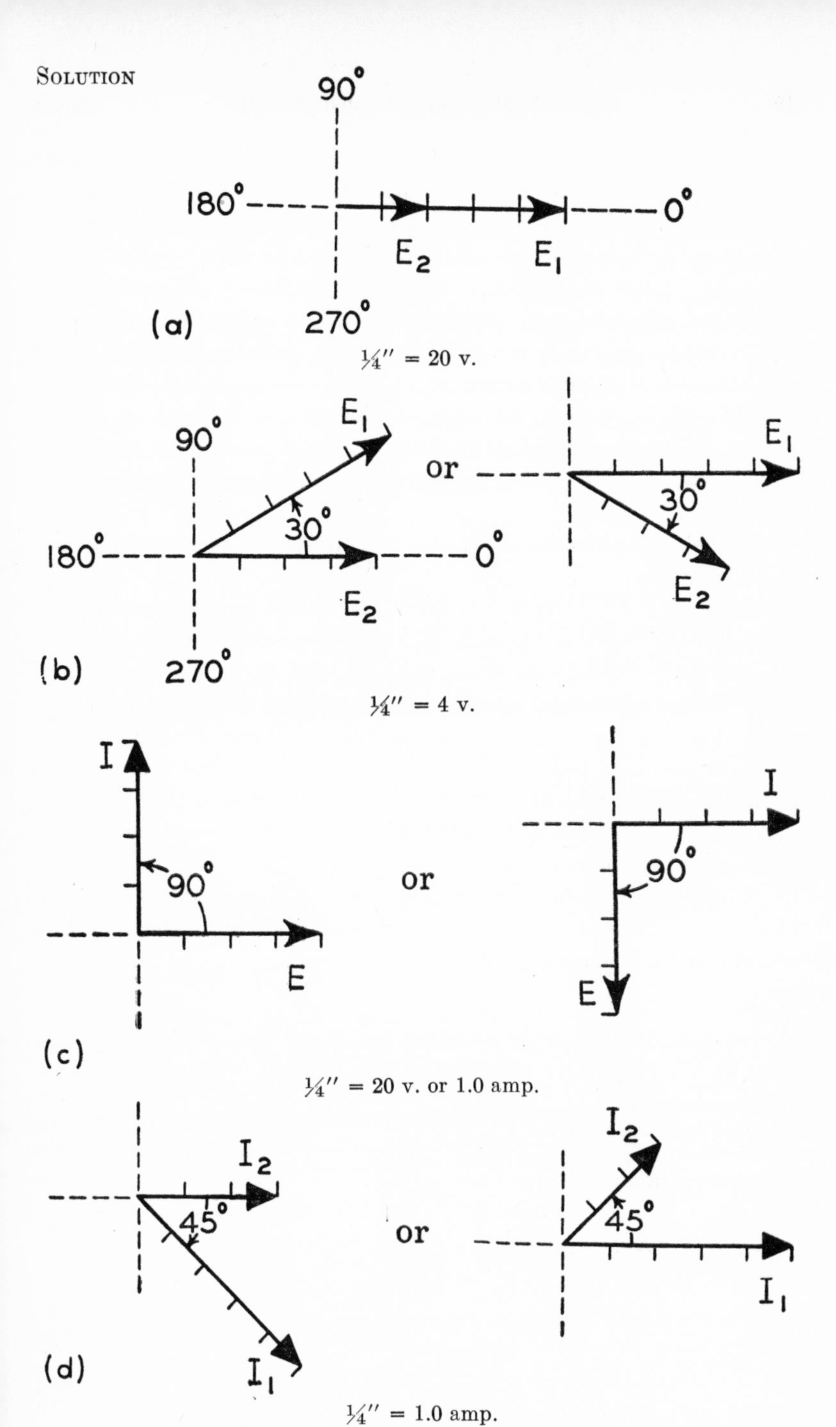

Fig. 3-8. Vector representation of sine waves.

This method of representing sine waves is not limited to just two at a time, but can be used for any number of sine waves simultaneously. There is one restriction. You will notice in Fig. 3-8 that there is a fixed phase angle between the two waves. This is true only if the waves are of the same frequency. Vector representation cannot be used with waves of different frequency, because they would apply only at ONE instant—a moment later all phase relations would have changed.

By use of vectors, addition of sine waves becomes a simple matter. However, remember that it can be used only when the sine waves are all of the same frequency. The procedure is as follows:

1. Pick a scale suitable to the magnitude of the given voltages or currents.
2. Draw the first vector to scale and at the given phase angle.
3. Where the first vector ends, start the second vector, draw it to scale and at the given phase angle.
4. Where the second vector ends, start the third vector . . . etc.
5. Join the starting point of the FIRST vector with the HEAD of the LAST vector. (See Fig. 3-9).
6. This line is the RESULTANT. Its length represents the magnitude of the resultant voltage or current, and its direction is the phase angle of the resultant.

If the given values are rms values, the resultant is also an rms value. If the given values were maximum values, the resultant would also be a maximum value.

EXAMPLE 2

The branch currents in a parallel circuit are (rms values): $I_1 = 10$ amps leading by 60°; $I_2 = 7$ amps at zero degrees; $I_3 = 6$ amps lagging by 30°. Find

(a) Resultant current.
(b) Phase angle of this current.
(c) Equation for the resultant current.

SOLUTION

See vector diagram on following page.

SOLUTION

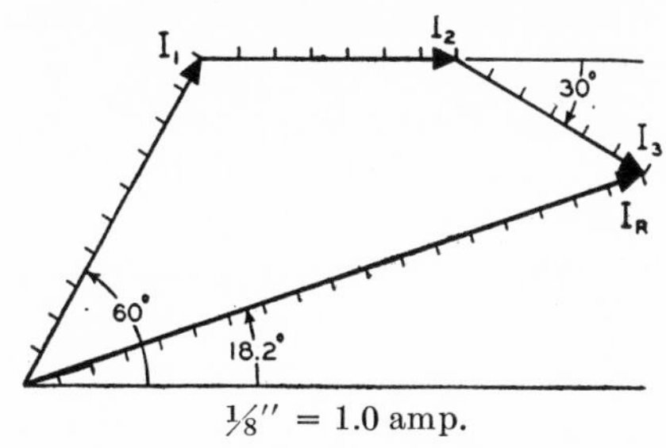

⅛″ = 1.0 amp.

Fig. 3-9. Graphical vector addition

(a and b) I_R = 18.1 amps leading by 18.2°.

(c) Maximum value of $I_R = \dfrac{18.1}{0.707} = 25.6$ amps.

$$i_R = 25.6 \sin (\omega t + 18.2°.)$$

This vector method for addition of sine waves is much simpler and quicker than the previous method where the individual sine waves were plotted and then added. The vector method will be used extensively in later chapters for the solution of A.C. problems involving only one frequency. In the preceding example, the problem was solved graphically. Careful plotting and large scales are necessary for accurate results. The vector method can also be solved by trigonometry or complex algebra. The diagram can then be merely a freehand sketch of the circuit values. Mathematical solutions will be treated later.

Review Problems

1. (a) Accurately sketch two cycles of a sine wave.

(b) Directly below, using the same time base, sketch a wave of twice the frequency.

(c) Repeat for a wave of four times the frequency.

(d) Repeat for a wave of one-half the frequency.

(e) Using (a) as the reference wave, what is the equation of each of the above curves?

2. (a) Accurately sketch $1\frac{1}{2}$ cycles of a sine wave.

(b) Directly below, using the same time axis, sketch a wave of the same frequency leading by 60 degrees.

(c) Repeat for a wave lagging by 45 degrees.

(d) Repeat for a wave lagging by 90 degrees.

(e) Using (a) as the reference wave, what is the equation for each of the curves?

3. In each of the following equations, specify amplitude, angular velocity, frequency, and angle of lead or lag:

(a) $e = 25 \sin (377t + 40°)$
(b) $p = 4 \sin (628t - 80°)$
(c) $i = 0.35 \cos 3150t$
(d) $e = -120 \sin 628t$

4. (a) Carefully sketch on graph paper one cycle of a sine wave having an amplitude of 10.

(b) On the same axis, sketch a second wave of the same frequency and amplitude, leading by 60 degrees.

(c) Plot the resultant of (a) and (b).

(d) What is the amplitude and phase angle of the resultant?

5. (a) Carefully sketch on graph paper one cycle of a sine wave having an amplitude of 10.

(b) On the same axis sketch a third harmonic having an amplitude of 5 and starting in phase.

(c) Plot the resultant of (a) and (b).

6. Represent the following sine wave values by vectors:

(a) $E_1 = 20$ v lagging $E_2 = 15$ v by 170 degrees.
(b) $E = 80$ v lagging $I = 10$ amps by 80 degrees.
(c) $I_1 = 40$ ma lagging $I_2 = 12$ ma by 40 degrees.
(d) $I_1 = 10$ amps leading $E_1 = 80$ v by 80 degrees.

7. Using the vector method (graphical) find the resultant (magnitude and phase angle) of the following voltages.

(a) Values from Problem 4.
(b) Values from Problem 6(a).
(c) Values from Problem 6(c).
(d) $E_1 = 40$ v lagging by 40 degrees.
$E_2 = 60$ v leading by 80 degrees.
$E_3 = 30$ v at zero degrees.

CHAPTER 4

Non-Sinusoidal or Complex Waves

FROM THE TITLE OF THIS CHAPTER you might be inclined to say, "Oh–oh, this is too tough, let's skip it." But wait, that is not fair! You have not even tried to see what it is all about. There is nothing complex about a complex wave—except its name. In fact, you have already seen an example of such a wave in the previous chapter (see Fig. 3-7). It was the resultant obtained when we added a fundamental sine wave and its second harmonic. Notice that this resultant wave shape is not a sine wave—and that, in a nutshell, is the whole story. *Any wave that is not a pure sine wave is called a complex wave. All complex waves are resultants of two or more sine waves of different frequencies.* One of the components of a complex wave may be of zero frequency—in other words, D.C. Now does it sound 'tough' any more?

But you are going to be from Missouri—so your next reaction is, "All right, that is simple enough, but why should I waste time on complex waves. I want to study electronics." The answer to that is equally simple. Complex waves occur in all phases of electronics. Music and speech (sound or audio waves) are complex waves because they are composed of fundamental and overtones or harmonics. Modulated carrier waves from transmitting stations, as shown in Fig. 1-4, are another example of such waves. Outputs from the rectifiers of a D.C. power supply, special wave shapes from electronic test equipment, radar, loran, navigational beacons, etc. are all complex waves. To analyze all of these waves would be impossible. Some wave shapes are of such common occurrence that special analysis is warranted.

Effect of odd harmonics on sine wave shape. Sometimes electronic equipment, such as an amplifier, although supplied with a sine wave input will have a complex wave output. This is a distortion of the original wave shape. Since all complex waves are the resultants from two or more sine waves of different frequencies, it means that the equipment has produced the new frequencies.

Usually these additional frequencies are harmonics of the input waves. When the output wave contains only odd harmonics of the input wave shape, it can be easily recognized. The two alternations of the wave are identical and the curve is said to have MIRROR IMAGE SYMMETRY. This effect can be seen in Fig. 4-1. If we cut the curve

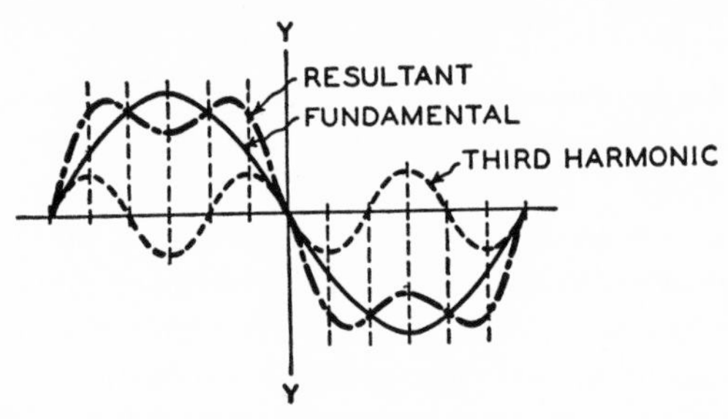

Fig. 4-1. Fundamental and third harmonic—in phase.

in half at the *Y*-axis, and slide the lower half to the left, under the upper half, you will notice that each half is a mirror image of the other.

Figure 4-1 shows the resultant of a fundamental and a third harmonic, in phase. The equation for such a wave is

$$e = E_1 \sin \omega t + E_2 \sin 3\omega t$$

When the third harmonic is not in phase, the output wave shape is entirely different, but the mirror image is maintained. Figure

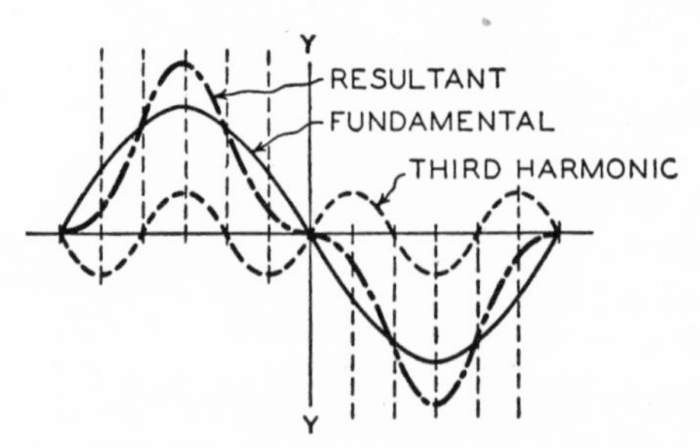

Fig. 4-2. Fundamental and third harmonic—180° out of phase.

4-2 shows the resultant wave when the third harmonic is 180 degrees out of phase with its fundamental. The equation for this wave is

$$e = E_1 \sin \omega t - E_2 \sin 3\omega t$$

In this illustration a third harmonic at 180 degrees was used for ease of visual interpretation. However, this same form of symmetry—*mirror image symmetry—is maintained for any odd harmonic at any phase angle.* Let us see why.

Each half-cycle of the fundamental will contain $n/2$ half-cycles of the harmonic (two and one-half for the fifth; four and one-half for the ninth; etc.). So—whatever the phase relation between the fundamental and harmonic at the start of the fundamental cycle, the same phase relation must exist at the start of the second half of the fundamental cycle. This makes each alternation of the resultant wave identical and gives us mirror image.

Effect of even harmonics on sine wave shape. When the output wave shape contains even harmonics (with or without odd harmonics) the mirror image is destroyed. However, each alternation of the output wave may be similar in shape. This is illustrated in

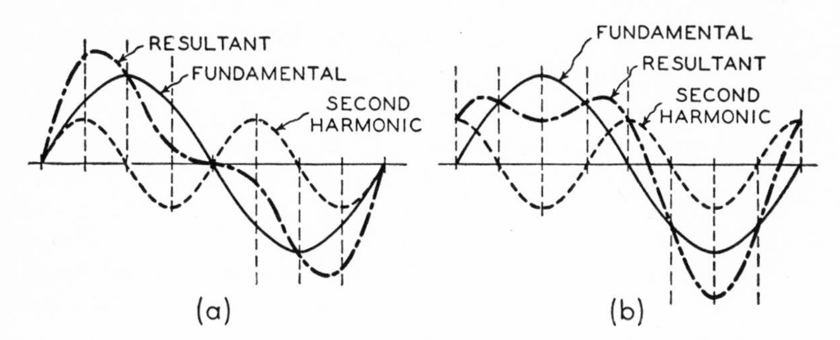

Fig. 4-3. Effect of even harmonics on sine-wave shapes: (a) Fundamental and second harmonic in phase. (b) Second harmonic leading by 90°.

Fig. 4-3, which shows the effect of a second harmonic in phase (a), and 90 degrees out of phase (*b*). The equations for these complex waves are

(a) $$e = E_1 \sin \omega t + E_2 \sin 2\omega t$$

(b) $$e = E_1 \sin \omega t + E_2 \cos 2\omega t$$

This lack of mirror image applies to any even harmonic. When each alternation of the output is similar (as in Fig. 4-3a), the even harmonics are either in phase or 180 degrees out of phase. Any other phase relation between fundamental and even harmonics results in unlike alternations.

Notice that neither of the curves in Fig. 4-3 has mirror symmetry. Yet a certain symmetry is still present in Fig. 4-3a. This type of symmetry may be called Z-axis symmetry. Hold a pencil at the intersection of the X and Y axes, perpendicular to the plane of the paper. Your pencil will represent the Z-axis. Now rotate the curves 180 degrees around the Z axis. The resulting wave shape will be identical to the original curve. This is Z-axis symmetry. Now if you apply the same idea to the curve in Fig. 4-3b, you will see that it does not have Z-axis symmetry. To illustrate the loss of Z-axis symmetry in Fig. 4-3b the even harmonic chosen was a second harmonic, and the phase angle between fundamental and harmonic was 90 degrees. These specific values were chosen merely for ease of drawing and ease of visual interpretation by inspection. However, it must be emphasized that *any even harmonic at any phase angle other than zero or* 180 *degrees will result in complete lack of symmetry.*

In summarizing the effects of harmonics, the following conclusions can be made:

1. If a complex wave has mirror symmetry it has no even harmonics. All its harmonics must be odd.

2. If a complex wave has Z-axis symmetry—but no mirror symmetry—it *must* have *even* harmonics. The even harmonics must be in phase or 180 degrees out of phase. It may also have ODD harmonics, but these also must be in phase or 180 degrees out of phase.

3. If a complex wave has no symmetry, it must have even harmonics (not at zero or 180 degrees), and it may also have odd harmonics.

Effect of D.C. on sine wave shape. Many wave shapes fed into or taken out of electronic equipment consist of D.C. plus some sine waves. For example, the input to the grid of a vacuum tube is usually made up of a D.C. bias voltage and the A.C. signal voltage. The output from this same tube will be A.C. (the amplified signal voltage) and the D.C. power supply voltage. When such a signal is fed through a capacitor, the D.C. component is removed. In television it is necessary to include a special circuit, the 'D.C. restorer,' in order to add the correct level of D.C. to the signal. This is necessary for proper background illumination of the scenes. So—let us examine the effect of D.C. on a sine wave.

Since D.C. can be considered a sine wave of zero frequency, addition of D.C. to a sine wave of any other frequency also results in a complex wave. The presence of D.C. in any complex wave can be easily recognized.

What was the average value of one full cycle of a sine wave? Zero—because the positive half-cycle is equal and opposite to the negative half-cycle. Check carefully the resultant wave in any of the above complex waves (Figs. 4-1 to 4-3). The average value in each case is still zero. This is obvious when you consider that the average value for each component is also zero! Now compare

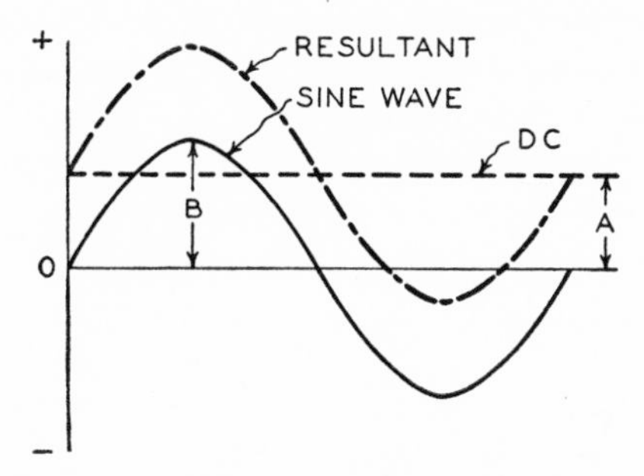

Fig. 4-4. Effect of D.C. on sine-wave shapes.

Fig. 4-4 showing the resultant of D.C. and a sine wave. The equation for this wave is:

$$e = A + B \sin \omega t$$

Notice that the sine wave shape is maintained, but it has been raised above the X-axis by an amount equal to the D.C. component. The positive portion of the complex wave is much greater than the negative portion. The average value for one full cycle of the complex wave is positive. Had the D.C. component been negative, the average value would also be negative. The illustration shown is a simple one, but the principle applies to any complex wave. *If the average value of any complex wave, for one full cycle is not zero, the wave has a D.C. component.*

Half wave rectifier output. Half wave rectifiers are often used in electronic equipment. One typical use is in low-current D.C.

power supplies as used for cathode-ray tubes, for example in the high voltage supply for oscilloscopes and television receivers. Circuits and applications will be shown later. If a sine wave is applied to such a rectifier, the output wave shape is shown in Fig. 4-5.

This wave shape has often been called 'pulsating D.C.' Well, it is true, but such a description does not give a complete picture. It is a complex wave! Let us analyze it:

1. Since the average value is not zero, this wave has a D.C. component. The average value for the sine wave half-cycle is $0.636E_{max}$. The average for the next half-cycle is obviously zero. Therefore, the average for one full cycle is $0.318E_{max}$. This is the value of the D.C. component.

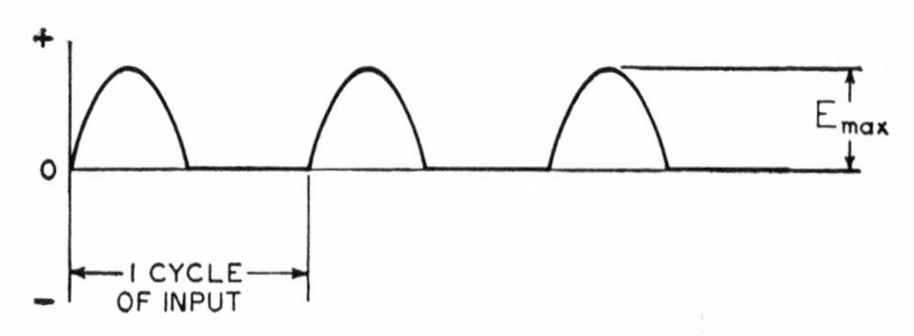

Fig. 4-5. Output of half-wave rectifier.

2. By means of a laboratory or mathematical wave analysis, it can be shown that the next component is the same as the input frequency—the fundamental, and that its peak is equal to one-half the peak value of the complex wave.

3. Since the output wave does not have mirror image symmetry, it is certain to contain even harmonics. A wave analyzer would show that the next component is the second harmonic of magnitude equal to $0.212E_{max}$.

4. The fourth component is the fourth harmonic of the input frequency of magnitude $0.042E_{max}$.

5. Notice that the magnitude of the harmonics is getting quite small. The output wave has sixth and eighth, etc., harmonics, but their magnitudes are so small as to be negligible.

Knowing the frequency and magnitude of each component, we can now write the equation for this wave:

$$e = 0.318E_{max} + 0.5E_{max} \sin \omega t - 0.212E_{max} \cos 2\omega t - 0.042E_{max} \cos 4\omega t$$

From the equation, what is the phase relation of the second and fourth harmonics to the fundamental? A minus cosine curve means a lag by 90 degrees. The presence of a lead or lag (other than 180 degrees) is obvious because the alternations of this wave shape are not similar. A simple proof of this analysis and equation is to plot the various components, add them, and compare the resultant with a typical half wave rectifier output. This will be left as an exercise for the student. (See Problem 6 under Review Problems.)

Full wave rectifier output. Another common complex wave shape is the output of a full wave rectifier as shown in Fig. 4-6. Full wave rectifiers are probably the most common type of rectifier used in power supplies. To understand the choice between half

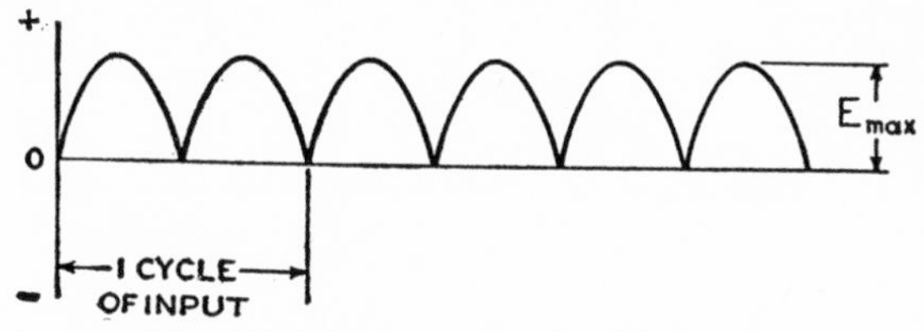

Fig. 4-6. Output of full-wave rectifier.

wave or full wave rectification and the operation of the filtering circuits needed with these rectifiers, we must be familiar with the composition of the rectifier output wave shape.

The components of this complex wave are as follows:

1. D.C. equal to $0.636E_{max}$. The average value of one full cycle is $0.636E_{max}$.

2. The next component is the second harmonic *of the input frequency* of magnitude $0.425E_{max}$. There is no fundamental frequency in the output wave.

3. The third component is the fourth harmonic of amplitude $0.085E_{max}$.

4. The last component of any consequence is the sixth harmonic of amplitude $0.036E_{max}$.

The equation of this curve is

$$e = 0.636E_{max} - 0.425E_{max} \cos 2\omega t - 0.085E_{max} \cos 4\omega t - 0.036E_{max} \cos 6\omega t$$

Comparing this equation with the equation for the output from a half wave rectifier, we notice that the full wave output has a higher D.C. component and lower A.C. components.

Square wave. Square waves are often used in electronic work for test purposes because they are rich in harmonics. Any unit which can 'pass' a square wave with little distortion is capable of handling a wide frequency range without discrimination. For example, let us assume that the audio amplifiers shown in block form in Chapter 1 must give true reproduction of frequencies up to 15,000 cycles. We can check this by feeding into the amplifier a square wave of 1500 cycles. If the output from the amplifier is still a good square wave, we know the amplifier is good to at least 15,000 cycles. Why this is so will be learned when studying the uses of the cathode-ray oscilloscope.

A typical square wave is shown in Fig. 4-7.

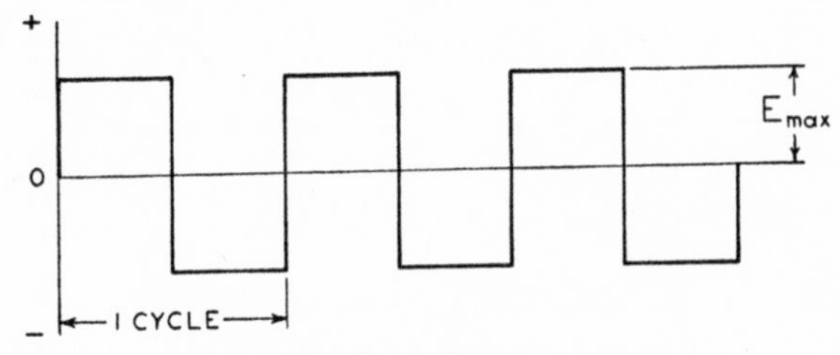

Fig. 4-7. Typical square wave.

Let us analyze this wave:

1. Since the average value for one cycle is zero, there is no D.C. component.
2. Since the curve has mirror image, there are no even harmonics.
3. The curve has steep sides, indicating a rapid change of instantaneous value with time. This means extremely high frequency, or high order of harmonics.

The equation for this curve is

$$e = E_{\max} \sin \omega t + \tfrac{1}{3}E_{\max} \sin 3\omega t + \tfrac{1}{5}E_{\max} \sin 5\omega t + \tfrac{1}{7}E_{\max} \sin 7\omega t \cdots$$

The composition of the square wave is shown graphically in Fig. 4-8.

With the addition of the seventh harmonic, the resultant wave shape approaches a square wave. As higher harmonics are added, the sides of the wave will get steeper and the ripples at the top will be smoothed out. In order to duplicate the square wave exactly, an infinite number of harmonics must be added.

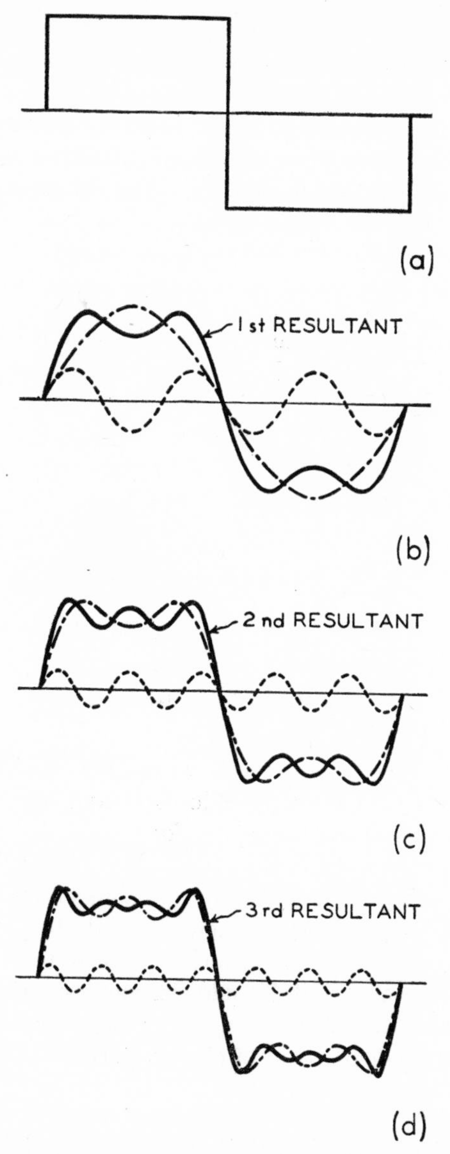

Fig. 4-8. Composition of a square wave: (a) Typical square wave. (b) Fundamental plus third harmonic. (c) First resultant plus fifth harmonic. (d) Second resultant plus seventh harmonic.

Triangular wave. A triangular wave is shown in Fig. 4-9.

From our earlier discussion, you should immediately summarize that this wave has:

1. No D.C. component (average value equals zero).
2. No even harmonics (mirror image symmetry). The harmonics must therefore all be odd harmonics. The equation of this wave is

$$e = E_{max} \sin \omega t - \tfrac{1}{9}E_{max} \sin 3\omega t - \tfrac{1}{25}E_{max} \sin 5\omega t - \tfrac{1}{49}E_{max} \sin 7\omega t \cdots$$

Since the amplitude of the harmonics is so low compared with the fundamental, it will be too difficult to show the composition of the triangular wave graphically.

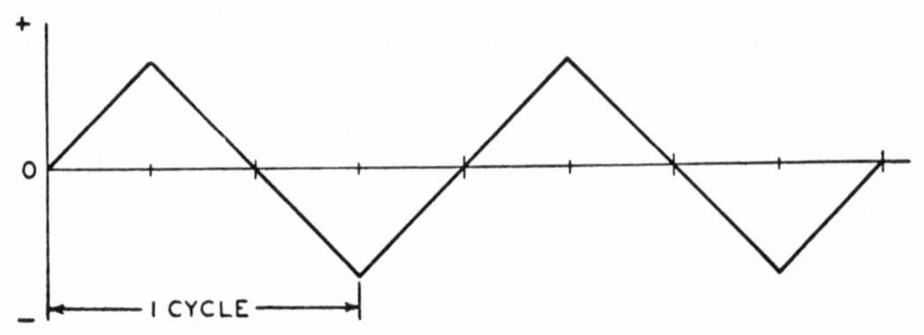

Fig. 4-9. Triangular wave.

Saw tooth wave. Saw tooth waves are used universally in sweep circuits of cathode-ray oscilloscopes and television receivers. They are also used quite frequently for trigger circuits. A typical saw tooth wave is shown in Fig. 4-10. It is obvious that the wave has no D.C. component since the area under each half-cycle is equal, and the average value is zero. In addition, the curve does not have mirror image. This means that it must contain even harmonics and may contain odd harmonics. However, Z-axis symmetry is present. Therefore, all harmonics present must either be in phase or 180 degrees out of phase with the fundamental. The actual equation for this curve is:

$$e = E_{max} \sin \omega t - \tfrac{1}{2}E_{max} \sin 2\omega t + \tfrac{1}{3}E_{max} \sin 3\omega t - \tfrac{1}{4}E_{max} \sin 4\omega t \cdots$$

The composition of this curve is also shown in Fig. 4-10.

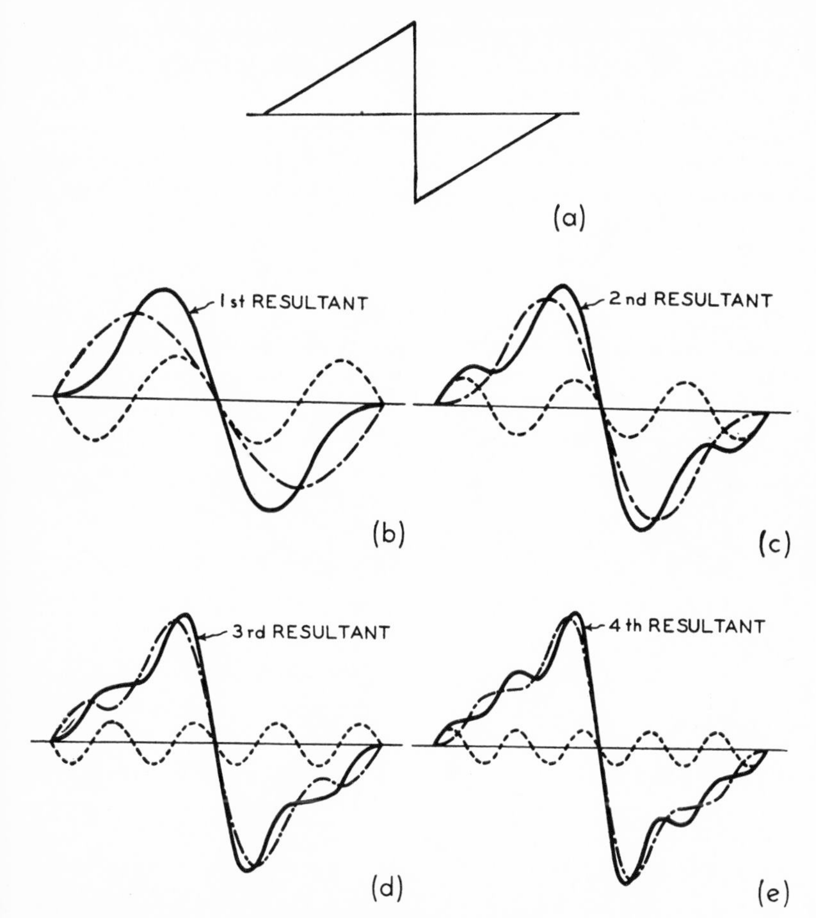

Fig. 4-10. Composition of saw tooth wave: (a) Typical saw tooth wave. (b) Fundamental plus second harmonic. (c) First resultant plus third harmonic. (d) Second resultant plus fourth harmonic. (e) Third resultant plus fifth harmonic.

Pulse waves. A pulse wave is similar to the output of a half wave rectifier, except that the duration of the pulse itself is only a very small fraction of the 'cycle' time. The pulse itself may have any shape—peaked, rectangular, etc. A typical pulse wave is shown in Fig. 4-11.

It is obvious that this is a complex wave having a D.C. component and many even harmonics. A detailed analysis of this wave is too complicated. Furthermore, since there are many shapes of pulses used, no one equation would apply to all. In general, however, the steeper the sides of the pulse, the higher the harmonic content. Also, the flatter (more horizontal) the top of the pulse, the lower the frequency of its lowest frequency component. This generalization is true for any complex wave.

When speaking of pulse waves, the terms 'frequency' and 'cycle' are not used. Instead they are identified by new terms: PULSE DURATION and REPETITION RATE. Since the pulse duration is usually extremely short, time is measured in microseconds. For example, the pulse duration may be 1 microsecond or 20 microseconds, etc. The repetition rate is a measure of the number of pulses produced in 1 second. If pulses are produced at the rate of 500 pulses per second, the wave is said to have a pulse repetition rate of 500.

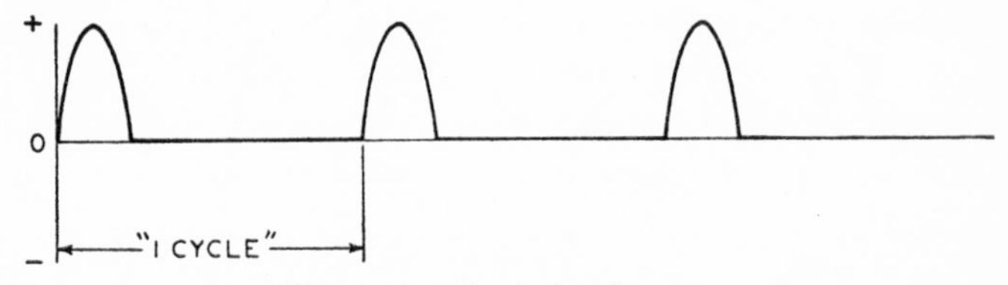

Fig. 4-11. Typical pulse wave.

Pulse waves have many applications in electronic circuits. They are used for triggering and synchronizing purposes due to the exact timing between pulses. (The horizontal synchronizing pulses used in television receivers are approximately 5 microseconds long and have a repetition rate of 15,750.) They are also used in radar, loran, and navigational beacons. In this latter application, tremendous power can be sent out in the pulses (increasing the range of transmission), with relatively low power input. The reason for this can be explained readily. The power input is low, but it flows continuously for the entire 'cycle.' This energy is stored and then released in one brief instant at tremendous peak power. Such a wave shape has a high ratio of peak-to-average power.

Average value of complex waves. When dealing with sine waves only, the average value (by convention) refers to the average for one half-cycle. This convention was adopted because each alternation is alike, and the average for a full cycle would be zero. However, when dealing with complex waves, the two alternations are not necessarily alike. The half-cycle average would have no meaning. This is especially true when the complex wave has a D.C. component. *The average value of complex waves should be taken for the* FULL *cycle.*

The method for obtaining an average is the same as explained for sine waves. A graphical method must be used unless the exact equation for the curve is known.

1. Plot or trace the wave (graph paper preferred).
2. Divide one FULL cycle of the wave into any number of equal parts (the more parts, the more accurate the final answer).
3. Measure the instantaneous values at each of these intervals—include all zero values.
4. Find the sum of all these instantaneous values.
5. Divide this sum by the number of values. This is the average value.

Another method of obtaining average values is sometimes easier:

1. Plot or trace the wave (graph paper preferred).
2. Calculate the net areas under the curve. If the curve has positive and negative values, the net area is the difference between the area under the positive and negative portions. For an irregular curve, a convenient way is to count the number of boxes (when using graph paper) under the curve.
3. Measure the length of the cycle. When boxes are used as a measure of area, then the length of the cycle can be measured in number of lines.
4. The average value is then: area divided by length of cycle (to the same scale as the curve is drawn.)

Both methods are illustrated in the following problem:

EXAMPLE 1

Find the average value of a half-wave rectifier output having a maximum value of 100 v.

SOLUTION

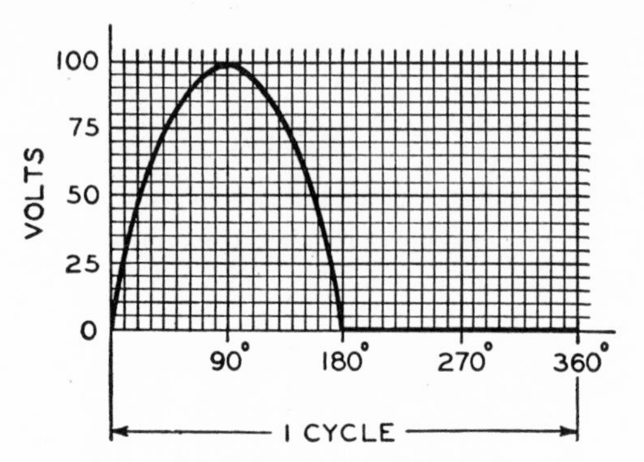

Fig. 4-12. Half-wave rectifier output.

(1) *By instantaneous values:*

Degrees	*e*	*Degrees*	*e*
15	26	195	0
30	50	210	0
45	71	225	0
60	86	240	0
75	96	255	0
90	100	270	0
105	96	285	0
120	86	300	0
135	71	315	0
150	50	330	0
165	26	345	0
180	0	360	0

Sum of instantaneous values = 758
Number of instantaneous values = 24
Average value = $\frac{758}{24}$ = 31.6 v

(2) *By area method:*

$$\text{number of squares under the curve} = 238$$
$$\text{number of lines for one cycle} = 36$$
$$\text{average value} = \frac{238}{36} \times 5 \text{ (volts per line)} = 33\text{v}$$

The exact answer to the above problem is 31.8 v. Notice that either method, if accurately done, gives reasonably accurate results.

Although all calculations in A.C. problems are based on sine waves, most wave shapes encountered in electronic work are complex waves. Calculations are therefore made on the various components of the complex wave. Where the individual frequencies in any complex wave are widely separated, circuits handling such complex waves are analyzed in terms of the lowest frequency component, medium frequency component, and maximum frequency component.

Review Problems

1. (a) Carefully sketch on graph paper a sine wave having an amplitude of 10.

(b) On the same axis, carefully sketch a fifth harmonic in phase, amplitude of 5.

(c) Plot the resultant of the two waves.

(d) What is the equation of this resultant?

2. Repeat Problem 1, using a third harmonic lagging by 90 degrees as the second wave.

3. Repeat Problem 1, using a second harmonic 180 degrees out of phase as the second wave.

4. Repeat Problem 1, using a fourth harmonic in phase as the second wave.

5. Repeat Problem 1, using D.C. as the second wave.

6. (a) On the same axis plot the following waves:

1. D.C., amplitude 31.8 v.
2. Sine wave, amplitude 50 v.
3. Second harmonic lagging the fundamental by 90 degrees, amplitude 21.2 v.
4. Fourth harmonic lagging the fundamental by 90 degrees, amplitude 4.2 v.

(b) Plot the resultant of these four voltages.

(c) Write the equation of each component.

(d) Write the equation for the resultant.

(e) Compare this curve with the output of a half-wave rectifier. Explain any difference.

7. When analyzing a complex wave for its components, explain how you can tell:

(a) Presence or absence of D.C. component.

(b) Presence or absence of even harmonics.

(c) When even harmonics are present whether they are in phase, 180 degrees out of phase, or at some other angle of lead or lag.

8. (a) A square wave has a frequency of 50 cycles. What is the frequency of the fundamental sine wave component?

(b) What is the equation of the 15th harmonic component?

9. In a triangular wave, what is the equation of the 9th harmonic component?

10. (a) In a saw tooth wave, how can you tell that the harmonics are not cosine curves?

(b) What is the equation of the 8th harmonic component?

11. (a) Figure 4-13 shows a saw tooth wave. How does it differ from Fig. 4-10?

(b) What is the equation of the saw tooth wave?

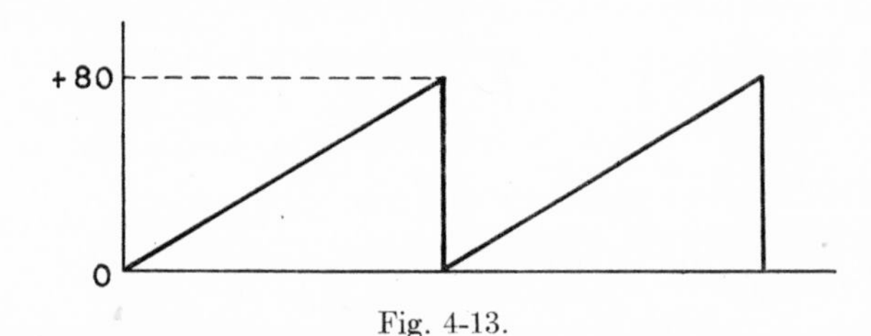

Fig. 4-13.

12. Draw a rectangular pulse wave having an amplitude of 10, pulse width of 0.02 sec, and a pulse repetition rate of 10.

13. Calculate the average value of the wave in Problem 12.

14. A radar transmitter sends out a rectangular pulse wave having a pulse duration of 5 μs. The pulse repetition rate is 500. The peak pulse power is 100 kw.

(a) Draw the pulse wave, showing time intervals.
(b) Calculate the average power per cycle.
(c) What is the energy per pulse?

CHAPTER 5

Resistance as a Circuit Element

IN ANY ELECTRICAL CIRCUIT you will find combinations of resistors, capacitors, and inductors used to control the circuit current in some desired manner. These components are called *circuit elements.* We have already discussed each of these elements from a D.C. standpoint.* Their behavior on A.C. circuits will be considered in the following chapters.

Resistance concept for A.C. In our study of direct currents, a resistor was considered as a definite piece of material (wire, carbon, or composition) having a definite length and cross-sectional area. When current passes through a resistor, electrical energy from the supply source is converted into heat energy in the resistor. The resistor dissipates electrical energy. This last statement is the basis for the concept of resistance in A.C. circuits. *Anything that dissipates electrical energy can be classified as a resistance.* It may be a real resistor such as was discussed in D.C. circuits, or it may be an *equivalent* resistance.

There are several ways by which these resistive effects are produced:

1. Eddy current and hysteresis losses in magnetic circuits dissipate electrical energy. These effects can be replaced by an equivalent resistance which will cause the same amount of power loss when inserted directly into the circuit. For example, a magnetic circuit carrying 100 ma has an iron loss (eddy currents and hysteresis) of 0.04 watt. The equivalent resistance due to this iron loss is

$$R = \frac{W}{I^2} = \frac{0.04}{0.01} = 4 \text{ ohms}$$

2. Dielectric losses and leakage losses in insulation or dielectric materials will dissipate electrical energy. They can be replaced by an equivalent resistance which would result in the same power loss.

---

* *Direct Current Fundamentals.*

3. Antennas are used in transmitting stations to radiate electromagnetic waves into space. The electromagnetic energy came from electrical energy supplied to the antenna circuit. As far as the circuit is concerned, power has been absorbed; therefore the circuit has an equivalent resistance. This radiation effect can be represented in the circuit by a resistance which will dissipate the same amount of power as was radiated into space. This resistance is known as the *radiation resistance* of the antenna. In an antenna, radiation is desirable. However, any wire or coil carrying current will also radiate electromagnetic energy to some degree. In this case, the power radiated because of the equivalent radiation resistance represents a power loss.

Effective resistance. Any component (wire, coil, resistor, or plate) having a certain resistance in a D.C. circuit, will be found to have a higher resistance in an A.C. circuit. At low frequencies the increase in resistance may be small (in some cases almost negligible), but as the frequency of the supply voltage is increased the resistance of the unit will increase markedly. The resistance of any component in an A.C. circuit is called the *effective resistance. Unless otherwise stated, when a resistance value is specified in an A.C. circuit, this value is the effective resistance of the unit.* In view of the previous paragraph, it is not surprising to find that the resistance of circuit elements is higher on A.C.

The effective resistance value of any unit is made up of the following components:

1. D.C. or *ohmic* resistance, due to its length, cross-sectional area, and specific resistance of the material.

2. Eddy current losses in the unit itself or in any metallic material within reach of the magnetic field produced when the unit carries current. This is particularly noticeable in radio coils with close-fitting shields.

3. Hysteresis losses in the iron of the unit itself or in any iron material within reach of its magnetic field.

4. Dielectric or leakage losses in the insulation of the unit or in surrounding objects within reach of the dielectric field around it.

5. Radiation losses, due to magnetic field energy which reaches out into the space surrounding the unit while the current is building up and does not return to the circuit when the current decays.

6. Skin effect (see page 63) which decreases the effective cross-sectional area of a wire.

Since all the preceding factors (except ohmic resistance) increase with frequency, effective resistance also increases with frequency. A resistance measurement made on D.C. or at low frequency may be valueless at radio frequencies. For accurate results at high frequencies, it is important that the effective resistance be known (or measured) at the frequency range desired.

Skin effect. As pointed out above, skin effect reduces the effective area of a wire. This is due to magnetic effects. When a wire carries current, a magnetic field is produced which encircles the wire. These lines of force are present not only around the outside of the conductor, but also *within* the conductor itself. As the current rises and falls (A.C.) these lines cut the conductor. Since the lines originate at the center of the conductor, more lines cut the center of the conductor than the outer layers. The induced voltage produced by the cutting will also be greater at the center. But induced voltages oppose the flow of current—less current flows through the center than through the outer layers! At high frequencies (greater speed of cutting) the induced voltage at the center is so high that practically no current flows through this section. The conducting area of the wire is reduced, thereby increasing the resistance of the path. Larger diameter wires would have to be used to compensate for this loss of effective area. Flat strip conductors are very poor. Current flows only along the outer edges, giving a very high ratio of effective to ohmic resistance.

In high current, high frequency circuits, where very low resistance is important, tubular conductors are often used in place of solid conductors. The center of the solid conductor would be ineffective, whereas all the material of the tube is effective. For the same weight of copper, the tube would have a much lower effective resistance.

Another way of reducing skin effect is the use of *Litzendraht* (Litz) wire. This conductor consists of a large number of small enameled wires, insulated from each other except at ends where they are carefully cleaned and paralleled. By proper interweaving of the strands, each single conductor will have the same average flux cuttings throughout its length. The current will divide equally among the strands. From another viewpoint, since current travels along the surface of the conductor (due to skin effect), using a larger surface area will reduce resistance. Many individual conductors of small diameter will have a larger surface area than a single conductor of the same total diameter.

Current flow in an A.C. circuit. In a D.C. circuit, one terminal is always positive, the other always negative. If the circuit is closed, electrons will flow from the negative terminal through whatever units are connected in the circuit, to the positive terminal; then, due to the action of the power supply, back to the negative terminal and round and round again if the circuit is closed for a long time. Such a circuit is shown in Fig. 5-1.

When the switch is closed, the ammeter indicates 2 amps. An electron from A has started to move toward J. The switch is now opened. That particular electron may only have reached point C. Meanwhile, an electron from B may have reached point D; another electron originally at C may have reached point E; others may have progressed from D to F, from E to G, from F to H, from G to I, from H to A, etc. No one electron went through the complete circuit,

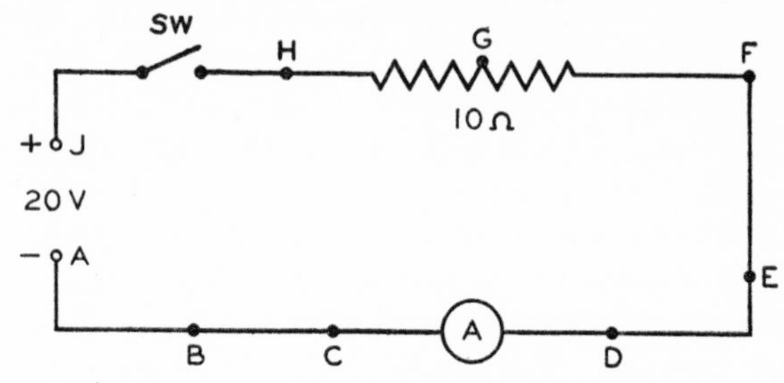

Fig. 5-1. Current flow in a D.C. circuit.

yet electrons were in motion *throughout* the circuit from A toward J. Current is flowing and power is being dissipated just as completely as if electrons had made complete 'trips.'

If the voltage were raised to 40 v, and the switch were closed and opened quickly, a current of 4 amps would flow for a short time. Again no electrons may move through the complete circuit. Since the current is higher it means that more electrons are in motion from A to J throughout the circuit. Remember that current is a measure of the number of electrons passing a given point in the circuit in a given time.

Now let us suppose that in the above circuit the switch is closed and then opened sooner. Again, during the time the circuit is closed, electrons throughout the circuit are in motion from A toward J. This time, however, an electron from A may only reach B, another at C may only reach D, from G to H, etc. Electrons will move a shorter distance—but these small electron motions take place everywhere in the circuit.

What is the nature of current flow in an A.C. circuit? The answer should now be obvious. Since the magnitude of the voltage is varying ($e = E_{max} \sin \theta$), the number of electrons in motion in any one direction is also varying. Since the polarity of the circuit reverses every half-cycle, electrons will move in one direction for one-half cycle and then move in the opposite direction for the next half-cycle. Current flow for a complete cycle would be as follows:

1. At the beginning of a cycle, the current is zero—no electrons are in motion in one particular direction.
2. For the first quarter-cycle, current starts to flow, more and more electrons start to move *toward* one supply terminal until the current reaches a maximum.
3. For the next quarter-cycle, current still flows in the same direction, but the number of electrons in motion is decreasing, until finally the current is again zero.
4. For the third quarter-cycle, current now starts to flow in the opposite direction. The number of electrons in motion increases until the current reaches a maximum.
5. During the last quarter-cycle, current still is flowing in this opposite direction, but the number of electrons in motion is decreasing until the current is once more zero.

How far does any one electron travel around the circuit? This depends upon how long does the supply voltage maintain any one polarity, or what is the frequency of the supply voltage. If the frequency is very low, the electrons will have more time to travel in any one direction and may move quite a distance around the circuit. But just imagine, at a frequency of 1 megacycle, the time for 1 cycle is 1 microsecond ($t = 1/f$) and for 1 half-cycle only half a microsecond. How far does an electron move around the circuit? It just about starts to move in one direction when it stops and moves in the opposite direction! *But electrons are in motion throughout the circuit, in one direction and then the other. No matter how short the distance traveled in any one direction, it still constitutes current flow.*

Current flow in an A.C. circuit may be considered as an oscillatory motion—like the motion of a pendulum—back and forth, with increasing and decreasing quantities of electrons in motion.

Current and voltage relations in resistive circuit. Figure 5-2a shows a resistor connected to an $833\frac{1}{3}$-cycle supply. The time for one cycle is $1/f$ or 0.0012 second. The accompanying figure, 5-2b, shows how the potential of point B (with respect to A), varies with time.

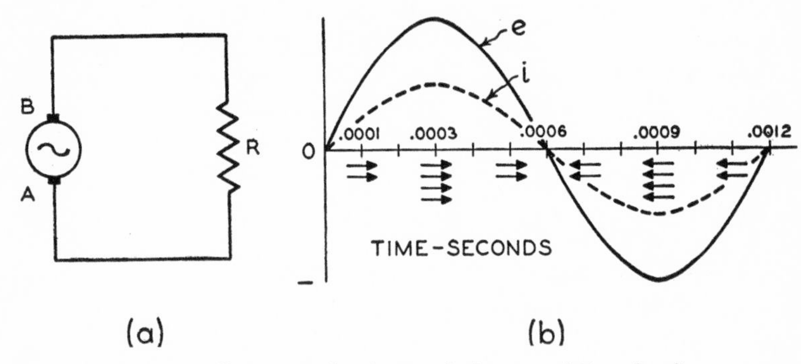

Fig. 5-2. Current and voltage relations—resistive circuit.

The current flowing in the circuit *at any instant* (i) is determined by the resistance of the circuit and the instantaneous voltage at that time. This is the same as Ohm's law in any D.C. circuit. However, since the voltage is varying, so must the current.

1. At time equals zero, the voltage is zero and no current is flowing.

2. At time equals 0.0001 second (30 degrees later), the potential of point B is positive, and the voltage has reached half its maximum value. A certain amount of current is now flowing. This is indicated by the double arrow in Fig. 5-2b. Electrons are in motion from terminal A toward B.

3. At time equals 0.0003 second (90 degrees), the potential of terminal B has reached a maximum. The current flowing from A toward B is also a maximum. In the diagram this is shown by four arrows.

4. Time equals 0.0006. There is no difference of potential between terminals A and B. No current flows.

5. Time equals 0.0009. Terminal B is now negative compared to terminal A, and the difference in potential is a maximum. The current flowing will be a maximum (four arrows) but electrons are moving *from B toward A*.

6. Elapsed time is 0.0012 second. There is no difference in potential between the two terminals. No current flows.

The instantaneous value of the current flowing in the circuit is shown in Fig. 5-2b by the dashed curve. Notice that it is also a sine wave, and that it is in phase with the applied voltage. *The current flowing through a resistor is always in phase with the voltage across it.*

Ohm's law A.C. resistive circuit. Ohm's law can be applied to an A.C. resistive circuit in exactly the same way as we did for a D.C. circuit. The only point to remember is that since A.C. values may be instantaneous, average, rms, or peak values, the same A.C. value must be used for both current and voltage. For example, if the voltage given is an instantaneous value, the current will also be an instantaneous value. If the voltage is a peak value, the current will be the maximum value. As stated earlier (Chapter 2) effective values are most commonly used in A.C. work and, unless otherwise stated, current and voltages are effective (rms) values.

EXAMPLE 1

A resistor of 20 ohms is connected across a 120-v 60-cycle supply. Find (a) the peak voltage across the resistor, (b) the current in the circuit and, (c) the maximum current through the resistor.

SOLUTION

(a) $$E_{\text{max}} = \frac{E}{0.707} = \frac{120}{0.707} = 170 \text{ v}$$

(b) $$I = \frac{E}{R} = \frac{120}{20} = 6.0 \text{ amps}$$

(c) $$I_{\text{max}} = \frac{I}{0.707} = \frac{6.0}{0.707} = 8.48 \text{ amps}$$

or $$I_{\text{max}} = \frac{E_{\text{max}}}{R} = \frac{170}{20} = 8.48 \text{ amps}$$

Vector representation—resistive circuits. In Chapter 3, we showed how vectors could be used to represent effective (or maximum) values of currents and voltages and the phase angles between them. Separate scales can be used for currents and voltages. However all currents (and all voltages) in the same problem must be to the same scale. The previous problem (Example 1) can be represented vectorially as shown in Fig. 5-3.

Notice that the current and voltage are drawn in phase. Also notice that the current vector is shown with a closed arrowhead. This system of differentiating current and voltage vectors will be used throughout the text to avoid confusion between them.

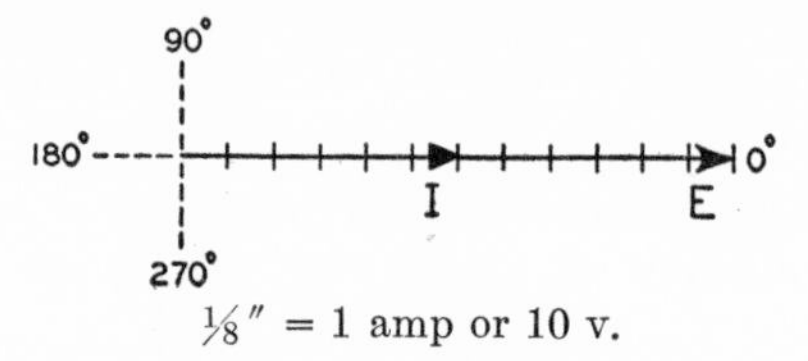

Fig. 5-3. Vector representation—resistive circuit.

Power in resistive circuits. In any given D.C. circuit, currents and voltages are constant and the power dissipated by the circuit is the product of the voltage and the current. On the other hand, currents and voltages in an A.C. circuit are continuously varying. But the power at any instant is equal to the product of the instantaneous values of the voltage and current at that instant, or

$$p = e \times i$$

A graphical plot of this relation is shown in Fig. 5-4. The ordinate of the power curve at any instant is the product of e and i.

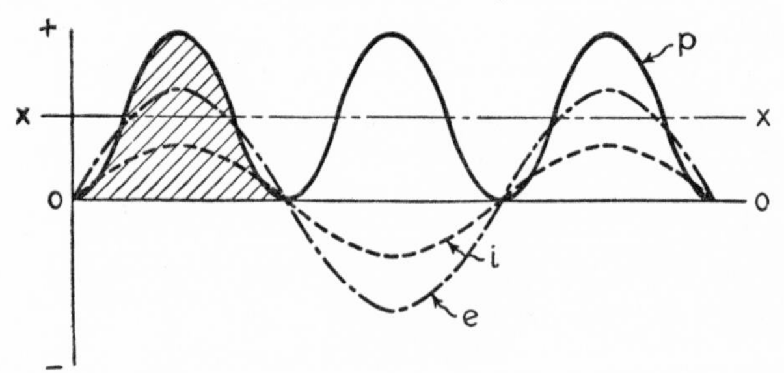

Fig. 5-4. Power in a pure resistive circuit.

Examine the power curve carefully. There are several important facts brought out:

1. The power curve is always positive. During the second half-cycle, current and voltage values are negative, but the power (product of two negative values) remains positive. *This means that a pure resistance takes power from the source during the entire cycle* regardless of the direction of current flow.

2. The instantaneous power varies from zero to a maximum value (equal to $E_{max}I_{max}$) twice during each cycle of the current and voltage wave.

3. The power curve is also of sine wave form, but of twice the frequency of the voltage (or current) wave. The zero axis of this curve is shifted upward from *O-O* (the normal axis) to *X-X*.

Since current and voltage are in phase, and their maximum values occur at the same time, the maximum power taken by the circuit is the product of the maximum value of current and voltage, or

$$P_{max} = E_{max} \times I_{max}$$

Line *X-X* occurs at half the maximum height of the power curve. But line *X-X* is the axis of this curve, or the power curve is symmetrical around line *X-X*. Therefore, line *X-X* represents the average heights of the power curve, or the average power delivered to the resistive load. The average power is one-half of the maximum power:

$$P_{av} = \frac{P_{max}}{2} = \frac{E_{max}I_{max}}{2}$$

Replacing the denominator, 2, by its equivalent $\sqrt{2} \times \sqrt{2}$, we get

$$P_{av} = \frac{E_{max}}{\sqrt{2}} \times \frac{I_{max}}{\sqrt{2}}$$

$\frac{E_{max}}{\sqrt{2}}$ and $\frac{I_{max}}{\sqrt{2}}$ equal $0.707E_{max}$ and $0.707I_{max}$ respectively.

But these are the rms values!

Therefore, the average power taken by a resistive load in an A.C. circuit is the product of the effective values of current and voltage, or

$$P = E \times I$$

EXAMPLE 2

A resistor of 700 ohms is connected to an A.C. supply having a maximum value of 400 v. What is the power taken by the circuit?

SOLUTION 1

1. $E = 0.707E_{max} = 0.707 \times 400 = 282.8$ v
2. $I = \frac{E}{R} = \frac{282.8}{700} = 0.404$ amps
3. $P = E \times I = 282.8 \times 0.404 = 114.3$ watts

SOLUTION 2

$$1.\ P = \frac{E^2}{R} = \frac{(0.707E_{\max})^2}{R} = \frac{0.5 \times 400 \times 400}{700} = \frac{800}{7} = 114.3 \text{ watts}$$

Measurement of power. As you learned in your earlier studies, the power taken by a load can be measured directly by use of a wattmeter.* The proper connections for a wattmeter are shown in Fig. 5-5.

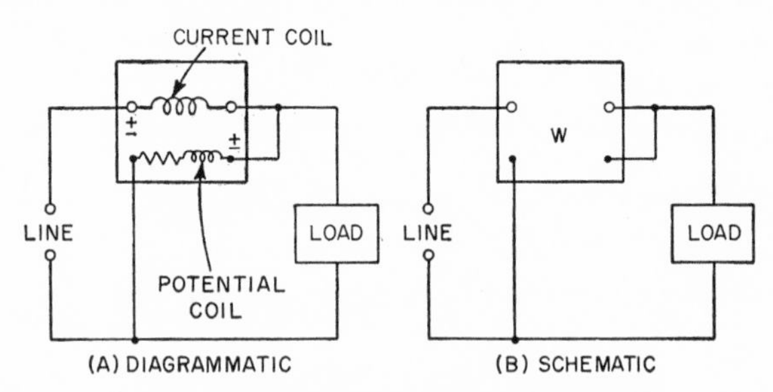

Fig. 5-5. Wattmeter connections.

The wattmeter has four terminals—two circuits. The *current coil* terminals (usually larger in size) are connected in series with the circuit just as for an ammeter. The *potential coil* terminals are connected across the circuit like any voltmeter. Notice, however, that the ± terminal of the current coil is connected to the *line* side of the circuit and that the ± terminal of the potential coil is connected to the same line lead as the current coil. Reversal of either winding will result in a backward deflection.

Review Problems

1. Name six factors that affect the resistance of any component in an A.C. circuit.

2. Explain briefly each of the six factors in Problem 1 above.

3. Explain two ways of reducing skin effect.

4. (a) How does current flow in a D.C. circuit differ from current flow in an A.C. circuit?

(b) What is the effect of frequency on the nature of the current flow?

---

* For details see *Direct Current Fundamentals*, Chapters 5 and 16.

5. The resistance of an air-core inductor as measured with a Wheatstone bridge is 129 ohms. It is connected to a 400-cycle aircraft supply. The line current and circuit power as measured by an ammeter and wattmeter, respectively, are 1.46 amps and 288 w.

(a) Find the resistance of the coil and account for the change.

(b) When a brass core is inserted through the center of the coil, the new instrument readings are 1.39 amps and 290 w. Find the new resistance and account for the change.

(c) The brass core is replaced by an iron core. The instrument readings drop to 0.90 amp and 145 w. Find the new resistance and account for the change.

(d) Why was there a drastic decrease in current in step (c) above?

6. A resistor of 4000 ohms is connected to a 500-cycle supply having a maximum value of 300 v.

(a) What value would an ammeter in the circuit indicate?

(b) Draw the vector diagram.

7. Find the average power dissipated in a resistive circuit, and either E, I, or R:

(a) $E_{max} = 200$ v, $I_{max} = 1.5$ amps.

(b) $E_{max} = 500$ v, $R = 1800$ ohms.

(c) $E = 300$ v, $I_{av} = 0.48$ amps.

(d) $E = 40$ v, $I = 30$ ma.

(e) $I_{max} = 90$ ma, $R = 2500$ ohms.

8. A transmitter is rated at 200 w output. When the transmitter is fully loaded, the antenna current is 2.5 amps. What is the radiation resistance of the antenna?

CHAPTER 6

Capacitance as a Circuit Element

CAPACITORS ARE USED IN electronic circuits for one of three basic purposes:

1. To 'couple' an A.C. signal from one section of a circuit to another.
2. To block out any D.C. potential from some component.
3. To by-pass or filter out the A.C. component of a complex wave.

In the 'power' field you will find capacitors used to supply starting torque and to improve the running characteristics of single-phase motors. In a later chapter you will also see their use for power factor correction. In preparation for this later section, let us now study the action of capacitors as circuit elements.

From your studies of the action of capacitors in a D.C. circuit* several important factors should be recalled. Let us review these briefly. We saw that when a capacitor is first connected to a steady voltage supply, the current flow is a maximum. Gradually the capacitor charges, building up voltage in opposition to the supply voltage. Due to this opposing voltage, the current drops slowly to zero. The time required to charge the capacitor and for the current to drop to zero depends upon the time constant of the circuit (R.C.). If the circuit contains no resistance, and the unit is a perfect capacitor (has no resistance), the time constant of the circuit is zero! This means that the capacitor will charge to the full supply voltage in zero time. Obviously, in a pure capacitive circuit, when the switch is first closed, the current is a maximum at the start, charges the capacitor to the full supply voltage, and drops to zero—all instantaneously! After that inrush transient condition, the current remains zero for as long as the supply voltage is constant.

---

* See *Direct Current Fundamentals*, Chapter 20.

In the same chapter we also pointed out that capacitance is the property of a circuit (or component) which allows a current to flow *when the voltage across it is changing.* The capacitance is 1 farad if 1 ampere flows through the circuit when the voltage changes at the rate of 1 volt per second. Now let us see how this applies to an A.C. circuit.

Current and voltage relation—pure capacitive circuit. Figure 6-1 shows a perfect capacitor connected to an A.C. supply. The sine wave, solid curve, shows the variation of the applied voltage with time.

Let us assume that the circuit is closed when the supply voltage is at its maximum positive value (point A). At this point the

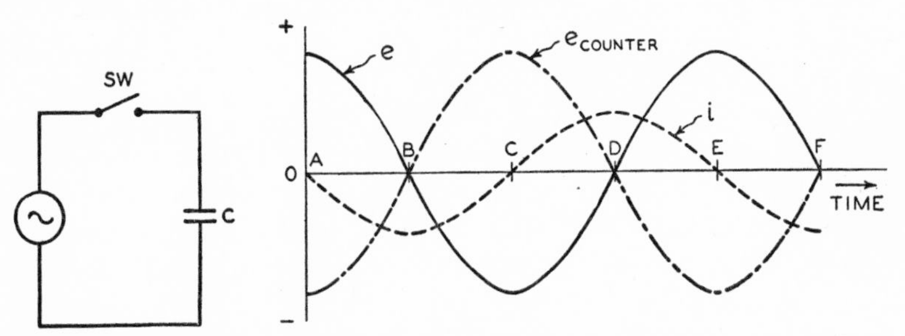

Fig. 6-1. Current and voltage relations—pure capacitive circuit.

voltage, for this brief instant, is constant. For this brief instant the situation is similar to a D.C. circuit—there is an inrush of current, the capacitor charges to the E_{max} value, and the current drops to zero.

Neglecting the brief transient condition, we have the following conditions:

1. Line voltage—maximum positive.
2. Capacitor countervoltage—maximum negative.
3. Current—zero.

This is shown in Fig. 6-2a. But the supply voltage does not remain constant. Between time interval A to B, the voltage drops. During this interval, the capacitor countervoltage tends to be higher than the supply voltage. The capacitor will discharge into the line! Current will flow in the circuit, but the current is negative. At the start, the supply voltage is dropping slowly. Therefore the net circuit voltage (capacitor voltage minus supply voltage) is very low. The current will be low (see Fig. 6-2b). As

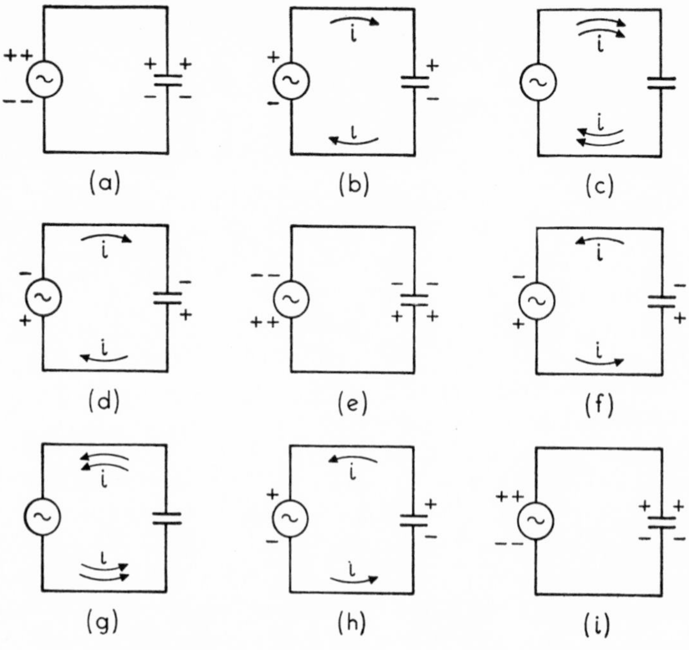

Fig. 6-2. Charge and discharge of a capacitor on alternating current (time references to Fig. 6-1).

(a) At time instant A: capacitor fully charged.
(b) During time interval A-B: capacitor discharging.
(c) At time instant B: capacitor fully discharged.
(d) During time interval B-C: capacitor charging with opposite polarity.
(e) At time instant C: capacitor fully charged again.
(f) During time interval C-D: capacitor discharging.
(g) At time instant D: capacitor fully discharged.
(h) During time interval D-E: capacitor charging with original polarity.
(i) At time instant E: capacitor fully charged.

time approaches point B, the supply voltage is dropping faster and faster. The net circuit voltage is increasing—the current will rise higher and higher. At point B, the line voltage is dropping at its fastest rate, and the current is a maximum. At this point, the new conditions are:

1. Line voltage—zero.
2. Capacitor completely discharged and its countervoltage—zero.
3. Current—maximum negative.

This condition is shown in Fig. 6-2c.

Between time B and C, the supply voltage is rising toward its negative maximum. Since the capacitor is discharged, and the voltage is at first rising rapidly, the line now sends maximum current into the capacitor. The line voltage is negative, the current is negative, and the capacitor starts to charge with reverse polarity (see Fig. 6-2d). As time approaches point C, the supply voltage rises more slowly, the capacitor countervoltage builds up as it charges, and the current drops rapidly. Finally, at point C, we again reach a momentary static condition:

1. Supply voltage—negative maximum
2. Capacitor countervoltage—positive maximum
3. Current—zero

This condition is shown in Fig. 6-2e.

During time interval C to D, the supply voltage is dropping. Again the capacitor countervoltage tends to exceed the supply voltage. But the capacitor is now charged of opposite polarity. Current will flow from the capacitor into the line. This time the current will be positive. As before, the current will at first be low in value (see Fig. 6-2f), but as time approaches point D, the supply voltage drops more rapidly and the current increases. At point D, the supply voltage is changing at its fastest rate—the current is a maximum. Meanwhile the flow of current out of the capacitor has discharged the capacitor. At point D, the conditions are (see Fig. 6-2g):

1. Line voltage—zero.
2. Capacitor countervoltage—zero.
3. Current—positive maximum.

From time equals D to E, the supply voltage is rising toward its positive maximum value. Since the capacitor is discharged, current flows into the capacitor, charging it in the original positive direction. The current flowing is still positive, but as the capacitor charges, and the line voltage rises more slowly, the current is dropping, till at point E the current is zero. Complete curves of supply voltage, capacitor countervoltage, and current are shown in Fig. 6-1. What are the phase relations?

1. Current leads the supply voltage by 90 degrees.
2. Capacitor countervoltage and line voltage are 180 degrees out of phase.

In any pure capacitive circuit, the line current leads the supply voltage by 90 degrees.

Current flow in a capacitive circuit. In D.C. theory, we learned that current will flow in a circuit only if the circuit is continuous and conducting. We also learned that a capacitor consists of two parallel conducting plates separated by the dielectric material, which is an insulator. Well, how does current flow in a capacitive circuit if the continuity of the circuit is broken by an insulating material? It does sound impossible—yet we know that it does!

The trouble is really in the terminology commonly used. We often speak of the current flow through a circuit, through a resistor, or through a capacitor, etc. In this text, we also have been using the same expressions. But notice that in starting this paragraph we have carefully used current flow *in* a circuit. You will recall that in Chapter 5 we covered current flow in A.C. circuits (page 64). In order for current to flow in a circuit, it was not necessary for electrons to flow completely around the circuit. Current flow was defined as *electrons in motion throughout the circuit in one general direction, regardless of how far they traveled in that direction.* Due to the alternating nature of the supply voltage, current flow in an A.C. circuit was found to be of an oscillatory nature—that is, the electrons move back and forth in the circuit.

A capacitor will allow such motion of electrons to take place. Therefore current can flow in a capacitive circuit. In each cycle of the supply voltage, during the time that the supply voltage is rising, electrons will flow from the negative line terminal *toward* one plate of the capacitor. Electrons will be stored on this plate, giving it a negative charge. Electrons from the other plate will be repelled by this negative charge and also will be attracted by the positive line terminal. Electrons will flow from this plate *toward* the positive line terminal. Electrons were in motion *throughout the circuit from negative to positive line terminals.* Therefore, from our previous definition, current is flowing in the circuit.

Quite often you hear the expression 'current flow through the capacitor.' In the preceding explanation, electrons were stored on one plate of the capacitor; electrons were removed from the opposite plate of the capacitor; *but no electrons actually went through the capacitor!* No electrons can pass through the unit unless the dielectric breaks down, in which case the capacitor is ruined.

Since a capacitor does allow current to flow in a circuit, we often simplify the mental picture by saying that current is flowing through the circuit and through the capacitor. This 'white lie' does not affect the accuracy of any calculations, and it does make reference to current flow in capacitive circuits much easier—so we will still use it, now that you know the true concept.

Capacitive reactance (X_c). You will recall that as a capacitor is charged it builds up a countervoltage across its plates. The voltage developed depends on the capacitance of the unit and the charge (number of electrons) stored on the plates: $E = Q/C$. The larger the capacitance, the lower the voltage built up across the unit by any given number of electrons on its plates.

Now let us consider a capacitor of infinite capacitance connected across the A.C. supply. As the line voltage rises, the capacitor starts to charge. But due to the large capacitance of the unit, no opposing voltage is built up across its plates, and there is no limiting action on the flow of current in the circuit.

What would happen if the unit had a low capacitance? As the line voltage rises, the capacitor would charge, but now the back voltage builds up rapidly. The net voltage in the circuit is reduced, and the current flow is limited to a low value. This reaction of a capacitor is called *capacitive reactance* (X_c). Since the current-limiting action of a capacitor is similar in effect to resistance in a D.C. circuit, reactance is also measured in ohms. The larger the capacitance of a capacitor, the lower the countervoltage built up across the capacitor and the lower the reactance. In other words, the reactance of a capacitor varies inversely with its capacitance.

Does frequency have any effect on the reactance of a capacitor? Definitely! The lower the frequency, the more time the capacitor has to charge up and the greater the limiting action. A more exact way of considering this relationship follows. Neglecting the initial transient charging current, no current flows in a capacitive circuit if the supply voltage is steady (D.C. circuit). If the voltage is increased, the capacitor charges further; current flows again. If the voltage decreases, current flows as the capacitor discharges. The amount of current flowing, in either case, will depend upon the *rate at which the voltage is changing.* On low frequencies, the voltage changes slowly; current is low. On high frequencies, the voltage changes rapidly with time; therefore, the current will be higher.

The reactance of a capacitor increases as the frequency of the applied voltage is decreased. On D.C., the reactance would be infinite. The rate of change of voltage in any A.C. circuit depends not only on frequency but more specifically on the angular velocity of the generating coil. In Chapter 2, we showed that the angular velocity (ω) was equal to $2\pi f$. Therefore, capacitive reactance varies inversely with angular velocity (ω) or $2\pi f$.

Since the reactance of a capacitor varies inversely with capacitance and with angular velocity ($2\pi f$ or ω), the equation for this effect is

$$X_c = \frac{1}{2\pi f C} = \frac{1}{\omega C}$$

If the frequency is expressed in cycles, and the capacitance in farads, then X_c will be in ohms. Since capacitor values are usually expressed in microfarads, we can convert the above equation by multiplying the numerator by 10^6. (For C in $\mu\mu$f use 10^{12}). Also, for slide rule calculations it is easier to replace $1/2\pi$ by its equivalent 0.159. Combining these two points we get

$$X_c = \frac{1}{2\pi f C} = \frac{0.159 \times 10^6}{fC} \qquad \text{where } C \text{ is in } \mu\text{f}$$

EXAMPLE 1

What is the reactance of a capacitor of 0.5 μf at 2000 cycles?

SOLUTION

$$X_c = \frac{1}{2\pi f C} = \frac{0.159 \times 10^6}{2000 \times 0.5} = 159 \text{ ohms}$$

This relationship between capacitance, frequency, and reactance is very important. Let us check if you understand it. How would you find the reactance of the above capacitor if the frequency is tripled? Would you go through the complete calculation as for Example 1? If so, you would get the correct answer—but you are not thinking! There is a much simpler way. We learned that the reactance, X_c, decreases with increase in frequency. Tripling the frequency will cut the reactance to one-third of the previous value or $\frac{159}{3} = 53$ ohms.

In general, if we know the reactance at any one frequency, we can find the reactance for any other frequency by multiplying the known reactance by the ratio of the two frequencies. The frequency ratio could be taken two ways: original to new frequency or new frequency to original. Which is correct? We could prove mathematically that the former ratio is correct. That means memorizing a formula. A little common sense is preferable. If the new frequency is higher, the new reactance must be lower: Use the ratio that will result in a smaller answer. Could anything be simpler? Let us try the idea in another example.

EXAMPLE 2

A capacitor has a reactance of 320 ohms at 5000 cycles. What is its reactance at 3500 cycles?

SOLUTION

1. Since the new frequency is lower the new reactance must be higher.

2. $X_{c_2} = X_{c_1}\frac{f_1}{f_2} = 320 \times \frac{50}{35} = 457$ ohms.

3. The answer is higher—check.

The third step of the solution may seem ridiculous to you. Please remember that when you forget to make this simple check, apply formulas blindly, and come out with opposite result. Such an answer is far more ridiculous!

One more problem—this time to see if your algebraic transformation is correct.

EXAMPLE 3

Find the capacitor needed in Example 2.

SOLUTION

$$C = \frac{1}{2\pi f X_c} = \frac{0.159 \times 10^6}{5000 \times 320} = 0.1\ \mu\text{f}$$

In case you forgot—the 0.159 is $\frac{1}{2\pi}$, and the 10^6 was used to get the answer in microfarads.

Ohm's law—capacitive circuit. Ohm's law can be applied to a capacitive circuit in the same manner that it is used for resistive circuits. Since reactance is measured in ohms, we merely replace resistance by reactance:

$$I = \frac{E}{X_c}$$

In this equation no subscripts are shown for I and E. This means they are effective values or rms values. This equation can be used equally well for maximum or instantaneous values as long as both current and voltage values are maximum or instantaneous values.

EXAMPLE 4

A capacitor of 0.02 μf is connected across a 500-v, 4000-cycle source. Find the current in the circuit.

SOLUTION

1. $X_c = \frac{1}{2\pi fC} = \frac{0.159 \times 10^6}{4000 \times 0.02} = 1990$ ohms.

2. $I = \frac{E}{X_c} = \frac{500}{1990} = 0.251$ amp.

Vector representation—capacitive circuits. Vector representation is applied to capacitive circuits in exactly the same way as for resistive circuits. Again different scales can be used for current and voltage. The only point to remember is that current in a pure capacitive circuit leads the voltage by 90 degrees. Figure 6-3 shows a vector diagram for the values in Example 4 above.

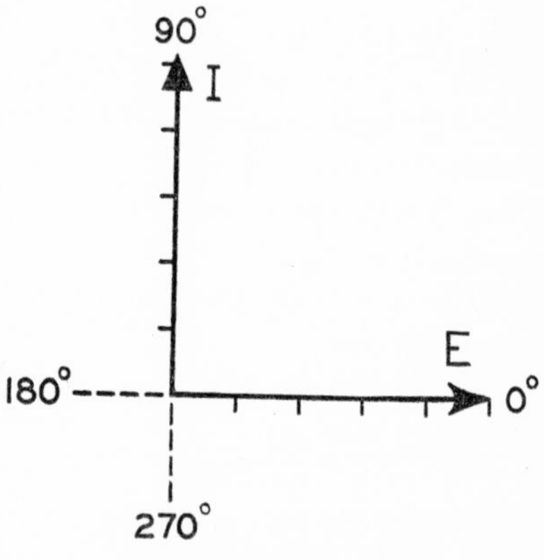

¼″ = .05 amp or 100 v.

Fig. 6-3. Vector diagram—capacitive circuit.

Power in pure capacitive circuits. We have already seen that the instantaneous power in an A.C. circuit is equal to the product of the instantaneous voltage and the instantaneous current. If we plot the current and voltage waves, with the proper phase relation, then for a number of values along the time axis, we multiply the instantaneous values of e and i and plot this new wave, and we have the power curve. Such a plot is shown in Fig. 6-4. Notice that, as in a resistive circuit, the power curve is a sine wave of twice the frequency of the current or voltage wave. However, the zero axis of the power curve is the same as the zero axis for the current and voltage waves. Let us analyze this curve more closely.

1. During the first quarter-cycle, the current is positive. Current is flowing into the capacitor, charging it. The power is also positive, again showing that the capacitor is charging. It takes energy from the source and stores this energy in its dielectric field.

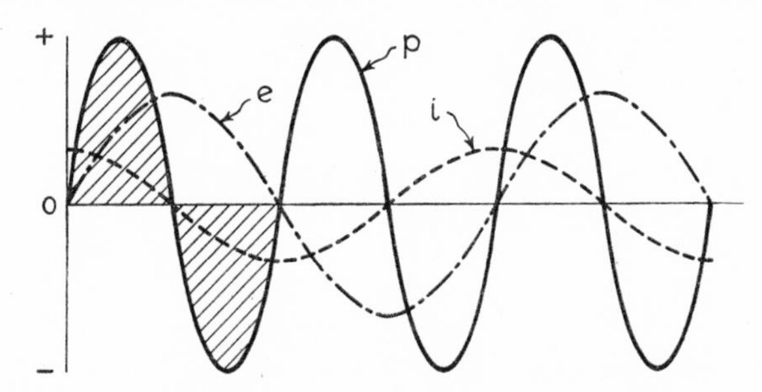

Fig. 6-4. Power in a pure capacitive circuit.

2. During the second quarter-cycle, the supply voltage is dropping, the capacitor is discharging, and the energy from the dielectric field is being *returned* to the line. The power is therefore negative.

3. Third quarter-cycle—the supply voltage is now rising to its negative maximum. The capacitor is charging again. It must take energy from the supply source and store it in its dielectric field. Therefore, the power is again positive.

4. Fourth quarter-cycle—line voltage is dropping. The capacitor must discharge and return its energy to the supply source. The power is negative.

During the first and third quarter-cycles, the capacitor takes power from the line, and the power is positive. In the other portions of the cycle, the capacitor returns this power to the line, and the power is negative. Therefore the total power dissipated in one full cycle is zero. *A perfect capacitor does not dissipate power.*

Power factor. If a capacitor is connected to an A.C. supply and a voltmeter, ammeter, and wattmeter are included in the circuit, we will find that:

1. The voltmeter will indicate the effective value of the supply voltage (E).

2. The ammeter will indicate the effective value of the circuit current (I).

3. The wattmeter will indicate zero! This is not surprising since we just explained by wave analysis that no power is dissipated by a pure capacitive circuit. Yet for resistive circuits we proved that the power dissipated is the product of the effective values of current and voltage. In a resistive circuit, the current and voltage are in phase, while in the capacitive circuit, current leads voltage by 90 degrees. Obviously, the phase angle between current and voltage is responsible for this discrepancy. Our power equation must be corrected by some term which includes phase angle. This term is called the *power factor* and is equal to the cosine of the phase angle. The general equation for power in an A.C. circuit is:

$$P = EI \cos \theta$$

where θ is the phase angle.

In a resistive circuit, current and voltage are in phase, the phase angle is zero, and the cosine of zero degrees is unity. Therefore the $\cos \theta$ term drops out, and the equation is the same as previously given for resistive circuits ($P = EI$). In a pure capacitive circuit, the phase angle is 90 degrees. The cosine of 90 degrees is zero. Therefore the power is zero.

$$P = EI \cos 90° = EI \times 0 = 0$$

This is in agreement with our theoretical conclusions.

The product of voltage and current is sometimes referred to as the *apparent power*. Since it is not actually a true power measurement, it is more commonly referred to as **volt-amperes** (**va**) or **kilovolt-amperes** (**kva**).

From the power factor of a circuit, we can immediately tell if there is a phase shift between current and voltage. The lower the power factor, the greater the phase shift (from 0 to 90 degrees). However, we cannot tell from power factor, ammeter, voltmeter, or wattmeter reading whether the current is leading or lagging.

Review Problems

1. (a) What is the phase relation between current and voltage in a pure capacitive circuit?

(b) Show this relationship by vector diagrams, first using voltage as the reference vector and then using the current as reference.

2. Explain current flow through a capacitor.

3. (a) What is meant by capacitive reactance?
(b) How is this reactance affected by frequency?
(c) How is this reactance affected by the size of the capacitor?

4. (a) What is the reactance of a 5 μf capacitor at 100 cycles?
(b) At 4000 cycles?

5. What size capacitor should be used to obtain 2000 ohms reactance at 1000 cycles?

6. At what frequency will a 100 $\mu\mu$f capacitor have a reactance of 10,000 ohms?

7. In audio work, it has sometimes been stated that a by-pass capacitor should have a reactance of not more than one-tenth the value of the resistor it is shunting at the lowest frequency. If the resistance value is 1500 ohms, what capacitance value should be used for:
(a) Speech frequency band of 200 to 3000 cycles.
(b) High fidelity band of 20 to 15,000 cycles.

8. A capacitor of 8 μf is connected to a 400-v 120-cycle supply.
(a) Find the current in the circuit.
(b) Draw the vector diagram.

9. When a capacitor is connected to a 120-v 60-cycle line, it draws a current of 0.54 amp. Find the capacitance of the unit.

10. In a pure capacitive circuit, the current and voltage are 8 ma and 350 v. The frequency is 15 kc. What is the capacitance of the circuit?

11. (a) What is the general equation for power in any A.C. circuit?
(b) What is meant by volt-amperes? How does it differ from power?

12. Calculate the power dissipated in each of the following:
(a) Pure capacitive circuit, $I = 5$ ma, $E = 300$ v.
(b) Pure resistive circuit, $I = 80$ ma, $E = 200$ v.
(c) $I = 50$ ma, $E = 200$ v, current leading the voltage by 80 degrees.
(d) $I_{max} = 100$ ma, $E_{max} = 500$ v, current lagging by 40 degrees.
(e) What is the power factor in each of the above?

CHAPTER 7

Inductance as a Circuit Element

HAVE YOU EVER BEEN CURIOUS ENOUGH to look up the circuit diagram of your radio receiver at home? Maybe you have seen the diagram of some other radio receiver. If so, you must have noticed inductances used in the tuning circuits that make it possible for you to tune in the desired station; or in the audio or power transformers; or as chokes in the power supply filter. These circuits and other applications of inductances will be covered in a subsequent text. Meanwhile, before we can analyze such circuits we must understand the role of inductances as circuit elements.

When D.C. is applied to an inductive circuit, the current at first is zero. A short period of time is required before the current reaches its maximum, steady state or Ohm's law value.* The time required for the current to reach its Ohm's law value depends on the time constant of the circuit (L/R). The lower the resistance of the circuit, the longer this time interval will be. This slow rise of current was due to the counter-electromotive force induced in a coil whenever the current *tends* to change. We also learned that the magnitude of this back emf depended upon the inductance value (L) and the rate at which the flux produced by the coil cuts its own turns—or the rate of change of current (i/t).

Current and voltage relation—pure inductive circuit. Let us consider a perfect inductance (resistance of the coil is zero) connected to an A.C. supply source, and that the circuit is closed at the instant the supply voltage reaches its positive maximum. The circuit and the sine waves of supply voltage, current and counter-emf are shown in Fig. 7-1.

At the instant the switch is closed, the situation is identical to a D.C. circuit. The voltage is at its maximum positive, and at this point it is constant for a short duration. Since the circuit has no

---

* See *Direct Current Fundamentals*, Chapter 19.

resistance, the current would tend to rise to a very high value. The rate of rise of current would be a maximum and a high induced voltage (cemf) is developed. This induced voltage is equal and opposite to the line voltage. Therefore, the current is actually zero. Another way of explaining this is that the time constant (L/R) for this circuit is infinite. (Remember—the resistance of the

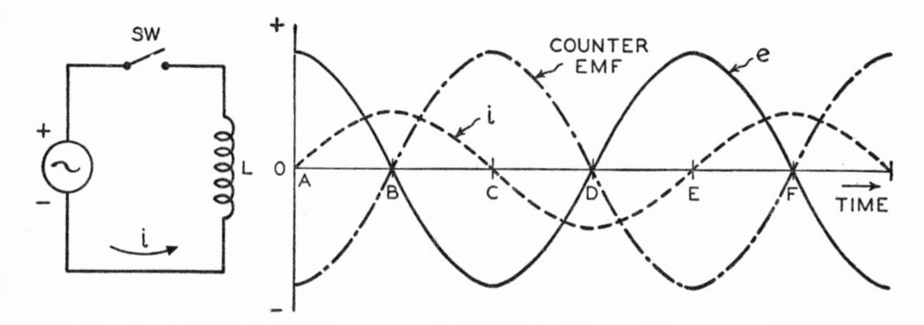

Fig. 7-1. Current and voltage relations—pure inductive circuit.

circuit is zero.) So, the current starts at zero and begins to rise to its Ohm's law value very gradually. As the current is rising, the line voltage starts decreasing. But the current still continues to rise! Why?

1. On D.C., the current rises slower and slower as it approaches its maximum value. (It is an exponential curve.)

2. Due to the fall in supply voltage on A.C., the current will rise even slower than in a D.C. circuit.

3. Since the rate of rise of current is decreasing, the induced voltage must also decrease.

4. The fall in line voltage is offset by the decrease in the opposing induced voltage—the current continues to rise until the line voltage reaches zero.

How can a high value of current flow when the supply voltage is zero? It sounds ridiculous! Let's take it slower. Just before the voltage reaches zero, it has some low value, let us say 0.001 v. Since the circuit resistance is zero (*pure inductive circuit*), the current, by Ohm's law, would be infinite. Even if the voltage were only one-tenth, one-hundredth, etc., of this value, the current would still be infinite. Of course, since the circuit is inductive as long as any line voltage is still applied and the current tends to rise just a hair more—a small amount of induced voltage is also present to limit the flow of current, and so the current rises to some finite value right up to the point of zero line voltage. We have completed the conditions for the first quarter-cycle of current flow (A to B). The current in the circuit diagram has been flowing counter-clockwise, starting at zero value and increasing to a maximum value.

During the first quarter-cycle above, the magnetic field strength was increasing, and energy was stored in the magnetic field. Now, at point B, the supply voltage reverses and starts to build up in the opposite direction. In a resistive circuit, the current would also reverse. The current in our circuit is now at its maximum value. It cannot continue to rise. It must drop to zero and then reverse. But this is an inductive circuit! Any tendency for the current to decrease will give rise to an induced voltage in a *positive* direction, that will try to maintain the current flowing in the original direction. Therefore, the current drops slowly from its maximum value toward zero. The magnetic field is giving up its energy.

As the energy in the magnetic field decreases, the current drops faster and faster. Since the current is changing more rapidly, the counter emf increases. Finally at point C, the supply voltage is a maximum negative; the current is zero, but it is changing at its fastest rate; the induced voltage is a maximum positive. This completes the first half-cycle.

During the next half-cycle, the conditions are similar to those discussed above—except that all values are reversed in polarity. The current now starts to flow in a clockwise direction. The explanation for the phase relations are the same as before. Now examine the entire curve shown in Fig. 7-1. The applied voltage leads the current (or vice-versa, the current lags the line voltage) by 90 degrees. Also, the induced voltage and supply voltage are 180 degrees apart. Comparing current and induced voltage, the induced voltage lags the current by 90 degrees. All three curves are sine waves of the same frequency. *In a pure inductive circuit, the current lags the supply voltage by 90 degrees.*

Inductive reactance (X_L). We have just seen that, due to the induced voltage in an inductive circuit, the current never reaches its D.C. value. Obviously, the inductance produces an opposition to current flow in an A.C. circuit. *This effect is called inductive* *reactance* (X_L). As in a capacitive circuit, this opposition to current flow is also measured in ohms.

What factors affect the inductive reactance of any coil? We know it depends upon the induced voltage. But the induced voltage increases with the value of the inductance. It also increases with the rate of change of current $\left(e = -L\frac{di}{dt}\right)$. But the current varies at the same frequency as the applied voltage or the angular velocity of the generating coil. Therefore, inductive reactance is equal to

$$X_L = 2\pi fL = \omega L$$

Example 1

Find the reactance of a 20-henry coil at 120 cycles.

Solution

$$X_L = 2\pi fL = 2\pi \times 120 \times 20 = 15{,}080 \text{ ohms.}$$

From our analysis of inductive reactance, and also from the equation, you can see that the reactance varies directly with frequency and with inductance. When it is necessary to find the reactance of a given coil at several frequencies, it is often more convenient (by slide rule) to use the ratio method.

Example 2

Find the reactance of the inductance in Problem 1 at 50 cycles.

Solution

1. Since the frequency is lower, the reactance should be lower, by the same proportion.

2. $X_{L_2} = X_{L_1}\frac{f_2}{f} = 15{,}080 \times \frac{5}{12} = 6280$ ohms.

3. $X_{L_2} = 2\pi f_2 L = 2\pi \times 50 \times 20 = 6280$ ohms (check).

Example 3

An R.F. circuit requires a choke coil (inductance) having a reactance of not less than 50,000 ohms at 500 kc. What is the minimum value of inductance that can be used?

Solution

$$L = \frac{X_L}{2\pi f} = \frac{0.159 \times 50{,}000}{500 \times 10^3} = 15.9 \text{ millihenries.}$$

Ohm's law inductive circuit. As in a capacitive circuit, Ohm's law can be used to show the relation between current, voltage and reactance:

$$I = \frac{E}{X_L}$$

The equation is stated in terms of effective values. Remember, it applies equally well to maximum, average and instantaneous values, as long as both current and voltage are the same type of values.

EXAMPLE 4

A coil of 50 millihenries is connected to a 20-v 12,000-cycle supply. Find the current in the circuit.

SOLUTION

1. $X_L = 2\pi fL = 2\pi \times 12{,}000 \times 50 \times 10^{-3} = 3770$ ohms.
2. $I = \dfrac{E}{X_L} = \dfrac{20}{3770} = 0.00531$ amps $= 5.31$ ma.

Vector representation—inductive circuits. How to use vectors to represent phase relations in an inductive circuit should be obvi-

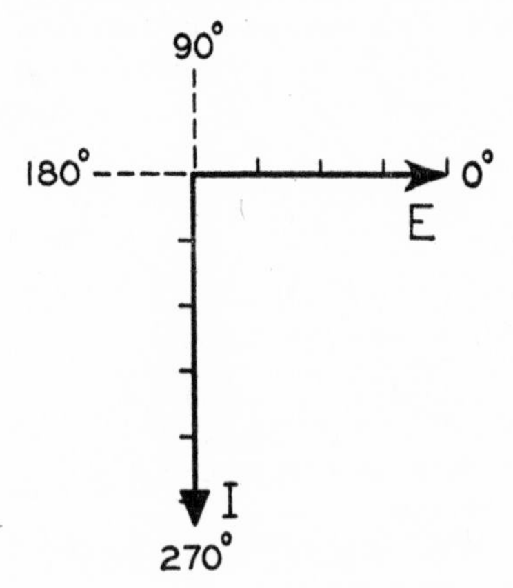

$\frac{1}{4}'' = 1$ ma or 5 v.

Fig. 7-2. Vector representation—inductive circuit.

ous. The method is the same as for capacitive and resistive circuits. The only point to remember is that the current lags the supply voltage by 90 degrees. As an illustration, we will use the results of Example 4 above. (See Fig. 7-2.)

Power in pure inductive circuits. Since the instantaneous power depends on the product of the instantaneous values of current and voltage, let us plot such curves. (See Fig. 7-3). Then for several

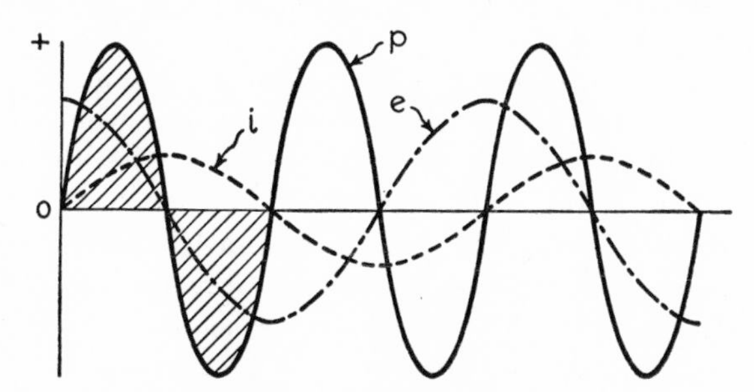

Fig. 7-3. Power in a pure inductive circuit.

points along the time axis, the product of e and i will give the points for the power curve.

As in the case of a pure capacitive circuit, notice that:

1. The power curve is a sine wave of double frequency.
2. The average power, for one full cycle of current, is zero.

During the first quarter-cycle, as the current is rising, a magnetic field builds up around the inductance. Energy is stored in the magnetic field. The line supplies power to the circuit. As the current drops to zero, in the second quarter-cycle, the magnetic field around the coil is collapsing. Energy is returned to the line—the power is negative. In the third quarter-cycle, the current builds up to a negative maximum. The magnetic field again grows stronger, but of reversed magnetic polarity. The line is now supplying power to the circuit. Energy is stored in the magnetic field. The fourth quarter-cycle is a repetition of the second quarter-cycle—current drops to zero, magnetic field collapses, energy of the field is returned to the line, power is negative. This analysis again shows that *a pure inductive circuit dissipates no power.*

In terms of power factor, what does this mean? The power factor in a pure inductive circuit must be zero. This should have been obvious to you—the phase angle between current and voltage is 90 degrees; therefore $\cos \theta$, or the power factor, is zero.

Losses in inductances. In the preceding descriptions, we have been considering a *pure* inductive circuit. This assumes that the inductance and wiring have no losses. Practically, such a circuit does not exist. A coil can be made to *approach* a perfect inductance. The better the quality of the coil, the closer we get to a pure inductance, but some losses still exist. These losses can be classified as follows:

1. *Ohmic (D.C.) resistance of the winding:* Since a coil is wound with wire, it still has a D.C. resistance, no matter what size wire is used. Naturally, the larger the diameter of the wire, the lower this loss.

2. *Effective resistance:* As you learned in Chapter 5, resistance in an A.C. circuit is higher than the ohmic value because of skin effect, core losses, and radiation losses. Since these were discussed before (page 62), nothing further need be added. With careful design, the effective resistance of a coil can be reduced to a minimum.

3. *Effect of coil shields:* For use at radio frequencies, coils are often enclosed in a copper or aluminum shield. These shields are needed to prevent interaction with stray fields from other units. But the shields are of conducting material! Therefore, if they are cut by the field of the coil, eddy-current losses result. Coils for use at low frequencies (power or audio) are often encased in heavy cast-iron shields. This shields the unit against magnetic fields. However, again we have eddy-current losses and, in addition, hysteresis losses. Shields will therefore increase the effective resistance or losses of a coil. Good practice recommends that a shield be at least twice the diameter of the coil in order to reduce these losses.

Shielding will also affect the inductance of air-core or open-core coils. A magnetic shield will act as a part of the magnetic path decreasing the reluctance. This increases the flux and, in turn, increases the inductance of the coil. Non-magnetic shields act oppositely. They are good conductors, and the resulting eddy currents set up their own flux, which is opposite to the coil flux. This reduces the net flux, lowering the inductance of the coil.

4. *Figure of Merit-Q:* In order to compare the quality of coils, a comparison is made between the inductive reactance and the

effective resistance of any coil. This is called the *figure of merit or Q* of a coil.

$$Q = \frac{X_L}{R} = \frac{\omega L}{R}$$

The Q of a coil varies with frequency. Both the inductive reactance and effective resistance increase with frequency but not at the same ratio. It is, therefore, important when specifying the figure of merit of any coil that it be calculated for the band of frequencies on which the coil is to be used.

EXAMPLE 5

A coil of 80 μh is to be used at a frequency of 500 kc. Its resistance at that frequency is 3.0 ohms. What is the figure of merit of the coil?

SOLUTION

1. $X_L = 2\pi fL = 6.28 \times 500 \times 10^3 \times 80 \times 10^{-6} = 251$ ohms.

2. $Q = \frac{X_L}{R} = \frac{251}{3.0} = 83.7$

High frequency effects. We have already seen that skin effect becomes more prominent at higher frequencies. This would increase the effective resistance and reduce the Q of a coil. To reduce this loss, litz wire or tubing is used to minimize the skin effect. With iron-core coils, core losses would become terrific. Laminating the iron is sufficient at low frequencies. At medium frequencies, powdered iron cores have proven satisfactory. With such cores, the inductance values are obtained with smaller windings. The reduction of effective resistance of the winding more than offset the core losses. The Q of the coil is increased. At higher frequencies, the core losses, even with powdered iron, are prohibitive.

At high frequencies, distributed capacity of coils becomes important. Each turn of wire is a conductor. The insulation between wires is a dielectric. A small capacitor is formed between each turn. At very high frequencies, the inductive reactance may be higher than the capacitive reactance. More current will flow through the distributed capacity of the coil than through the winding itself! Unless special precautions are taken, an inductor may actually act as a capacitor.

To reduce distributed capacitance, the winding of a radio frequency choke coil is often sectionalized. In addition, use of fine wire, space winding, and criss-cross winding in place of parallel winding also minimize the capacitance between turns. Figure 7-4 shows the use of criss-cross winding and sectionalized winding.

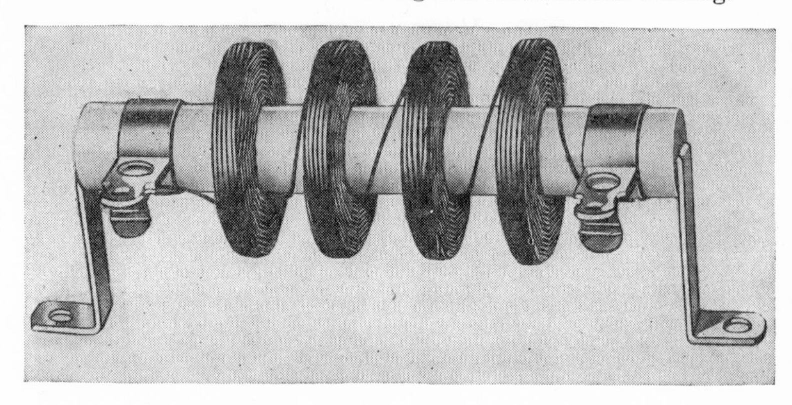

Fig. 7-4. Coil construction to reduce distributed capacity. (*Courtesy J. W. Miller Co.*)

Nomograms. Nomograms are often used in electronic work to avoid calculations. You may have seen these charts before. Typical applications are for calculation of:

1. Resistors in parallel.
2. Inductors in parallel.
3. Capacitors in series.
4. Inductive reactance.
5. Capacitive reactance.
6. Capacity-inductance-frequency relations.

The use of nomograms is very simple. Merely locate the two given values on the chart. Lay a straight edge across these points. Where it intersects the third axis, read the answer. Figure 7-5 shows nomograns for inductive and capacitive reactance. An illustration will best explain their use.

In Example 1 Chapter 6, we found that the capacitive reactance of a $0.5\mu f$ condenser at 2000 cycles was 159 ohms. On the nomogram the answer is approximately 170 ohms. The second illustration is for Example 1 in this chapter. The mathematical solution showed that the reactance of a 20-henry coil at 120 cycles was 15,080 ohms. From the nomogram, the answer is approximately 15,000 ohms.

Use of nomograms is NOT recommended for such simple calculations. The nomogram shown covers too wide a range of values, and the results are only approximations. The accuracy of the answers can be increased by dividing the nomogram into several interrelated sheets, with each chart covering only a small portion

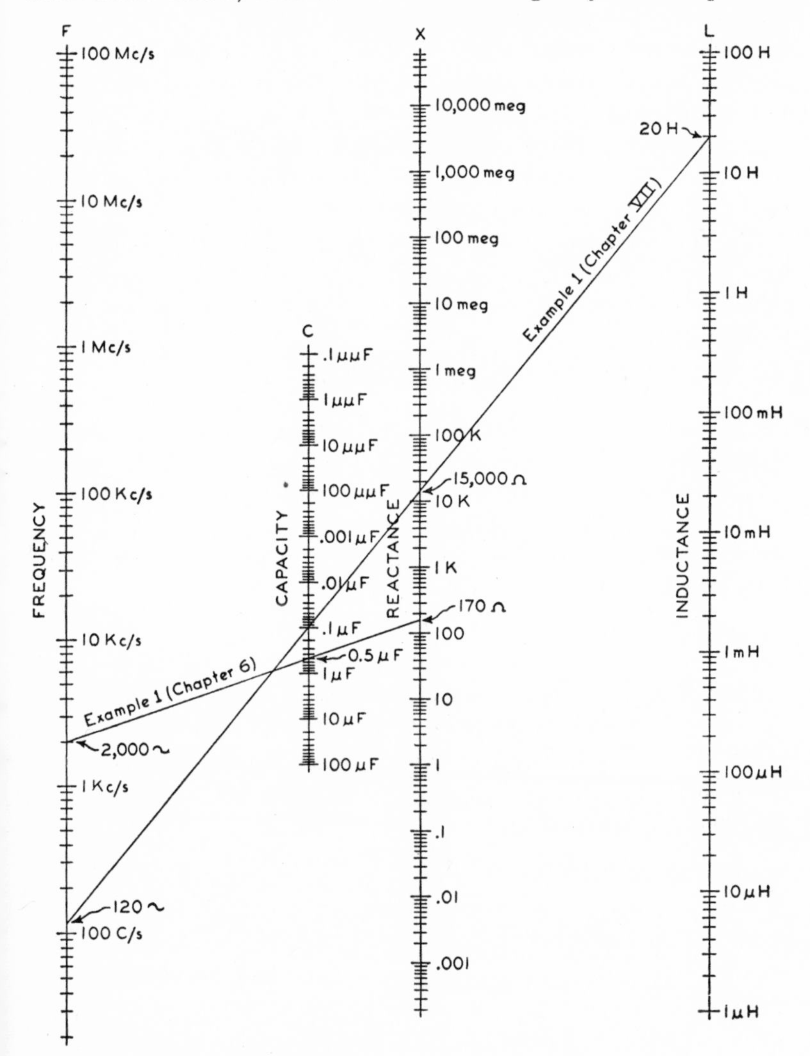

Fig. 7-5. Inductive and capacitive reactance nomogram.

of the full range. Any saving in time by use of such devices is extremely doubtful. First, you must have the series of charts and a straight edge (preferably a transparent one, such as a drafting triangle). Second, selecting the correct chart and finding the given values takes time. Third, accurate setting of the straight edge is important. Last, you must interpolate the answer. A slide rule applied to the formula is just as quick and more accurate. Since their use is not recommended, then why were they even mentioned? For two reasons:

1. Where repetitive calculations are to be made, or where the solution of the equations involved is very laborious, nomograms are used to great advantage in industry.

2. You may run across their use on the job. Ignorance is not bliss. Now at least you know what they are, know their limitations, and if you do use them on occasions, you can use them judiciously.

Review Problems

1. Explain why the current in an inductive circuit does not rise immediately to full value.

2. How do the inductance and resistance of the circuit affect the time delay in the rise of current?

3. (a) What is the phase relation between current and voltage in a pure inductive circuit on A.C.?

(b) Show this phase relation by vector diagram, using voltage as the reference vector.

(c) Repeat (b), using current as reference.

4. (a) What two factors influence the inductive reactance of a coil?

(b) How does the reactance vary with each?

5. What is the reactance of a 20-mh coil at 1500 kc?

6. What value inductance would be needed to obtain a reactance of 250,000 ohms at 4000 kc?

7. At what frequency will a coil of 300μh have a reactance of 3000 ohms?

8. A coil of 80 mh is connected across a supply of 30 v, 800 cycles.

(a) What is the current in the circuit?

(b) Draw the vector diagram.

9. In a pure inductive circuit, the current and voltage are 120 ma, 40 v, respectively. If the frequency is 1200 cycles, what is the inductance value?

10. An inductance of 250 μh has a resistance of 45 ohms at 2000 kc. What is the figure of merit of the coil?

11. What is the resistance of a 75-μh coil if its Q is 90 at 1.5 megacycles?

12. A 320-μh coil, for use at 500 kc, has a Q of 120. Find its resistance.

13. Explain the effect of shielding on the resistance and inductance of a coil.

(a) For a shield made of magnetic material.
(b) For a shield made of nonmagnetic material.

14. What is meant by 'distributed capacitance' in a coil? How is it minimized?

CHAPTER 8

Series Circuits—Basic Principles

ALTERNATING-CURRENT SERIES CIRCUITS 'obey' all of the principles previously discussed for direct-current circuits.* The correlation is complete if the circuit contains resistors alone. Where more than one type of circuit element (resistance, capacitance, or inductance) is involved, phase angles must be considered. However, the principles are still the same:

1. The current is the same in all the components. In vector diagrams, the current is therefore used as the reference vector.

2. The current in the circuit depends on the total opposition in the circuit. This opposition may consist of resistance, inductive reactance, capacitive reactance, or any combination thereof.

3. The total opposition is the sum of the oppositions of each component.

(a) If the circuit contains resistors alone, this total opposition is a resistance:
$R_T = R_1 + R_2 + R_3 \cdots$, as in any D.C. circuit.

(b) If the circuit contains capacitors alone, the total opposition is a reactance:
$X_{C_T} = X_{C_1} + X_{C_2} + \cdots$.

(c) If the circuit contains inductors alone, the total opposition is a reactance:
$X_{L_T} = X_{L_1} + X_{L_2} + \cdots$.

(d) If the circuit contains a combination of circuit elements, we cannot call the total opposition a resistance nor can we call it a reactance. It is given a new name, IMPEDANCE.

Each of these cases will be taken up in more detail in this chapter. It is recommended, particularly where the circuit con-

---

* See *Direct Current Fundamentals*, Chapter 7.

tains more than one type of circuit element, that a vector diagram be drawn, even if a mathematical solution is used.

Resistors in series. In a pure resistive circuit, whether the circuit contains one or a hundred resistors, the current is in phase with the line voltage. Since the current flows through each of the resistors, there is a voltage drop across each:

$$E_1 = IR_1; \qquad E_2 = IR_2 \cdots$$

Each of these voltage drops is in phase with the current. Since the phase angle is zero for the entire circuit, and also for any part of the circuit, this case is identical to a D.C. circuit and can be treated in the same manner. Therefore, no further discussion is necessary.

Capacitors in series. When capacitors are connected in series, the circuit is still a pure capacitive circuit. In such a circuit, we know that the current leads the applied voltage by 90 degrees. How much current flows in the circuit? That will depend upon the applied voltage and the *total* reactance. The total reactance depends on the total capacitance. In the previous volume,* we learned that when capacitors are connected in series the total capacitance is less than that of the smallest unit, or

$$\frac{1}{C_T} = \frac{1}{C_1} + \frac{1}{C_2} + \frac{1}{C_3} \cdots$$

1. From this relation we can find the total capacitance, C_T.
2. From C_T we can find the total reactance, X_{C_T}.
3. From the applied voltage we can find the line current, I.
4. Knowing that the current through each component is the same, we can find the voltage across each unit:

$$E_1 = IX_{C_1}; \qquad E_2 = IX_{C_2}; \qquad E_3 = IX_{C_3}; \cdots$$

This is exactly the same as we would do with a resistive circuit to find voltage drops.

5. Since the total circuit is a pure capacitive circuit, and since each unit is a pure capacitor, *the line voltage, and also the voltage across each capacitor, will lag behind the line current by 90 degrees.*

---

* *Direct Current Fundamentals*, Chapter 20.

EXAMPLE 1

A 2-μf, 4-μf, and 8-μf capacitor are connected in series across a 1000-cycle 150-v supply. Find the line current and the voltage across each unit.

SOLUTION

1. $\dfrac{1}{C_T} = \dfrac{1}{2} + \dfrac{1}{4} + \dfrac{1}{8}; \qquad C_T = 1.14\ \mu\text{f}.$

2. $X_{C_1} = \dfrac{1}{2\pi f C_1} = \dfrac{0.159 \times 10^6}{1000 \times 2} = 79.5$ ohms.

$X_{C_2} = \dfrac{1}{2\pi f C_2} = \dfrac{0.159 \times 10^6}{1000 \times 4} = 39.8$ ohms.

$X_{C_3} = \dfrac{1}{2\pi f C_3} = \dfrac{0.159 \times 10^6}{1000 \times 8} = 19.9$ ohms.

$X_{C_T} = \dfrac{1}{2\pi f C_T} = \dfrac{0.159 \times 10^6}{1000 \times 1.14} = 139$ ohms.

3. $I = \dfrac{E_T}{X_{C_T}} = \dfrac{150}{139} = 1.08$ amps.

4. $E_1 = IX_{C_1} = 1.08 \times 79.5 = 85.8$ v.
$E_2 = IX_{C_2} = 1.08 \times 39.8 = 43.0$ v.
$E_3 = IX_{C_3} = 1.08 \times 19.9 = 21.3$ v.
Check 150.1 v.

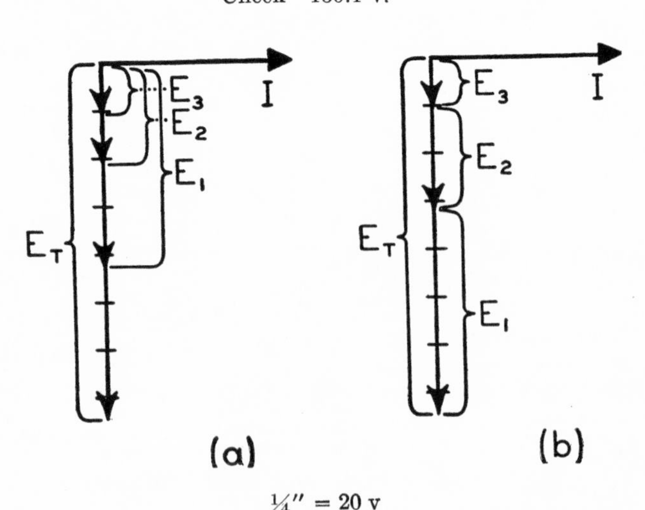

¼″ = 20 v

Fig. 8-1. Vector diagram—capacitive series circuit. (a) Individual voltages from zero reference. (b) Additive voltage reference.

Since all the voltages are in phase (with each other) we can add them numerically. Their sum is equal to the applied voltage. A vector diagram of this problem is shown in Fig. 8-1. Notice that the current is being used as the reference vector (0 degrees), and that each voltage lags the current by 90 degrees. Vector diagrams are best drawn on graph paper for convenient scales.

Inductors in series. We have already learned that when inductors are connected in series, the total inductance is the sum of the individual inductances:*

$$L_T = L_1 + L_2 + L_3 \cdots$$

We have also seen that in a pure inductive circuit, the current lags the applied voltage by 90 degrees. This, coupled with the treatment we just went through for capacitors in series, should make solution of such a type problem obvious:

1. Find the total inductance.
2. Find the total reactance and the reactance of each unit.
3. Find the current in the circuit by Ohm's law.
4. Find the voltage across each unit.

The vector diagram will be similar to Fig. 8-1. However, since we shall use current as the reference vector and since current now *lags* the applied voltage by 90 degrees, all voltages will be drawn *upward* instead of downward. Rather than using a similar type of problem to illustrate inductors in series, we will try a variation.

EXAMPLE 2

Three inductances, 30, 50, and 60 millihenries (mh) are connected in series to an A.C. supply. The current in the circuit is 0.5 amp. The voltage across the 30-mh coil is 40 v. Find the supply voltage, frequency, and voltage across each coil.

SOLUTION

1. $X_{L_1} = \frac{E_1}{I} = \frac{40}{0.5} = 80$ ohms.
2. $f = \frac{X_{L_1}}{2\pi L_1} = \frac{80}{6.28 \times 30 \times 10^{-3}} = 425$ cycles.
3. $X_{L_2} = 2\pi f L_2 = 6.28 \times 425 \times 50 \times 10^{-3} = 133$ ohms.
4. $X_{L_3} = 2\pi f L_3 = 6.28 \times 425 \times 60 \times 10^{-3} = 160$ ohms.

---

* *Direct Current Fundamentals,* Chapter 19.

5. $L_T = L_1 + L_2 + L_3 = 30 + 50 + 60 = 140$ mh.
$X_{L_T} = 2\pi f L_T = 6.28 \times 425 \times 140 \times 10^{-3} = 374$ ohms.
6. $E_1 =$ *Given* 40.0 v
$E_2 = IX_{L_2} = 0.5 \times 133 = 66.6$ v
$E_3 = IX_{L_3} = 0.5 \times 160 = 80.0$ v
$E_T = E_1 + E_2 + E_3 = 186.6$ v
$E_T = IX_{L_T} = 0.5 \times 374 = 187.0$ v (check)

Since all the voltages are in phase with each other, we can add them numerically for a check.

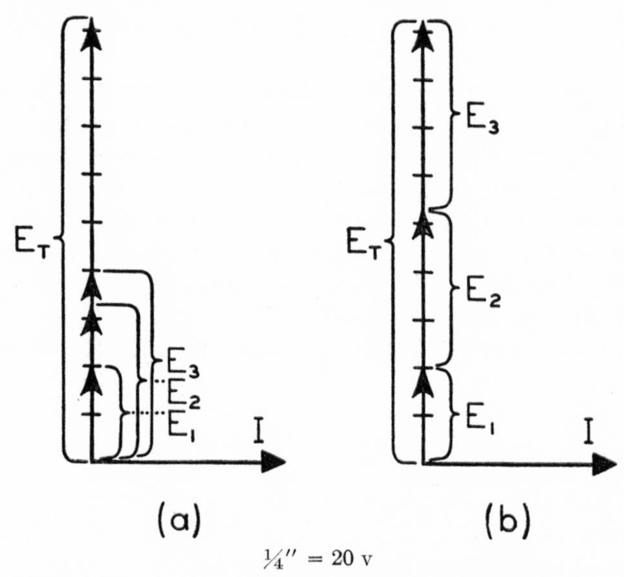

¼″ = 20 v

Fig. 8-2. Vector diagram—inductive series circuit. (a) Individual voltages from zero reference. (b) Additive voltage reference.

Resistance and Capacitance in Series

So far we have been considering series circuits containing only one type of circuit element. These circuits were comparatively simple because phase angles were the same in all parts of the circuit, as well as for the total circuit (zero for pure resistive circuits and 90 degrees for pure reactive circuits). We were therefore able to add oppositions and voltage drops numerically. Now, however, we begin to analyze circuits that contain more than one type of circuit element. Such circuits are very common in all types of electronic equipment.

If a resistor and a capacitor are connected in series, the current that flows in the resistor must be the same current that flows through the capacitor. This is true because it is a series circuit. We know that the volt drop across a resistor (IR) is in phase with the current. But the voltage across a capacitor (IX_c) *lags* the current by 90 degrees. As in any series circuit, the total voltage is equal to the sum of the voltage across each unit. Since the individual unit voltages are out of phase, this addition must be a *vector* addition.

Impedance, *Z*. In order to find the current in a series circuit, we must know the total opposition of the circuit. An *R-C* circuit has two types of oppositions, a resistance (due to R) and a reactance (due to C). Each of these oppositions is measured in ohms. We have already learned (page 96) that the total opposition in this type of circuit is called *impedance* (Z), and that it also is measured in ohms. Can we add resistance and reactance numerically to get impedance? No! The explanation is simple:

1. Current flowing through the resistor produces a voltage, IR, in phase with the current.

2. Current flowing through the capacitor produces a second voltage, IX_c, lagging the current by 90 degrees.

3. The total voltage must be equal to the product of this same current and the total opposition, IZ. But we also know that the total voltage is equal to the *vector sum* of IR and IX_c. Therefore, IZ is equal to the vector sum of IR and IX_c.

Let us consider an *R-C* series circuit where $R = 15$ ohms, $X_c = 20$ ohms, and the current in the circuit is 2 amps.

1. The voltage across the resistor, $E_R = IR = 30$ v, in phase with the current.

2. The voltage across the capacitor, $E_c = IX_c = 40$ v, lagging the current by 90 degrees.

3. To get the total voltage, IZ, we add IR and IX_c using the vector method explained on page 41.

This is shown in Fig. 8-3. Measuring the length of the resultant, IZ, we find that the total voltage is 50 v! Obviously, the voltages IR and IX_c cannot be added numerically.

Notice, in Fig. 8-3, that IR, IX_c and IZ form a right triangle, with IZ as the hypotenuse of the triangle. Also notice that the current, I, is the same for each of these voltages. Therefore, if we divide each value by I, we still have a right triangle with each

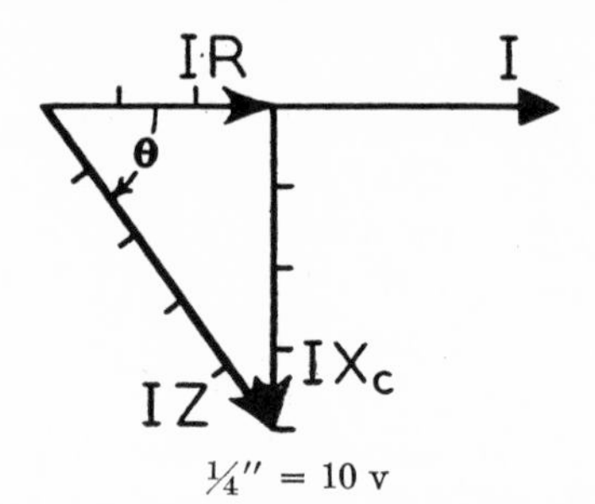

¼″ = 10 v

Fig. 8-3. Vector diagram—*R-C* series circuit.

side reduced in scale, by the value of I (in this case reduced by 2, since $I = 2$ amps). This new triangle is called the *impedance triangle* (see Fig. 8-4). The sides are $R = 15$ ohms, $X_c = 20$ ohms, and $Z = 25$ ohms. This shows definitely that to find the imped-

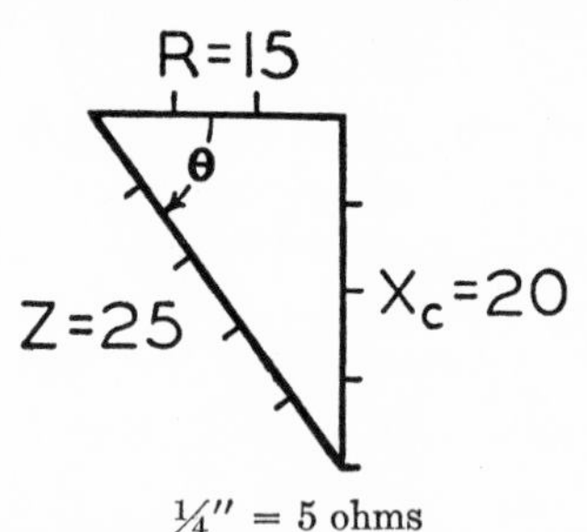

¼″ = 5 ohms

Fig. 8-4. Impedance triangle—*R-C* series circuit.

ance of a circuit, the resistance and reactance values cannot be added numerically. They must be added in vector fashion.

In drawing the impedance triangle, notice that no arrows are shown. This is because resistance, reactance, and impedance by themselves are *not* vector quantities. They act with the current, which is a vector, to produce voltages which are also vectors. Since resistance and reactance 'operate' on the current to produce voltages of different phase angles, they must be drawn at their 'operating' angle. That is, resistance must be drawn horizontally (zero phase angle), and reactance must be drawn vertically (90-degree phase rotation).

The preceding solution for impedance was a graphical one. We drew the values to scale and then measured the resultant. Graphical solutions are never too accurate, unless they are drawn to large scale and with great care. But we saw that the impedance triangle is a right triangle, with the impedance, Z, as the hypotenuse. We can, therefore, solve for Z trigonometrically. The hypotenuse of any triangle is equal to the square root of the sum of the squares of the sides. Therefore

$$Z = \sqrt{R^2 + X_c^2}$$

Using this method with our values of R and X_c above, we get

$$Z = \sqrt{R^2 + X_c^2} = \sqrt{(15)^2 + (20)^2} = 25 \text{ ohms}$$

This checks with our graphical answer.

Phase angle: *R-C* series circuit. In the problem illustrated in Fig. 8-3, we have three phase angles to consider:

1. The phase angle between the current and the voltage across the resistor, $E_R(=IR)$ = zero degrees.

2. The phase angle between the current and the voltage across the condenser, $E_c(=IX_c)$ = 90 degrees.

3. The circuit phase angle (θ). This is the angle between the line current and the total voltage (IZ). Applying a protractor to Fig. 8-3, this angle is measured as 53 degrees. If we apply the protractor to the impedance triangle (Fig. 8-4) we get the same answer, 53 degrees.

This gives us another means for getting the circuit phase angle—by trigonometry. We can use sine, cosine, or tangent function:

1. The cosine of the circuit phase angle is the ratio of the adjacent side (R) to the hypotenuse (Z) or:

$$\cos \theta = \frac{R}{Z}$$

and since arc cosine means '*the angle whose cosine is*'

$$\theta = \text{arc cosine } \frac{R}{Z} = \text{arc cosine } \frac{15}{25} = 53.1 \text{ degrees}$$

2. The sine of the circuit phase angle is the ratio of the opposite side (X_c) to the hypotenuse (Z) or

$$\sin \theta = \frac{X}{Z}$$

and $$\theta = \text{arc sin } \frac{X}{Z} = \text{arc sin } \frac{20}{25} = 53.1 \text{ degrees}$$

3. The tangent of the circuit phase angle is the ratio of the opposite side (X_c) to the adjacent side (R) or

$$\tan \theta = \frac{X}{R}$$

and $$\theta = \text{arc tan } \frac{X}{R} = \frac{20}{15} = 53.1 \text{ degrees}$$

Ohm's law: *R-C* series circuit. We have already covered all the theory pertinent to Ohm's law in an R-C series circuit. We have discussed the principles applicable to series circuits, and we have seen how to calculate impedance and phase angles. All we need to do now is to apply all of this to a problem.

Example 3

A resistor of 500 ohms is connected in series with an 0.05-μf capacitor across a 100-v, 8000-cycle supply. Find:

(a) Current in the circuit.
(b) Voltage across each unit.
(c) Circuit phase angle.
(d) Draw a vector diagram.

Solution

1. $X_c = \frac{1}{2\pi fC} = \frac{0.159 \times 10^6}{8000 \times 0.05} = 398$ ohms.

2. $Z = \sqrt{R^2 + X_c^2} = \sqrt{(500)^2 + (398)^2}$
$= 640$ ohms.

(a) $I = \frac{E}{Z} = \frac{100}{640} = 0.156$ amp.

(b) $E_R = IR = 0.156 \times 500 = 78.2$ v.
$E_c = IX_c = 0.156 \times 398 = 62.2$ v.

(c) $\theta = \text{arc tan } \frac{X}{R} = \text{arc tan } \frac{398}{500} = 38.5°$.

(d)

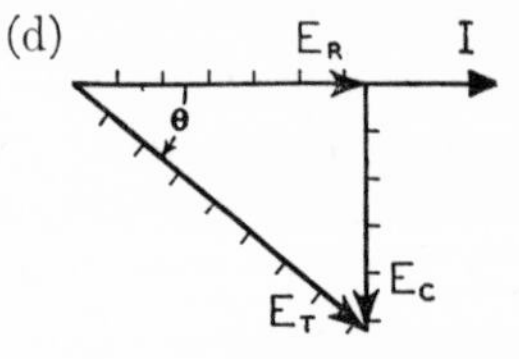

$\frac{1}{8}'' = 12$ v

Fig. 8-5. Vector diagram—R-C series circuit.

The above solution was by formulas throughout. In such cases the vector diagram need not be drawn to scale but can be a sketch to represent circuit conditions. If a graphical solution were used, it could only be applied to find impedance (Step 2) and circuit phase angle (Step 2c). The other portions of the problem must still be solved by formulas. With a graphical solution, the impedance triangle must be drawn accurately. The vector diagram could still be a sketch, since both Z and θ could be obtained from the impedance triangle.

Power in an *R-C* circuit. In a pure resistive circuit (page 68), we saw that the power curve (versus time) was always positive. On the other hand, in a pure capacitive circuit (page 80), the power curve was half positive and half negative—the average power for the cycle was zero. This was because the capacitor absorbed energy

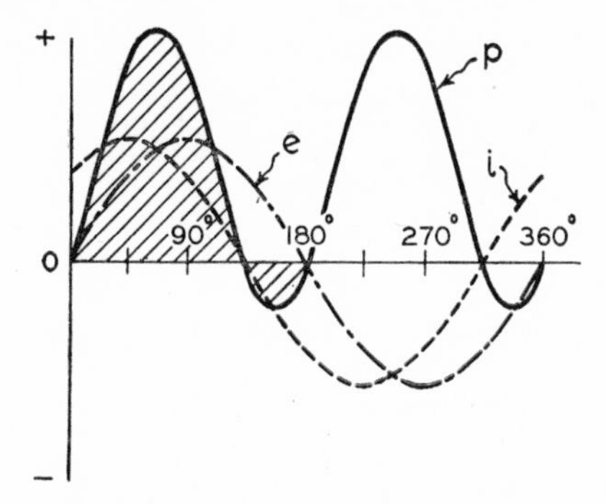

Fig. 8-6. Power in an *R-C* series circuit.

while charging and returned energy to the line when it discharged. What happens to the power curve when the circuit contains capacity and resistance in series? For simplicity, we will analyze such a circuit where the frequency of the input voltage, and the value of capacitance and resistance, are so selected that X_c is equal to R. In the impedance triangle, the tangent function (X_c/R) is equal to 1.0. The phase angle between current and line voltage is 45 degrees, with the current leading. Now we can plot the curves for e, i, and p with time. These curves are shown in Fig. 8-6.

Now carefully examine this curve (Fig. 8-6).

1. The power curve is partly negative, but mainly positive.

2. The total power (positive areas minus negative areas) for the cycle is positive. The energy is dissipated in the resistance of the circuit.

The power dissipated by the circuit is obviously less than the product of current and voltage. This checks with our previous analysis $P = EI \cos \theta$. Now let us examine this same circuit from a vector representation. The vector diagram is shown in Fig. 8-7.

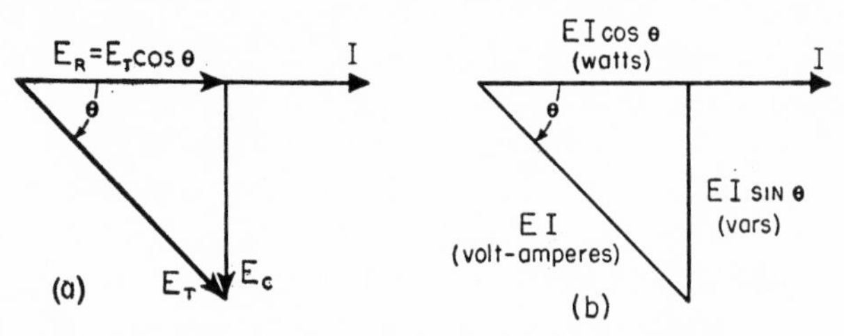

Fig. 8-7. Vector diagram—*R-C* series circuit.

We know that the power in any circuit where current and voltage are out of phase is given by

$$P = E_T I_T \cos \theta$$

Let us rewrite this as

$$P = (E_T \cos \theta) I_T$$

Now look at the vector diagram (Fig. 8-7); $E_T \cos \theta$ is equal to E_R! The power dissipated is therefore the product of current and *voltage across the resistor*. This should not be surprising. We know the capacitor dissipates no power, and therefore all the power dissipated in the circuit must be dissipated by the resistor.

Reactive volt-amperes (vars). Let us reëxamine the vector diagram Fig. 8-7(a). We see that $E_R = E_T \cos \theta$. But from our knowledge of trigonometry we can also see that $E_c = E_T \sin \theta$. Now if we multiplied our three voltage values by the *numerical* value of the current in the circuit, we would have another right triangle of the same relative proportions but larger in size. This new triangle is shown in Fig. 8-7(b). The horizontal line (vectorially in phase with I) would now be $EI \cos \theta$, or would represent the circuit power. The hypotenuse would now be EI and would represent the circuit volt-amperes. The third side, the vertical component (vectorially in quadrature with I) would now be

$EI \sin \theta$. Since it also is a product of voltage and current (amperes), it is called the *reactive volt-amperes* of the circuit. The basic unit for reactive volt-amperes is the *var*. This term is often used in 'power' circuits containing resistance and reactance and is equal to the product of line voltage, line current, and the *sine* of the circuit phase angle, or

$$\text{reactive volt-amperes (var)} = EI \sin \theta$$

Measurement of power. We saw in Chapter 5 how a wattmeter could be used in a pure resistive circuit to measure power directly. If a wattmeter were connected into a circuit containing resistance and reactance, would the meter indicate the true power ($EI \cos \theta$) or the volt-amperes (EI) taken by the circuit? We know that the torque or deflecting force in a wattmeter depends on the voltage across its potential coil and the current through its current coil. Before you jump to any rash conclusion, let us qualify that statement. The torque *at any instant* is proportional to the product of voltage and current *at that instant*. Now examine the wave diagrams of Fig. 8-6. The product of voltage and current at any instant is the instantaneous power curve p, and is the true circuit power. Since the wattmeter movement, due to its inertia, cannot follow the instantaneous variation in power, the meter indication will be proportional to the average power per cycle, or the true power taken by the load.

Commercial loads, particularly where motors are used, have both resistance and reactance. (Although the reactance is generally inductive, its effect on circuit power is similar to capacitance.) In such cases, since the circuit constants (R, L, C) or circuit power factor are seldom known, wattmeters are indispensable for finding the power taken by the load. In fact, when circuit power factor is desired, it is calculated from wattmeter, voltmeter, and ammeter readings.

EXAMPLE 4

A $\frac{3}{4}$-ton air conditioner draws 8.0 amps from a 120-v 60-cycle line. The power taken by this load, from a wattmeter reading, is 720 w. Find

(a) The volt-amperes of the load.
(b) The power factor of the load.
(c) The phase angle between line current and voltage.
(d) The reactive volt-amperes.

SOLUTION

(a) volt-amperes $= EI = 120 \times 8.0 = 960$ va.
(b) From $P = EI \cos \theta$,

$$\cos \theta = \frac{P}{EI} = \frac{720}{960} = 0.75$$

(c) $\theta = \text{arc} \cos 0.75 = 41.4°$.
(d) vars $= EI \sin \theta = 960 \times 0.6613 = 635$ vars.

Resistance and Inductance in Series

Here again we are faced with a circuit containing more than one type of circuit element. The analysis will be quite similar to an R-C series circuit. When a resistor and an inductor are connected in series, the current that flows through the resistor must be the same current that flows through the inductance. This current will produce a voltage drop (IR) across the resistance. We know that this voltage is in phase with the current. However, the voltage drop across the inductance (IX_L) will lead the current by 90 degrees. As in any series circuit, the total voltage is the sum of the voltages across each unit—but due to the phase angles of these voltages, the addition must be vectorial.

EXAMPLE 5

A current of 150 ma is flowing through a resistance of 1000 ohms and an inductance of 2 henrys. The frequency of the supply voltage is 50 cycles. Draw a vector diagram and find the supply voltage, and circuit phase angle.

SOLUTION

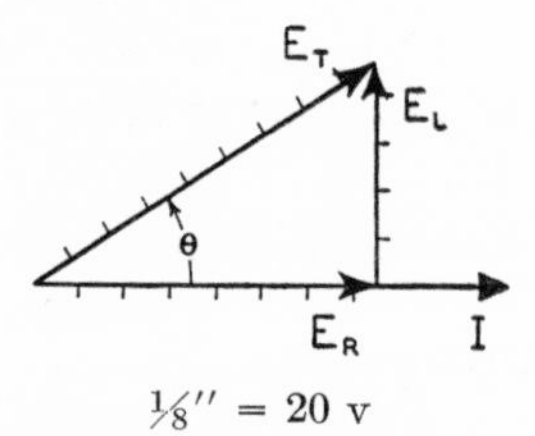

$\frac{1}{8}'' = 20$ v

Fig. 8-8. Vector diagram—R-L series circuit.

1. $E_R = IR = 0.15 \times 1000 = 150$ v.
2. $X_L = 2\pi fL = 6.28 \times 50 \times 2 = 628$ ohms.
3. $E_L = IX_L = 0.15 \times 628 = 94.2$ v.

4a. Graphical (Fig. 8-8): $E_T = 175$ v, leading by $\theta = 32°$.

4b. Mathematical: Since E_L and E_R are at right angles, we can solve for line voltage and circuit phase angle by trigonometry:

(1) $E_T = \sqrt{E_R^2 + E_L^2} = \sqrt{(150)^2 + (94.2)^2} = 177$ v.

(2) $\theta = \text{arc} \tan \dfrac{E_L}{E_R} = \text{arc} \tan \dfrac{94.2}{150} = 32.1°$.

Impedance: *R-L* circuit. Compare Fig. 8-8, for an inductive circuit, with Fig. 8-3, for the capacitive circuit. Notice that E_L is drawn upward (leading the current by 90 degrees), whereas E_c was drawn downward (lagging the current by 90 degrees). Since the voltage triangle

$$E_T = IZ; \qquad E_L = IX_L; \qquad E_R = IR$$

is the basis for the impedance triangle, the impedance triangle for an *L-R* circuit should be drawn upward.

Example 6

Find the impedance and phase angle for the circuit in Example 5.

Solution A—Graphical:

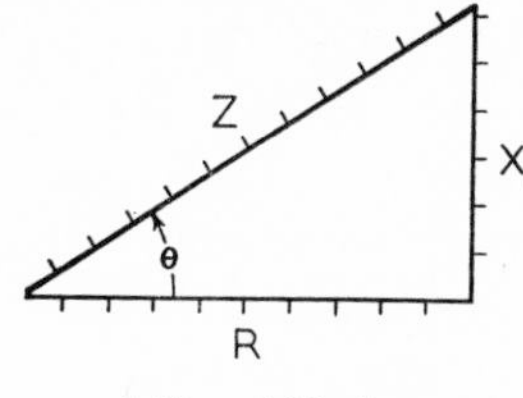

Fig. 8-9. Impedance triangle—*R-L* series circuit.

$\frac{1}{8}'' = 100$ ohms

Solution B—Trigonometric:

$$Z = \sqrt{R^2 + X_L^2} = \sqrt{(1000)^2 + (628)^2} = 1180 \text{ ohms.}$$

$$\theta = \text{arc tan } \frac{X_L}{R} = \text{arc tan } \frac{628}{1000} = 32.1°.$$

Solution C—Ohm's law:

$$Z_T = \frac{E_T}{I} = \frac{177}{0.15} = 1180 \text{ ohms.}$$

θ — no other method.

You have noticed that the impedance triangle was drawn *upward* for an inductive circuit (Fig. 8-9) and *downward* for the capacitive circuit (Fig. 8-4). This is strictly correct. And yet, very often the impedance triangle for the capacitive circuit is also drawn upward. Since impedance, reactance, and resistance are not true vectors, this variation is permissible. This does not affect the value of impedance, nor the *value* of circuit phase angle. However, be careful to remember that this phase angle should be *negative*, that is, the line voltage in the *R-C* circuit lags the current.

R-L series circuit—commercial coil. In the above R-L illustrations, we assumed the coil was a perfect inductance, and therefore the current through the coil lags the voltage drop across the coil by 90 degrees. But a commercial coil has resistance as well as inductance! If the resistance of the coil is low, it can be neglected, and the above assumptions are correct. For example, a coil with a Q of 100 or better would introduce an error of less than 0.6 degree. ($Q = X_L/R = 100$, but X_L/R is also the tangent of the phase angle. Arc tan 100 = 89.45 degrees. This is almost the 90-degree shift of the perfect coil.) But when the Q of the coil is low, we cannot assume that the coil resistance is negligible. How do we handle such a case?

If we know the resistance and inductance of the coil, the problem is easily solved. Merely add the coil resistance in series with the coil, and proceed as before.

EXAMPLE 7

A coil of 5 h and 400-ohms resistance is connected in series with a 600-ohm resistance across a 120-v, 60-cycle supply. Find:

(a) Line current.
(b) Circuit phase angle.
(c) Coil voltage.
(d) Coil phase angle.
(e) Coil Q.

SOLUTION

1. $X_L = 2\pi fL = 6.28 \times 60 \times 5 = 1885$ ohms.
2. $R_T = R + R_L = 600 + 400 = 1000$ ohms.
3. $Z_T = \sqrt{R_T^2 + X_L^2} = \sqrt{(1000)^2 + (1885)^2} = 2140$ ohms.

(a) $I = \dfrac{E_T}{Z_T} = \dfrac{120}{2140} = 0.0561$ amps $= 56.1$ ma.

(b) Circuit phase angle $= \text{arc tan}\,\dfrac{X_L}{R_T} = \text{arc tan}\,\dfrac{1885}{1000} = 62°$.

4. Impedance of coil $Z_L = \sqrt{R_L^2 + X_L^2} = \sqrt{(400)^2 + (1885)^2} = 1930$ ohms.

(c) Coil voltage $= IZ_L = 0.0561 \times 1930 = 108$ v.

(d) Coil phase angle $= \text{arc tan}\,\dfrac{X_L}{R_L} = \text{arc tan}\,\dfrac{1885}{400} = 78°$.

(e) $Q = \dfrac{X_L}{R_L} = \dfrac{1885}{400} = 4.71$.

5. $E_R = IR = 0.0561 \times 600 = 33.6$ v.
6. $E_{R_L} = IR_L = 0.0561 \times 400 = 22.4$ v.
7. $E_{X_L} = IX_L = 0.0561 \times 1885 = 106$ v.

The above problem was simple to solve, because we knew the component values R and L of the coil. When we know the inductance and Q of the coil, the solution is equally simple. Q is equal to X_L/R. Therefore, we first find X_L from L and the frequency of the applied voltage. Then, from the Q value, we can find the resistance of the coil. The problem is now the same as before.

Sometimes we are given an unknown commercial inductance. We would like to know its resistance and inductance. If we have

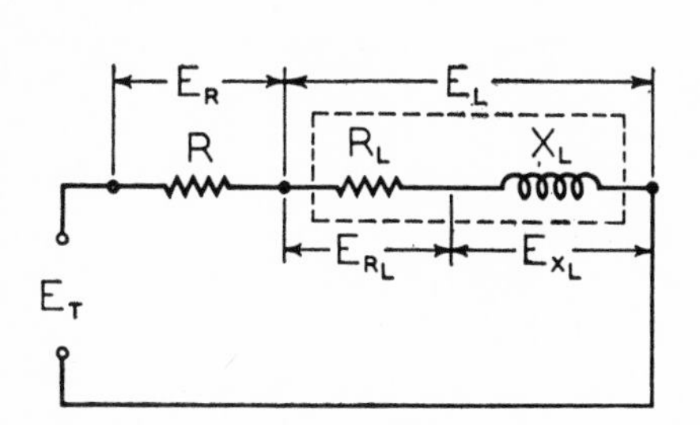

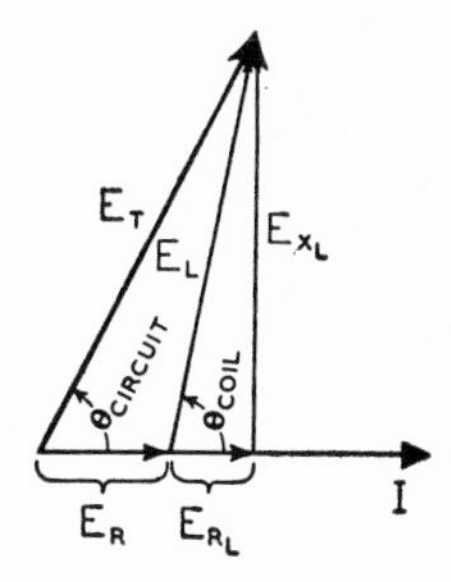

Fig. 8-10. Vector diagram—commercial-coil series circuit.

a wattmeter, ammeter, and voltmeter of proper ranges, we can measure the resistance of the coil. An ohmmeter will not do. It only gives the ohmic resistance; we want the effective resistance! Figure 8-10 shows us a method for getting R and L of the coil, using only a voltmeter.

1. Connect the coil in series with a known resistor across an A.C. supply voltage.

2. Measure E_T, E_R, and E_L. We know that the vector sum of E_R and E_L must equal E_T. Therefore:

3. Draw E_R to scale, horizontal direction. E_L starts at the end of E_R. We know its magnitude, and we know its direction is at some angle between zero and 90 degrees, upward. Therefore, from the end of E_R, strike an arc of radius equal to E_L. We also know the magnitude of E_T and that it starts at the origin of E_R. With radius equal to E_T and with center at the start of E_R, strike a second arc to intersect the E_L arc. Draw E_T and E_L.

4. Measure the circuit phase angle and coil phase angle.

5. From the intersection point, drop a perpendicular to the horizontal axis. This resolves E_L into its two components E_{X_L} and E_{R_L}.

6. From E_R and R calculate the current in the circuit.

7. Using this value of current and the E_{X_L} and E_{R_L} values from (5) above, we can now calculate R_L and X_L.

EXAMPLE 8

An unknown coil is connected in series with a 500-ohm resistor across a 40-v, 25-cycle supply. The voltage across the resistor is 20 v; across the coil 28 v. Find the inductance and resistance of the coil.

SOLUTION

1. Draw the vector diagram.

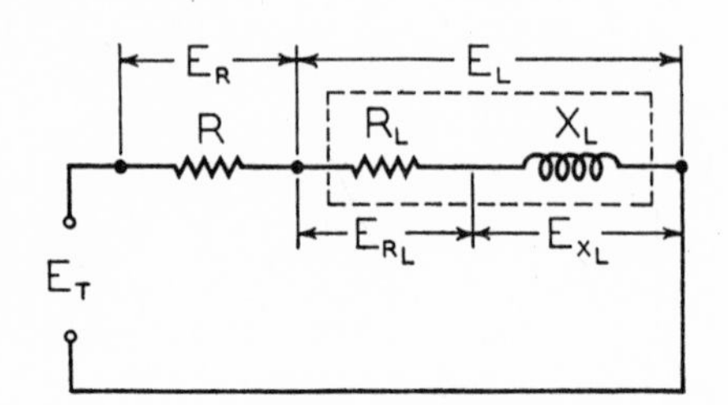

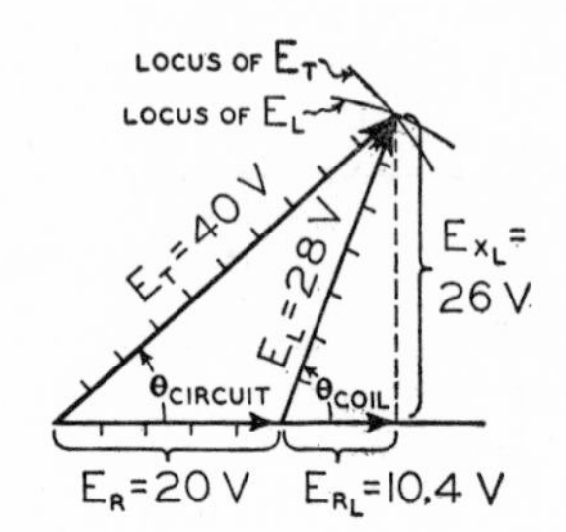

FIG. 8-11. Vector solution—commercial coil.

2. By measurement from the diagram:
   (a) $E_{R_L} = 10.4$ v.
   (b) $E_{X_L} = 26$ v.
   (c) Circuit phase angle = 39°.
   (d) Coil phase angle = 66.5°.

3. $I = \dfrac{E_R}{R} = \dfrac{20}{500} = 0.04$ amp.

4. $R_L = \dfrac{E_{R_L}}{I} = \dfrac{10}{0.04} = 250$ ohms.

5. $X_L = \dfrac{E_{X_L}}{I} = \dfrac{25}{0.04} = 625$ ohms.

6. $L = \dfrac{X_L}{2\pi f} = \dfrac{625}{6.28 \times 25} = 3.98$ h.

Power in *R-L* series circuit. In a circuit containing resistance and inductance in series, the voltage will lead the current by some angle less than 90 degrees. If we plot the sine waves of e, i, and p, we shall find that the power curve has positive and negative portions. But the positive portions are greater than the negative portions. The circuit takes power from the line. The inductance itself does not dissipate power. We already know that it stores energy in its magnetic field and returns it to the line. The power taken by the circuit is the power dissipated in the series resistance (IE_R). If we draw a vector diagram of such a circuit, it will be seen that $E_R = E \cos \theta$, where E is the line voltage. The power dissipated is therefore $EI \cos \theta$. This is quite similar to the analysis of power in an R-C circuit. Again, no further discussion is necessary.

Resistance, inductance and capacitance in series. We now shall consider circuits containing all three types of circuit elements. Circuits containing resistance, inductance, and capacitance in series are very common in electronic work. Since we have already considered the effect of each of these circuit elements alone, and in combinations containing resistance and either inductance or capacitance, very little new theory is necessary. In fact, all we need to do is put previous knowledge together.

Impedance: *L-C-R* circuit. Let us consider an R-C series circuit connected to a source of A.C. The current flowing in the circuit will be limited to some value by the combined opposition ($\sqrt{R^2 + X_c^2}$) of the circuit elements. We shall use an ammeter to measure the current. Now we open the circuit and insert an inductance in series. The current, as indicated by the ammeter, *increases*. But why? We have added another circuit element. The total opposition should be greater—*No!* The total opposition is *less*.

Think back. In a pure capacitive circuit, the voltage across the capacitor lags the current by 90 degrees. But the voltage across an inductance leads the current by 90 degrees. These two voltages are 180 degrees apart! *The net reactance voltage is decreased.* It is the difference between E_c and E_L. The net opposition in the circuit is decreased.

From another point of view, check back on the impedance triangle for a capacitive and inductive circuit. You will recall that X_c was drawn downward, while X_L was drawn upward. Again we see that these reactances counteract each other, and the *net reactance* (X_0) is less than either X_L or X_c alone.

In any *L-C-R* series circuit, the impedance can be found as follows:

1. Calculate X_L and X_c.
2. Find the net reactance $X_0 = X_L - X_c$. If X_L is greater, the circuit is inductive; X_0 will be positive, meaning upward in direction when drawing the impedance triangle. If X_c is greater, the circuit is capacitive; X_0 will be negative, meaning downward in direction in the impedance triangle.
3. Calculate the impedance $Z = \sqrt{R^2 + X_0^2}$.

Steps (2) and (3) are sometimes combined as

$$Z = \sqrt{R^2 + (X_L - X_c)^2}$$

Either method is acceptable. Once we have found the impedance of the circuit, it is a simple matter to solve for the current and voltage relations in the circuit.

EXAMPLE 9

An *L-C-R* series circuit has the following circuit constants: $L = 1$ henry, $R = 20{,}000$ ohms, and $C = 0.005\ \mu$f. The circuit is connected to a 100-v, 1000-cycle supply. Find:

(a) Line current.
(b) Voltage across each component.
(c) Circuit phase angle.
(d) Draw the vector diagram.
(e) Power dissipated.

SOLUTION

1. $X_L = 2\pi fL = 6.28 \times 1000 \times 1 = 6280$ ohms.
2. $X_c = \dfrac{1}{2\pi fC} = \dfrac{0.159 \times 10^6}{1000 \times 0.005} = 31{,}800$ ohms.
3. $X_0 = X_L - X_c = 6280 - 31{,}800 = -25{,}520$ ohms.

The circuit is capacitive.

4. $Z_T = \sqrt{R^2 + X_0^2} = \sqrt{(20{,}000)^2 + (25{,}520)^2} = 32{,}400$ ohms.

(a) $I = \dfrac{E_T}{Z_T} = \dfrac{100}{32{,}400} = 0.00308$ amp $= 3.08$ ma.

(b) $E_L = IX_L = 3.08 \times 10^{-3} \times 6280 = 19.2$ v.
$E_R = IR = 3.08 \times 10^{-3} \times 20{,}000 = 61.4$ v.
$E_c = IX_c = 3.08 \times 10^{-3} \times 31{,}800 = 98.0$ v.

(c) $\theta = \text{arc tan}\ \dfrac{X_0}{R} = \text{arc tan}\ \dfrac{25{,}520}{20{,}000} = 52°$.

Since the circuit is capacitive, the current leads the line voltage by 52 degrees.

(d)

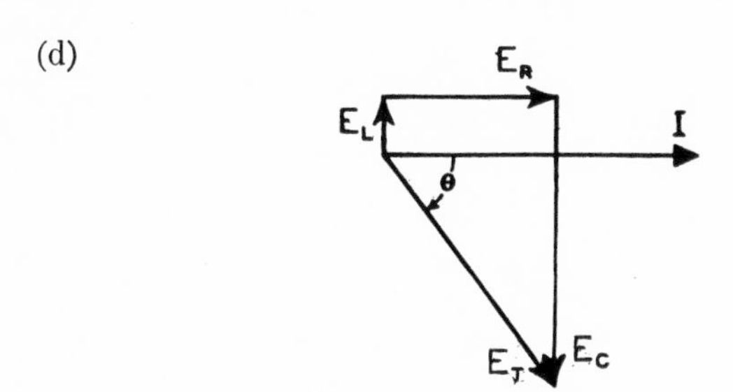

Fig. 8-12. Vector diagram —*L-C-R* series circuit.

(e) $P = EI \cos \theta = 100 \times 3.08 \times 10^{-3} \times 0.616 = 0.19$ w.

or: $P = I^2R = (3.08 \times 10^{-3})^2 \times 20{,}000 = 0.19$ w.

or: $P = IE_R = (3.08 \times 10^{-3}) \times 61.4 = 0.19$ w.

As in D.C. circuits, series circuits can assume many variations. It would be impossible to give illustrations of each variation. However, the same general rules apply to all series circuits:

1. The total opposition—impedance—is the *vector* sum of each individual opposition.
2. The current in the circuit depends on the total impedance.
3. The same current flows through each component of the series circuit.
4. The applied voltage is the *vector* sum of the voltage across each component.
5. Ohm's law can be applied to the entire circuit or to any portion of the circuit, as long as *all* the values used (E, R, X, or Z) apply to the entire circuit or to the same portion of the circuit.

We have now covered the basic principles that apply to any A.C. series circuit. The steps used in solving any specific case will vary depending on the data given. A thorough mastery of these principles is necessary in order for you to understand the analysis of electronic circuits that will follow in the next volume. And so, to insure mastery of these fundamentals, numerous problems are included in the Review Problem section.

Review Problems

1. In A.C. series circuits, why is the current used as the reference vector?

2. What is the name given to the total opposition in a series circuit, if it contains:

(a) Resistors only.
(b) Inductors only.
(c) Capacitors only.
(d) Combinations of resistors, inductors, and capacitors.

3. Why can we treat an A.C. series circuit containing only resistors exactly as a D.C. circuit?

4. Three resistors, 20, 40, and 50 ohms, are connected in series across a 120-v, 60-cycle supply. Find the line current, circuit phase angle, and voltage across each unit.

5. Three capacitors, 0.1, 0.25, and 0.05 μf, are connected in series across a 20-v, 5000-cycle supply. Find the line current, voltage across each unit, circuit phase angle, and draw the vector diagram.

6. Two capacitors, 50 $\mu\mu$f and 200 $\mu\mu$f, are connected in series to a 30-kc supply. The voltage across the 200-$\mu\mu$f capacitor is 40 v. Find:

(a) Line current.
(b) Voltage across the 50-$\mu\mu$f capacitor.
(c) Line voltage.
(d) Total reactance of the circuit.

7. Three choke coils are connected in series across a 50-v, 120-cycle supply. The inductances are 10 h, 15 h, and 3 h. Find:

(a) Line current.
(b) Voltages across each unit.
(c) Circuit phase angle.
(d) Vector diagram.

8. Two coils are connected in series across a 30-v, 1000-cycle supply. The voltage across L_1 is 12 v. L_2 has an inductance of 20 h. Assuming both coils are perfect inductances, find:

(a) Voltage across L_2.
(b) Line current.
(c) Inductance of L_1.
(d) Draw the vector diagram.

9. A resistor of 600 ohms is connected in series with a capacitor of 800-ohms reactance, across a 120-v supply. Find:

(a) Line current.
(b) Voltage across each unit.
(c) Circuit phase angle.

10. Find the impedance of the following R-C series circuits, if $R = 1000$ ohms and:

(a) $C = 0.1\ \mu f, f = 1000$ cycles.
(b) $C = 500\ \mu\mu f, f = 200$ kc.
(c) $C = 500\ \mu\mu f, f = 50$ kc.
(d) $C = 500\ \mu\mu f, f = 30$ kc.
(e) $C = 500\ \mu\mu f, f = 1500$ kc.
(f) $C = 0.005\ \mu f, f = 200$ kc.

11. From an analysis of the values in Problem 10, when can R or X_c be neglected in computing impedance?

12. A 100-ohm resistor is connected in series with a 200-$\mu\mu$f capacitor, across a 500-v, 1500-kc supply. Find:

(a) The circuit impedance.
(b) Line current.
(c) Voltage across each unit.
(d) Circuit phase angle.
(e) Draw the vector diagram.

13. A capacitor of 10 μf is connected in series with a resistor of 120 ohms, across a 440-v, 60-cycle supply. Find:

(a) Current in the circuit.
(b) Voltage across each unit.
(c) Circuit phase angle.
(d) Power dissipated.

14. In a series R-C circuit, the current voltage and power dissipation are 1.5 amps, 120 v, 60 cycles, and 50 w, respectively. Find the values of R and C.

15. A commercial load draws a current of 120 amps from a 220-v line at a power factor of 0.8 lagging. Find:

(a) The power taken by the load.
(b) The reactive volt-amperes.

16. Data taken at full load on a repulsion-induction motor shows that it takes 1600 w from a 230-v line at a current of 9.6 amps. Find:

(a) The power factor of the load.
(b) The reactive volt-amperes.

17. A series circuit contains a resistor of 150 ohms and an inductance of 0.5 h. The supply voltage is 220 v, 60 cycles. Find:

(a) Circuit impedance.
(b) Line current.
(c) Voltage across each unit.
(d) Circuit phase angle.
(e) Power dissipated.

18. In an L-R series circuit, a current of 0.6 amp flows when the supply voltage is 220 v, 120 cycles. The current lags the voltage by 70 degrees. Find:

(a) The power dissipated.
(b) The impedance of the circuit.
(c) The values of R and L.

19. The impedance of a commercial coil is 150 ohms at 200 cycles. Its resistance is 42 ohms. What is its inductance? What is the Q of the coil?

20. A commercial coil (having resistance and inductance) is connected in series with a resistor. Draw the vector diagram, and find the circuit phase angle and coil phase angle when (use graphical solution):

(a) $E = 120$ v, $E_R = 80$ v, $E_L = 70$ v.
(b) $E_L = 200$ v, $E = 450$ v, $E_R = 300$ v.
(c) $E = 5$ v, $E_L = 3.5$ v, $E_R = 2.5$ v.

21. In each of the above problems, find L and R_L if:

(a) $R = 80$ ohms, and $f = 100$ cycles.
(b) $R = 30{,}000$ ohms, and $f = 1000$ cycles.
(c) $R = 5$ ohms, and $f = 60$ cycles.

22. A coil having a reactance of 500 ohms is connected in series with a resistor of 200 ohms. If the current in the circuit is 0.8 amp, find:

(a) Voltage across each unit.
(b) Line voltage.
(c) Circuit phase angle.
(d) Power dissipated.

23. In each of the following cases, a coil, capacitor, and resistor are connected in series. Find the impedance of the circuit, circuit phase angle, and state whether the circuit is capacitive or inductive:

(a) $L = 3.5$ h, $C = 12\ \mu$f, $R = 500$ ohms, $f = 60$ cycles.
(b) $L = 90\ \mu$h, $C = 250\ \mu\mu$f, $R = 20$ ohms, $f = 1000$ kc.
(c) $L = 1.5$ h, $C = 5\ \mu$f, $R = 200$ ohms, $f = 60$ cycles.

24. In each of the cases of Problem 23 above, if the applied voltages are 400 v, 1.5 v and 230 v, respectively, find (1) line current; (2) voltage across each component; (3) power dissipated.

25. Find the applied voltage in a series circuit containing R, C, and L, when the voltage drops are:

$E_c = 25$ v, pure capacitance.
$E_L = 10$ v, pure inductance.
$E_R = 15$ v, pure resistance.

26. Repeat Problem 25, for:

$E_c = 100$ v, lagging the current by 90 degrees.
$E_R = 120$ v, in phase.
$E_L = 80$ v, coil Q equal to 5.

27. Repeat Problem 25, for:

$E_L = 12$ v ($X_L = 100$ ohms, $R_L = 50$ ohms).

$E_R = 20$ v, pure resistance.

$E_c = 10$ v, capacitor has no losses.

28. In each of the following cases, the circuit consists of a coil, capacitor and resistor in series. The coil and capacitor may not necessarily be pure reactances. All phase angles given are with respect to the line current:

(a) $E_T = 80$ v, leading by 30 degrees.

$E_R = 50$ v, in phase.

$E_c = 25$ v, lagging by 90 degrees.

Find E_L, both magnitude and phase angle.

(b) $E_T = 20$ v, lagging by 20 degrees.

$E_R = 15$ v, in phase.

$E_L = 8$ v, leading by 70 degrees.

Find E_c, both magnitude and phase angle.

(c) $E_T = 45$ v, lagging by 10 degrees.

$E_c = 20$ v, lagging by 85 degrees.

$E_L = 15$ v, angle unknown.

Find (1) E_R; (2) phase angle of E_L.

CHAPTER 9

Series Circuits—Electronic Aspects

IN THE PREVIOUS CHAPTER we discussed the basic principles applicable to any series circuit. The topics covered and the treatment of each topic was general and applied equally well to the power or electronic fields. But in electronics, series circuits have special significance. So now we are going to analyze these circuits in more detail with regard to their electronic aspects.

Resonance. The condition known as *resonance* occurs only in circuits containing both inductance and capacitance. The circuits may also have resistance—but although resistance greatly affects the current and voltage values when a circuit is in resonance, it does not determine *when* resonance will occur. Any circuit containing inductance and capacitance will be 'resonant' at some frequency —or by proper choice of these circuit elements we can make resonance occur at any desired frequency. You will learn later that resonance is obtained when the inductive reactance equals the capacitive reactance. For example, the choice of L and C values in the R.F. carrier generator and R.F. amplifiers of the transmitter shown in Fig. 1-4 will determine the carrier frequency of that station. In Chapter 1 we also presented the salient features of a receiver—the need for *selectivity* and *bandwidth*. Again resonance is the underlying principle that makes it possible for you to tune in any desired station, and that gives the circuits the necessary selectivity and bandwidth.

Notice that in both of the above illustrations, the circuits used were operated at radio frequencies (R.F.). It is in R.F. circuits, where only one frequency or a relatively narrow band of frequencies is desired at any one time, that reasonance plays an important role. Whereas in the audio amplifiers, such as shown in Figs. 1-3, 1-4, and 1-5, the frequencies these units must handle at any one time may range from 30 to 15,000 cycles. Video amplifiers used in television should have uniform characteristics from 20 cycles to 4.5 megacycles. Resonance is undesirable in these units. In fact these amplifiers could well be called non-resonant amplifiers.

Since resonance is mainly applicable to R.F. circuits, complete discussion will be delayed to a later text on resonant circuit applications. At this time we shall develop:

1. How to find the resonant frequency of a circuit.
2. How to make a circuit resonant at a given frequency.
3. What are the characteristics of a circuit when in resonance.

Any series circuit containing both inductance and capacitance will have a resonant frequency regardless of the values of these components. Resonance will occur whenever the reactances X_L and X_C are equal. Quite often in electronic circuits we need to know at what frequency this resonant condition will result. The solution is quite simple. Since X_L must equal X_C, then

$$2\pi fL = \frac{1}{2\pi fC}$$

solving for f, we get

$$f_0 = \frac{1}{2\pi\sqrt{LC}}$$

Let us apply this to a problem.

EXAMPLE 1

A series circuit contains the following components: A 1250-ohm resistor, an inductance of 5 mh, and a capacitor of 500 $\mu\mu$f. At what frequency will the circuit become resonant?

SOLUTION

1. The resistance of the circuit is of no consequence in determining the resonant frequency.

2. $f_0 = \dfrac{1}{2\pi\sqrt{LC}} = \dfrac{0.159}{\sqrt{5 \times 10^{-3} \times 500 \times 10^{-12}}} = 100.6$ kc.

Now that we have a resonant circuit, let us investigate the characteristics of this circuit. This can best be seen by another problem.

EXAMPLE 2

In Example 1 above, if the applied voltage is 100 v at the resonant frequency (100.6 kc), find:

(a) Total circuit impedance.
(b) Line current.
(c) Voltage across each unit.
(d) Circuit phase angle.

SOLUTION

1. It is always wise to start by drawing the circuit diagram (see Fig. 9-1a)

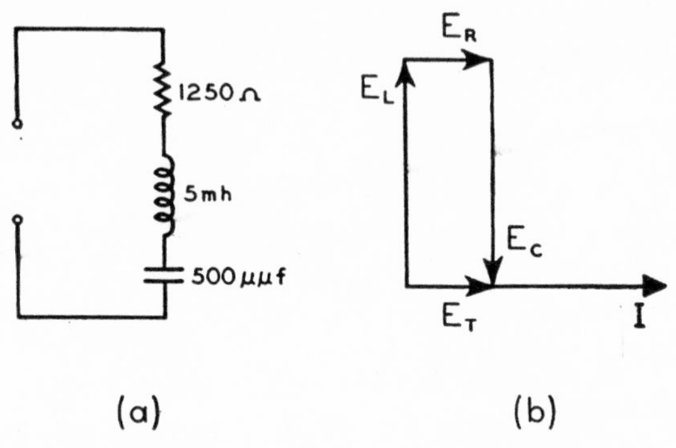

Fig. 9-1. Series resonant circuit.

2. The total impedance is given by $Z_T = \sqrt{R^2 + X_0^2}$
Therefore let us first find the net reactance (X_0)

(a) $X_L = 2\pi fL = 6.28 \times 100.6 \times 10^3 \times 5 \times 10^3 = 3160$ ohms.

(b) $X_c = \dfrac{1}{2\pi fC} = \dfrac{0.159 \times 10^{12}}{100.6 \times 10^3 \times 500} = 3160$ ohms.

(c) $X_0 = X_L - X_c = 3160 - 3160 = 0$ ohms.

This result should have been obvious, since the resonant frequency found in Problem 1 was the frequency at which X_L would equal X_c. A word of caution: Due to slide rule inaccuracies in determining the resonant frequency, X_L or X_c, this cancellation may not at times seem perfect.

(d) $Z_T = \sqrt{R^2 + X_0^2} = \sqrt{(1250)^2 \times (0)^2} = 1250$ ohms.

Notice that the total impedance is equal to the resistance of the circuit!

3. $I_T = \dfrac{E_T}{Z_T} = \dfrac{100}{1250} = 80$ ma.

4. $E_R = IR = 80 \times 10^{-3} \times 1250 = 100$ v.

$E_L = IX_L = 80 \times 10^{-3} \times 3160 = 253$ v.

$E_c = IX_c = 80 \times 10^{-3} \times 3160 = 253$ v.

Notice that the voltage across the reactive components is higher than the line voltage. This can readily happen in an *R-L-C* circuit if close to resonance, and the circuit resistance is low compared with X_L or X_c. Remember that the reactive voltages are 180 degrees out of phase and will cancel out. A voltmeter across both *L* and *C* will read zero!

5. To find the circuit phase angle, first draw the vector diagram showing the relation between line current and component voltages. Use current as the reference vector. (See Fig. 9-1b). Obviously, the line voltage is

in phase with the line current; the circuit is operating at unity power factor; and the circuit phase angle is zero, just as if it were a purely resistive circuit.

Let us go back to Example 9 in the previous chapter (page 114), and examine the given data and calculated results. It was also a series L-C-R circuit:

Given: $L = 1$ h, $C = 0.005\ \mu$f, $R = 20{,}000$ ohms.

$E = 100$ v and 1000 cycles.

Calculated: $X_L = 6280$ ohms, $X_c = 31{,}800$ ohms.

$Z_T = 32{,}400$ ohms, $I_T = 3.08$ ma.

$\theta_c = 52°$ (current leading).

Is this circuit in resonance? No! How can we tell? There are several ways:

1. X_L does not equal X_c.
2. Z_T is higher than the resistance value.
3. θ_c is not zero—current is leading.

The next question is how could we make this circuit resonant? Again there are several answers possible:

(1) Any circuit containing L and C is resonant at some frequency. We could change the frequency. Which way—increase or decrease? Since X_L is too low, and X_c is too high, the frequency should be increased. As the frequency is increased, X_L will increase. At the same time X_c will decrease. At some higher frequency, X_L will be equal to X_c. The correct value of frequency will be given by the equation

$$f_0 = \frac{1}{2\pi\sqrt{LC}}$$

Example 3

At what frequency will the above circuit be in resonance?

Solution

$$f_0 = \frac{1}{2\pi\sqrt{LC}} = \frac{0.159}{\sqrt{1 \times 0.005 \times 10^{-6}}} = 2250 \text{ cycles}$$

But suppose we wanted the circuit to be resonant at the given frequency of 1000 cycles. We still have two other methods for making $X_L = X_c$.

(2) Change the value of the inductance. In our problem, X_L is too low. Therefore, we must increase the inductance.

EXAMPLE 4

What value of inductance is needed to bring the circuit into resonance at 1000 cycles with the given capacitor of 0.005 μf?

SOLUTION

1. X_c was found previously to be 31,800 ohms.
2. X_L must equal X_c or 31,800 ohms.
3. $L = \frac{X_L}{2\pi f} = \frac{0.159 \times 31{,}800}{1000} = 5.05$ h.

(3) The circuit could also be brought into resonance by changing the capacitance value. Since X_c is too high, the value of capacitance must be increased.

EXAMPLE 5

Find the capacitance value that would give a resonant condition at 1000 cycles with an inductance of 1 h.

SOLUTION

1. X_L at 1000 cycles = 6280 ohms.
2. X_c must equal X_L or 6280 ohms.
3. $C = \frac{1}{2\pi f X_c} = \frac{0.159 \times 10^6}{1000 \times 6280} = 0.0253$ μf.

In practical applications either method is used to 'tune' a circuit into resonance. For example, in broadcast band receivers, tuning is done by varying capacitance, whereas in television tuners and in many F.M. tuners, inductance variation is used.

Let us summarize the main points concerning resonance:

1. Resonance is obtained when $X_L = X_c$.
2. Resonant condition can be obtained by varying L, C or frequency.
3. At resonance:
   (a) The impedance is a minimum and is equal to the resistance of the circuit.
   (b) The current is a maximum.
   (c) Current and line voltage are in phase.
   (d) The circuit acts as a pure resistive circuit.
   (e) The voltage across L and C may exceed the supply voltage.
4. Below resonance, X_c is greater than X_L, and the circuit acts as an R-C circuit.

5. Above resonance, X_L exceeds X_c, and the circuits acts as an *L-R* circuit.

If there is any possibility that a circuit might operate at or close to resonance, the voltage ratings of the coil and capacitor must be checked carefully. We have seen that the voltage across these units may exceed the supply voltage. This is particularly true if the circuit resistance is low compared with the reactance of the coil or capacitor. For example, in Problem 2, if the resistance were only 125 ohms, the current would have been ten times higher (800 ma). But the voltages across the coil and the capacitor would have been 2530 v! It is, therefore, important that the units used have the proper voltage rating.

As mentioned earlier in this discussion, the details such as effect of resistance and *L-C* ratio on the resonance curve, will be discussed in a later volume.

Phase shift *R-C* circuits. We know that in a pure capacitive circuit, the current leads the voltage by 90 degrees. But we saw in the previous chapter that if we have resistance and capacitance in series, the current leads by some angle less than 90 degrees. Obviously, the combination of resistance with capacitance reduced the angle of phase shift between current and voltage. This phase angle can be obtained from the impedance triangle for the circuit. (See Fig. 8-4, page 100.) In Fig. 9-2a is shown a group of imped-

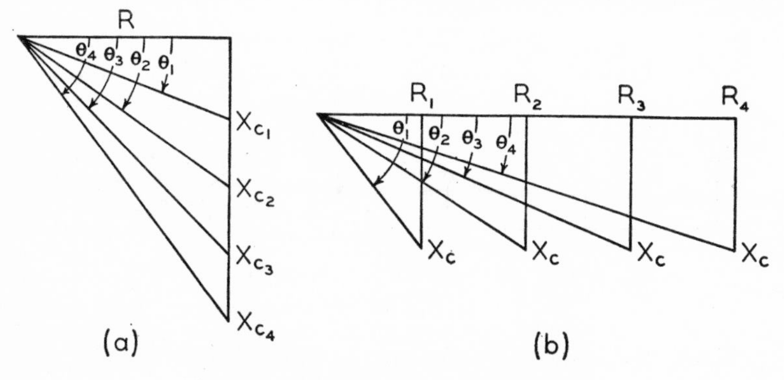

Fig. 9-2. Effect of *R* or *C* on phase shift.

ance triangles with fixed resistance value and several values of capacitive reactance. Notice that the larger the X_c value, the greater the phase shift.

Now refer to Fig. 9-2b. This time the reactance value is kept constant, while the resistance value is increased. What is the effect of resistance on the phase angle? The greater the resistance value, the smaller the phase shift. Obviously, the degree of phase shift depends not on resistance or reactance values alone, but on the ratio of reactance to resistance. This merely confirms what we had previously seen—the circuit phase angle, θ, is the angle whose tangent is equal to the ratio of reactance to resistance:

$$\theta = \text{arc tan } \frac{X_c}{R}$$

Very often in electronic work, R-C series circuits are used to feed the A.C. output of one circuit or 'stage' to the input of the next stage. This is called *coupling.* R-C coupling is widely used in audio amplifiers, video amplifiers (television), and special circuits such as used in loran, radar, and timing or trigger circuits. Sometimes phase shift is not too important (simple audio amplifiers). In video circuits, phase shift is undesirable, particularly at the lower frequencies. But we know that reactance (X_c) increases at lower frequencies! Therefore, unless capacitance and resistance values of the coupling circuit are carefully chosen, phase shift in television circuits would distort the picture. On the other hand, in some special circuits a definite phase shift is desired. Now the problem is to pick R and C values to produce the desired phase shift.

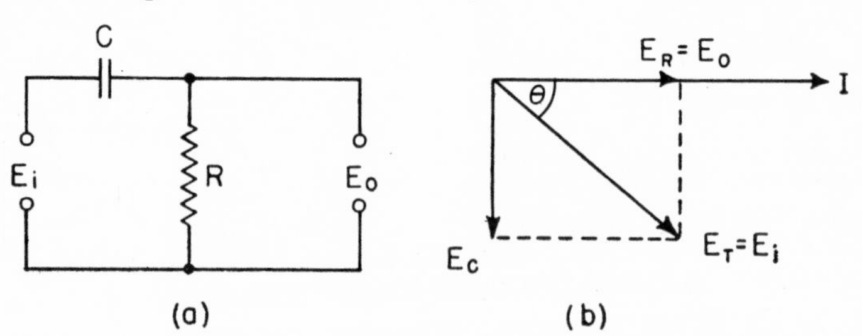

Fig. 9-3. Typical R-C coupling circuit.

Figure 9-3 shows a typical R-C coupling circuit. The input voltage (E_i) is fed to the total circuit, while the output (E_o) is taken off the resistor, and fed to the grid of the next tube. Since grid circuits, in general, are very high-impedance circuits, we can neglect the shunting effect of such loads across the resistor R.

Calculation of phase shift between the input and output voltage is simple. We know how to find the phase angle between the applied voltage (E_i) and the circuit current. The output voltage is the voltage across the resistor. But we know that this voltage is in phase with the current. Therefore the phase angle between input and output voltage is the same as the circuit phase angle, and the output voltage *leads* the input voltage. This is shown in the vector diagram, Fig. 9-3b.

Example 6

In Fig. 9-3, find the phase relation between input and output voltage, if $R = 50{,}000$ ohms, $C = 0.05\ \mu f$, and the frequency of the applied voltage is 1000 cycles.

Solution

1. $X_c = \dfrac{1}{2\pi fC} = \dfrac{0.159 \times 10^6}{1000 \times 0.05} = 3180$ ohms.

2. $\theta = \arc\tan \dfrac{X_c}{R} = \arc\tan \dfrac{3180}{50{,}000} = 3.6°.$

If the frequency of the applied voltage were increased to 15,000 cycles, would the phase shift be greater or less? At the higher frequency, X_c is less—15 times less; the phase shift would be less than 0.3 degree. But if the frequency were to be reduced to say 50 cycles, the reactance would be 20 times greater, and the phase shift would increase to 51.7 degrees! Certainly, if phase shift is undesirable, and the circuit must operate on a frequency range that goes as low as 50 cycles, this circuit is inadequate.

How can we eliminate or reduce phase shift to a negligible value? Merely select a capacitor and resistor value, such that *at the* LOWEST *frequency* that the circuit will operate, the reactance is small compared with the resistance. How small? Well, if X_c is less than 1/50 of R, then the tangent of the phase angle is less than 0.02, and the phase shift is less than 1.2 degrees. At any higher frequency, the phase shift is even lower. Notice that this does not specify the value of the capacitor or resistor, but only the ratio of their respective oppositions. Quite often the value of either one or the other circuit component is fixed or limited by other circuit considerations.

EXAMPLE 7

An R-C coupling circuit is to operate on a frequency range of 30 to 50,000 cycles. The maximum capacitor value is fixed by other considerations at 0.1 μf. What value resistor must be used in order to limit the phase shift to 3.0 degrees?

SOLUTION

1. $X_c = \dfrac{1}{2\pi fC} = \dfrac{0.159 \times 10^6}{30 \times 0.1} = 53{,}000$ ohms.
2. For 3.0°, $\tan\theta = 0.0524$.
3. From $\tan\theta = \dfrac{X_c}{R}$

$$R = \frac{X_c}{\tan\theta} = \frac{53{,}000}{0.0524} = 1{,}012{,}000, \text{ or approx. } 1.0 \text{ megohm.}$$

When a high degree of phase shift is desired, the capacitance value is made small and the resistance is reduced. This results in a high X_c to R ratio. The phase shift will be large.

We have seen how we can reduce undesired phase shift to negligible values or how we can produce any given phase shift. In the latter case, the output voltage (taken across the resistor) leads the input by an amount equal to the circuit phase angle. Suppose, however, that we want a phase shift, but that the output voltage should *lag* the input. Can this be done with our simple R-C circuit? Yes—examine Fig. 9-3b again. Notice that the voltage E_c across the capacitor lags the input voltage. So if we reverse C and R in Fig. 9-3a and take the output across the capacitor we can achieve the desired result. The next question is: "How do we obtain a specific value of phase shift?" Again, reference to the vector diagram (Fig. 9-3b) will show that the angle between E_c and E_T is $(90 - \theta)$, where θ is the circuit phase angle. An example will clarify the procedure.

EXAMPLE 8

What value of capacitor is needed in an R-C phase-shift circuit to produce an output voltage that will lag the input voltage by 30 degrees at 2000 cycles? The resistor value is 10,000 ohms.

SOLUTION

1. The circuit used will be similar to Fig. 9-3a but with R and C reversed and the output taken across the capacitor.

2. Since 30-degree phase shift is desired, the circuit phase angle θ must be (90 − 30), or 60 degrees.

3. $\tan\theta = \frac{X_c}{R} = \tan 60° = 1.732.$

4. $X_c = R\tan\theta = 10{,}000 \times 1.732 = 17{,}320$ ohms.

5. $C = \frac{1}{2\pi f X_c} = \frac{0.159 \times 10^6}{2000 \times 17{,}320} = 0.00458\ \mu\text{f}.$

Phase-shift *L-R* circuits. Just as a capacitor causes a phase shift between line current and line voltage—so will an inductance. However, since the voltage across a pure inductance leads the current by 90 degrees, the phase shift in any series *L-R* circuit will cause the line voltage to lead the line current—just the reverse of the conditions we saw for an *R-C* circuit. The amount of phase shift will depend on the amount of resistance and inductance in the circuit. The greater the resistance, the smaller the phase shift. Remember that if the circuit contains resistance only, the phase shift is zero. On the other hand, the greater the inductance, the greater will be the reactance (or the higher the frequency, the greater the reactance). This will cause a greater angle of shift. This can be verified by reference to the impedance triangle: The circuit phase angle, and therefore the phase shift, are given by

$$\theta = \arctan\frac{X_L}{R}$$

Circuits containing resistance and inductance in series are used as coupling and filter circuits. Since these circuits produce phase shifts, the component values must be carefully selected if negligible phase shift or a definite phase shift is required. Phase-shifting circuits are shown in Fig. 9-4. If the output voltage is taken off the resistor, it will lag the input voltage by an angle equal to the circuit phase angle. When the output voltage is taken off the inductor, the output will lead the input voltage by an angle equal to 90 minus the circuit phase angle. This should be obvious from the vector diagram for each condition.

Example 9

It is desired to build a circuit that will cause the output voltage to lead by 30 degrees at 10,000 cycles. The resistance value is fixed at 50,000 ohms. What value inductance must be used?

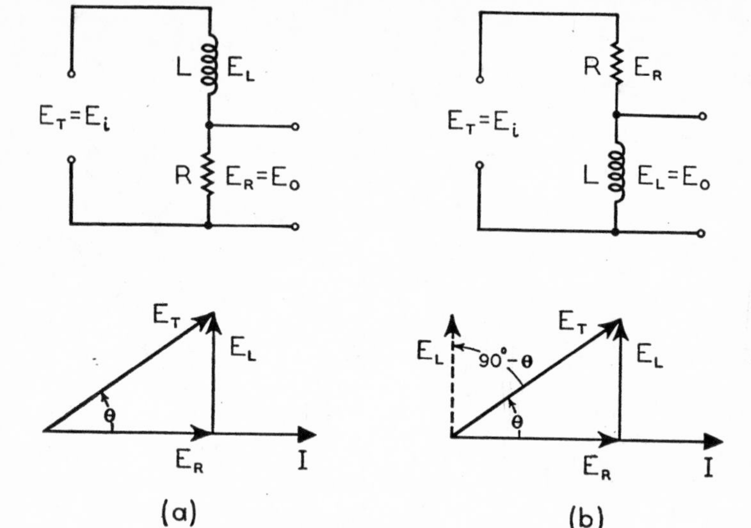

Fig. 9-4. Phase shift in *L-R* circuits. (a) E_o lags E_i by $\theta°$. (b) E_o leads E_i by $(90 - \theta°)$.

SOLUTION

1. Since the output voltage is leading, the circuit should be that of Fig. 9-4b. The output voltage is taken off the inductor.

2. E_o will lead E_i by 30 degrees, if the circuit phase angle is 60 degrees, $(90 - \theta)$.

3. $\theta = \text{arc tan } \frac{X_L}{R} = 60°$.

4. tan 60 degrees = 1.73 (table).

5. $\frac{X_L}{R} = 1.73$; $X_L = 50{,}000 \times 1.73 = 86{,}500$ ohms.

6. $L = \frac{X_L}{2\pi f} = \frac{86{,}500}{6.28 \times 10{,}000} = 1.38$ h.

Frequency discrimination: *R-C* filter. In our study of D.C. circuits, we saw that voltage dividers could be made by using several resistors in series and taking the output voltages from taps.* Such a circuit is shown in Fig. 9-5. The output voltage is obviously less than the input voltage. Now if the output voltage is fed to a high-impedance circuit, the shunting effect of the 'load' across R_2 is

* *Direct Current Fundamentals,* Chapter 10.

negligible. (A typical example is when the output voltage is fed to the grid input circuit of a tube.) Under such conditions, the output voltage is less than the input voltage by the same ratio that R_2 bears to the total resistance $(R_1 + R_2)$, or

$$E_o = E_i \frac{R_2}{(R_1 + R_2)}$$

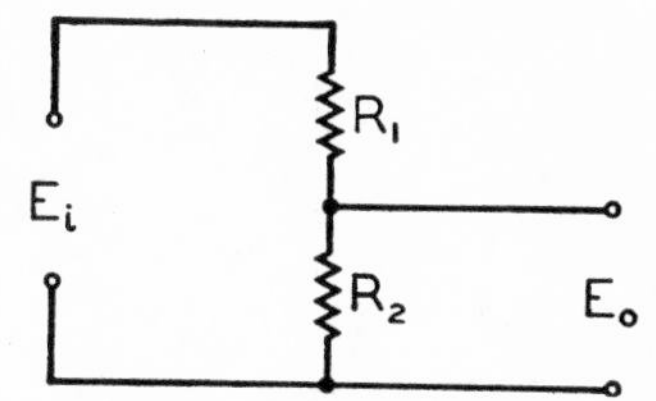

Fig. 9-5. Simple voltage divider (attenuator).

This same circuit works equally well with A.C. Regardless of frequency, the above voltage relation will still hold true. Any change in resistance value or distributed capacitance or inductance in the resistors will affect R_2 and $(R_1 + R_2)$ in the same ratio. A resistive voltage divider will, therefore, show no frequency discrimination; that is—if the frequency of the input voltage is varied, the ratio of output to input voltage remains constant. What is the purpose of such a circuit? When the amplitude of the input voltage is too high for the circuit components that follow, this circuit will reduce the amplitude of all input signals. Obviously, such a circuit introduces a loss in energy—the drop in the resistor R_1. Any circuit that reduces the amplitude of the input signal voltage is called an ATTENUATOR. (The volume control in your radio receiver is an example of a variable attenuator.) A resistive voltage divider attenuates all frequencies by the same proportion.

Sometimes the input voltage is too high at only certain frequencies. In this case we should attenuate only those frequencies. Other times certain frequency components of the input voltage (either at the high or low end) are undesirable. For example, scratch produced by the phonograph needle is mainly in the high end of the audible frequency range. Under these conditions, we would like to attenuate only the undesirable frequencies. An *R-C* voltage divider will do the trick. In Fig. 9-6 are shown two methods of connecting the circuit.

Which of these circuits will attenuate the higher frequencies? Let us consider the circuit in Fig. 9-6a. As the frequency increases, X_c will decrease, and more of the input voltage will appear across R. The output has increased with frequency. Whereas, at the lower frequencies, X_c increases, the drop across the capacitor increases, and the output voltage will decrease. This circuit, therefore, attenuates the lower frequencies. What about the circuit shown in Fig. 9-6b? The output voltage is the drop across X_c. As the input frequency increases, X_c decreases, and the voltage drop across the capacitor decreases. The output voltage must decrease with frequency. This circuit obviously attenuates the higher frequencies. Notice that, depending upon the relative position of R

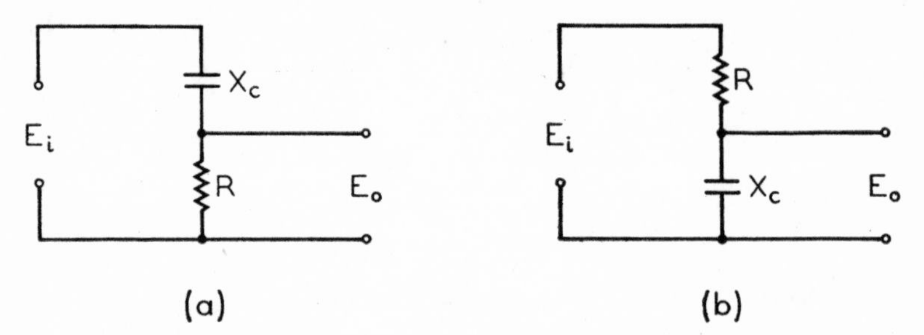

Fig. 9-6. *R-C* frequency discriminating circuits. (a) Low frequency discrimination. (b) High frequency discrimination.

and C, the circuit can act to attenuate high or low frequencies. This circuit is often used as a simple tone control merely by making the resistance element variable.

In Fig. 9-6a, the output voltage (E_o) is equal to IR. In turn, $I = E_i/Z$; replacing current I by its equivalent we get:

For low-frequency attenuation

$$E_o = E_i \frac{R}{Z}$$

By similar reasoning:

For high-frequency attenuation

$$E_o = E_i \frac{X_c}{Z}$$

From these relations, we can calculate the variation of output voltage with frequency for any given circuit, or the circuit values required in order to reduce the output voltage to some definite value at any desired frequency.

Example 10

In Fig. 9-6b, $R = 100{,}000$ ohms, $C = 0.003\ \mu f$. The input is 10 v. Calculate the output voltage for a frequency range of 50 to 20,000 cycles. Plot. (Start at 50 cycles and double the frequency each time.)

Solution

1. At 50 cycles $X_c = \dfrac{1}{2\pi fC} = \dfrac{0.159 \times 10^6}{50 \times 0.003} = 1.06$ megohm.

2. $Z = \sqrt{R^2 + X^2} = \sqrt{(0.1)^2 \times (1.06)^2 \times 10^6} = 1.06$ megohm.

f	X_c	Z	X_c/Z	E_o
50	1.06 meg.	1.06 meg.	1.00	10.0
100	0.53 meg.	0.539 meg.	0.985	9.85
200	0.265 meg.	0.283 meg.	0.936	9.36
400	0.132 meg.	0.166 meg.	0.795	7.95
800	66,300	120,000	0.55	5.50
1,600	33,100	106,000	0.31	3.10
3,200	16,600	101,500	0.163	1.63
6,400	8,300	100,000	0.083	0.83
12,800	4,140	100,000	0.0414	0.414
25,600	2,070	100,000	0.0207	0.207

3. See Fig. 9-7, page 134.

In checking the above tabulated values, try some 'short cuts.' Since the frequency is doubled in each successive step, X_c should be half of the previous value. Therefore only one calculation need be made for X_c. Next, notice in the calculations that when X_c is greater than $10R$, $Z = X_c$, and R is negligible. Also, when R is greater than $10X_c$, $Z = R$, and X_c is negligible. These facts will often save you many unnecessary calculations.

Look at Fig. 9-6a again. Have we discussed this circuit before? What was it used for? It is a typical coupling circuit such as is used in audio and video amplifiers. But we just learned that this circuit is a frequency discriminating circuit that attenuates the lower frequencies! What will happen to the fidelity of the output voltage? If the values of R and C are properly chosen, the frequency discrimination is negligible. From the equation for this circuit $E_o = E_i \dfrac{R}{Z}$ (and also from common sense analysis), the larger the capacitance and the larger the resistance, the closer the output

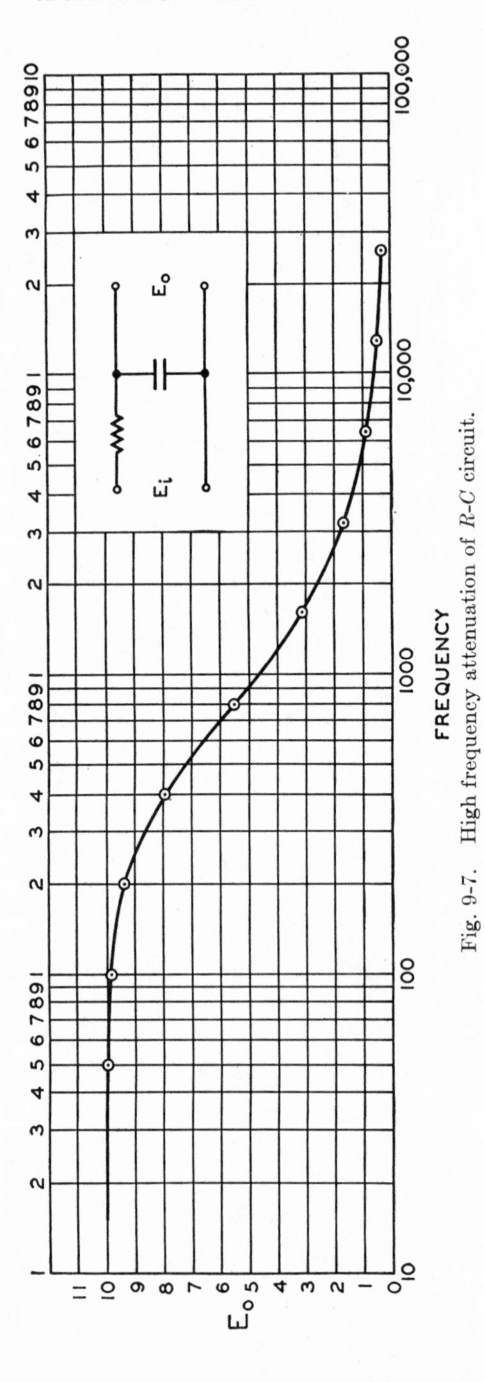

Fig. 9-7. High frequency attenuation of *R-C* circuit.

voltage approaches the input value. Again, either the capacitance or resistance value may be fixed by other circuit considerations.

EXAMPLE 11

In an *R-C* coupling circuit, the resistor value is 250,000 ohms. What value capacitor should be used in order to obtain an output voltage of at least 95% of the input voltage at 30 cycles?

SOLUTION

1. For $E_o = 0.95E_i$, R/Z must equal 0.95.
2. $Z = \dfrac{R}{0.95} = \dfrac{250{,}000}{0.95} = 263{,}000$ ohms.
3. $X_c = \sqrt{Z^2 - R^2} = \sqrt{(692 - 625) \times 10^8} = 82{,}000$ ohms.
4. $C = \dfrac{1}{2\pi f X_c} = \dfrac{0.159 \times 10^6}{30 \times 82{,}000} = 0.0645\ \mu\text{f}.$

The above problem illustrates how, by proper design, an *R-C* coupled amplifier can be made to give good low-frequency response.

Frequency discrimination: *R-L* circuit. The *R-L* series circuits shown in Fig. 9-4 also act as voltage dividers. The output voltage will be less than the input voltage due to the drop in the series circuit element. Since X_L varies with frequency, it is obvious that the ratio of output to input voltage will vary with frequency. These circuits inherently are, therefore, frequency discriminating circuits. The higher the frequency, the greater the X_L value and the higher the voltage developed across the inductance. When the output is taken off the resistor (Fig. 9-4a), the output decreases with frequency. This circuit will attenuate high frequencies. Using the connections shown in Fig. 9-4b, the drop across the inductance increases with frequency, giving a greater output voltage. This circuit attenuates low frequencies. If frequency discrimination is desired, one or the other of the two *R-L* circuits can be used, depending upon which end of the frequency range it is desired to attenuate. The choice of *R* and *L* values will depend upon the amount of discrimination desired at any particular frequency. Since the action of these circuits is quite similar to the *R-C* circuits previously studied, no further discussion is necessary.

Differentiator and integrator circuits. The title of this section is enough to make you want to skip these next few pages. But don't let the names of these circuits scare you. It requires no calculus to explain their action. In fact, they are nothing more than the R-C series circuits we have been discussing, but now specifically designed to distort the output waveshape. In a differentiator circuit the output is taken across the resistor, and for good differentiating action *the time constant of the R-C circuit must be short.* If the time constant is too long, the distorting effect is lost and we revert to the simple coupling action of the circuit in Fig. 9-3. Conversely, if the output is taken across the capacitor and *the circuit has a long time constant*, good integrator action will be achieved.

The distorting effect of differentiating and integrating circuits is apparent only when the input is a complex wave, because each component frequency of the complex wave is shifted in phase by a different amount. With sine-wave input, there is no apparent distortion. The output will be reduced in amplitude (voltage-divider action of R-C circuits) and shifted in phase (phase-shift action of R-C circuits) as compared with the input voltage, but that is all.

Those of you who are familiar with calculus will recall that the differential of the sine of an angle is + cosine. This would mean that if a sine wave is applied to a differentiating circuit, the output should be a + cosine wave, or leading by 90 degrees. That this is so can be readily seen from circuit analysis. The circuit for differentiating action is the same as shown in Fig. 9-3a. Remembering that the time constant should be very short, it would mean that X_c should be very large (C is small), and that R should be small. The impedance approaches pure capacitive reactance, and the current I will lead the input voltage E_i by 90 degrees. The output voltage E_o taken across the resistor is in phase with I, and therefore also leads E_i by 90 degrees. This is a + cosine wave.

Similarly, by calculus, the integral of the sine of an angle is the $-$cosine; by vector diagram analysis (remember that an integrating circuit should have a long time constant—low X_c and large R), θ_c approaches 0° and the output across the capacitor will lag the input voltage by $(90° - \theta)$, or 90 degrees. The output lagging by 90 degrees is a $-$cosine wave.

Before we can discuss the action of these circuits, it will be necessary to review briefly the charging action of a capacitor in an R-C series circuit with D.C. supply—particularly the concept of time constant.* Such a circuit is shown in Fig. 9-8. At the instant that the power is turned on, there is no charge on the capacitor. Therefore the only opposition to current flow is the series resistor R. The initial value of current ($I = E/R$) will be a maximum. But just as soon as current starts to flow, the capacitor begins to

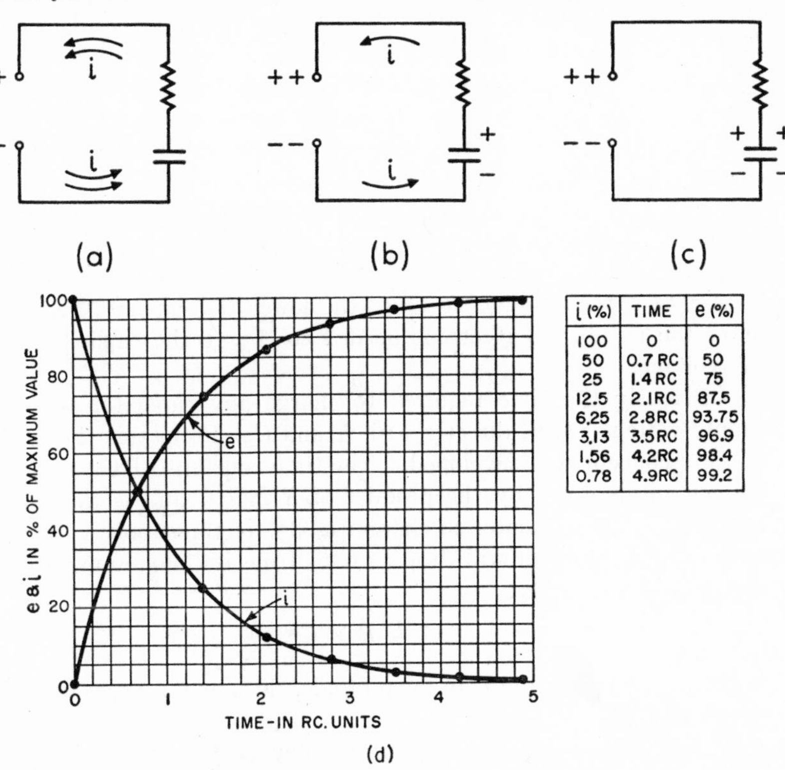

i (%)	TIME	e (%)
100	0	0
50	0.7 RC	50
25	1.4 RC	75
12.5	2.1RC	87.5
6.25	2.8RC	93.75
3.13	3.5RC	96.9
1.56	4.2RC	98.4
0.78	4.9RC	99.2

Fig. 9-8. Charge of capacitor in a D.C. *R-C* circuit.

charge and a countervoltage is built up across its plates. The net voltage, which causes the current to flow, is the difference between the line voltage and this countervoltage. Obviously the current flow will decrease. Finally, when the capacitor is fully charged and the countervoltage equals the supply voltage, the current drops to zero. These conditions are shown pictorially in Fig. 9-8a, b, and c.

* For details see *Direct Current Fundamentals*, Chapter 20.

Will the capacitor charge increase linearly with time? No! At first the current flowing in the circuit is high, and the capacitor charges rapidly. But as the capacitor charges, the increase in countervoltage causes the current to drop. Due to the reduced current flow, the capacitor charges more slowly. With time, this effect is cumulative—the current drops more and more slowly, and the capacitor charges more and more slowly. The curves for e and i are shown in Fig. 9-8d. Curves of this shape are called *exponential* curves.

The next question is how long will it take for the capacitor to charge completely? This depends on two factors:

1. *The amount of resistance in the circuit*—the lower the series resistance, the higher the current, and the quicker the capacitor will charge.

2. *The capacitance of the unit*—the lower the capacitance, the fewer the number of electrons needed to charge the capacitor to full voltage.

Obviously the time required to charge any capacitor to full supply voltage varies directly with R and C. From this the *time constant* concept was developed. The time constant (T.C.) of any R-C circuit is given by the product of R and C and is the time required for the capacitor to charge to 63% of the supply voltage. Naturally the current will drop *by* 63% from its maximum value. Expressed by formula:

$$\text{T.C.} = R \times C$$

If R is in megohms and C in microfarads, this time interval will be in seconds.

A more practical time constant was developed as $0.7RC$. This was the time interval for a 50% increase in voltage (from its previous value toward maximum). This method is used for the data and graph in Fig. 9-8d:

1. In the first unit of time, the capacitor charges to 50% of its total value.

2. In the second time unit, the charge increases by 50% of the remaining amount, or +25%. Now it has only 25% more to go.

3. In the third time unit, the charge increases by 50% of this remainder, or +12.5%, giving a total of 87.5%. Remainder now 12.5%.

4. Increase in charge is now +6.25%, for a total of 93.75%.
5. Increase is +3.12%; total 96.87%.

Theoretically, the capacitor is never fully charged. Practically, however, in seven of these time units ($7 \times 0.7RC$), or approximately $5RC$, the capacitor is more than 99% charged and can be considered fully charged.

EXAMPLE 12

How long will it take for a capacitor of 0.5 μf to charge completely if it is connected in series with a 200,000-ohm resistor across a 200-v supply?

SOLUTION

1. T.C. = $RC = 0.2 \times 0.5 = 0.1$ sec.
2. Full charge = approx. $5RC = 0.5$ sec.

The curves of Fig. 9-8d show how the charging current and voltage across the capacitor vary with time, time being expressed in RC units. Offhand, this seems like a poor method of measuring time. Seconds would seem the more logical unit. However, there are two good reasons for the unit employed. First, in Fig. 9-8, no specific values were selected for R and C. Therefore we cannot calculate the time constant in seconds. Second, had we chosen specific values for R and C, calculated the actual time in seconds, for each step of the curve, and plotted the curve with 'time in seconds' as the abscissa, this curve would now apply *only* to this specific situation. A new curve would have to be drawn for any other value of C and/or R, whereas the curve as shown is a *universal* time constant curve and can be applied for any value of C or R.

EXAMPLE 13

A circuit contains a capacitor of 0.1 μf and a resistor of 220,000 ohms. The supply voltage is 230 v.

(a) Find the time constant of the circuit.
(b) How long will it take for the capacitor voltage to reach 190 v?

SOLUTION

1. T.C. = $RC = 0.22 \times 0.1 = 0.022$ sec.
2. 190 v is 190/230 or 82.6% of the maximum.
3. From the universal curve (Fig. 9-8d), 82.6% corresponds to 1.8 T.C. units. Time = $1.8 \times 0.022 = 0.04$ sec.

The degree of distortion produced by differentiating and integrating circuits depends upon the time constant of the circuit as compared to the *period* (time for one cycle) of the input wave. For example, if the frequency of the complex wave input is 100 cycles, its period is 0.01 sec. At this frequency, a time constant of 0.1 sec or longer can be considered long, whereas a time constant of 0.001 sec (or less) should be considered short. For pulse waves, the period of the wave has little meaning. These waves are specified in terms of pulse width (or duration) and pulse repetition rate. The degree of distortion produced by differentiating and integrating circuits again depends on the time constant of the circuit, but now this time constant must be compared to the time duration of the pulse. In general, *if the time constant exceeds ten times the period of the input wave shape* (*or ten times the pulse width*) *the circuit is said to have a long time constant; and when the circuit has a time constant less than one tenth of the period of the input wave shape,* (*or one tenth the pulse width*) *the time constant is short.*

EXAMPLE 14

A pulse wave has a repetition rate of 500 and a pulse width of 80 μs. What value of time constant would be considered (a) long, (b) short?

SOLUTION

(a) Long time constant $= 10 \times 80 = 800$ μs (or more).
(b) Short time constant $= 80/10 = 8$ μs (or less).

EXAMPLE 15

At a frequency of 5000 cycles, what value of time constant will be considered (a) long, (b) short?

SOLUTION

1. Period $= \dfrac{1}{f} = \dfrac{1}{5000} = 0.0002$ sec $= 200$ μsec.
   (a) Long time constant: $10 \times 200 = 2000$ μsec (or more).
   (b) Short time constant: $\frac{200}{10} = 20$ μsec (or less).

Differentiating and integrating circuits are used quite commonly in pulse wave equipment such as loran, radar, racon, and also in timing, trigger, and synchronizing circuits, as in television. The best way to explain their action is to analyze the action of such a circuit, with inputs like square waves or saw tooth waves.

Figure 9-9 shows an *R-C* series circuit with square wave input. The values of *R* and *C* are so chosen, with respect to the period of the input wave, that the time constant is short, in order to give good differentiator action. A short time constant means that

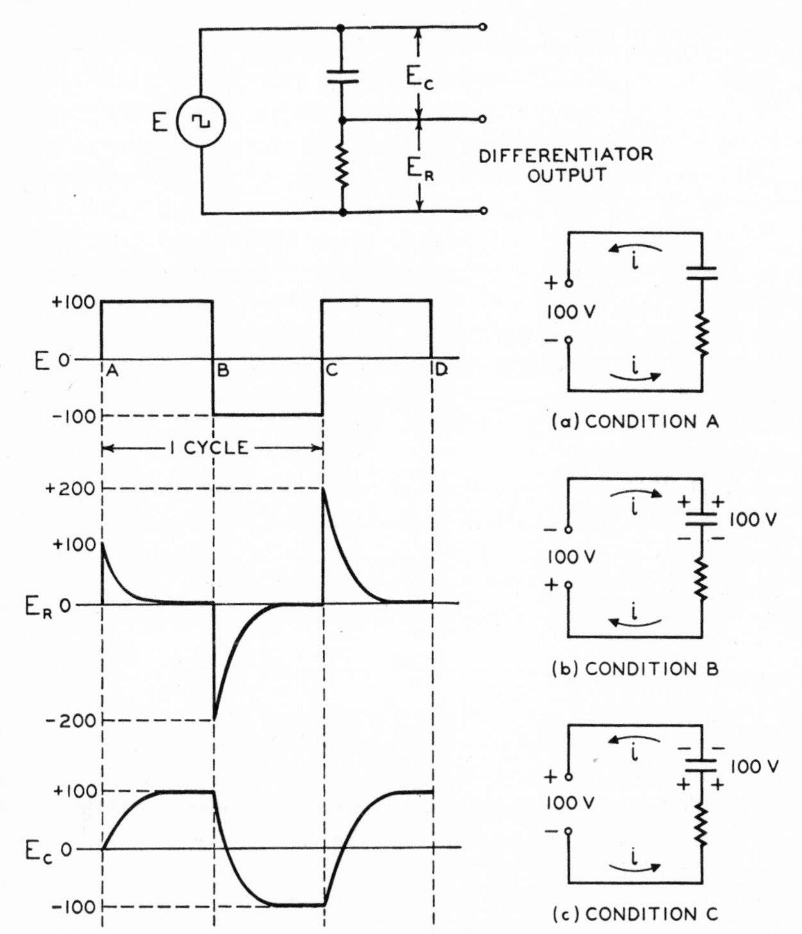

Fig. 9-9. Output of differentiator circuit with short time constant.

the capacitor will charge completely in less than one-half cycle. (Remember that a short time constant is less than one tenth of the period of the wave, and full charge—$5RC$ units—will be less than five tenths of the period, or less than one-half cycle).

1. When the circuit is closed at A, the voltage rises immediately from zero to +100 v. Since the capacitor is not charged, the only opposition to current flow is the resistance R. The current will rise immediately to its Ohm's law value. The voltage drop across the resistor will equal IR, or 100 v.

2. During time period A to B, the action is similar to a D.C. circuit. The capacitor starts to charge, and as the voltage across the unit builds up, the current and E_R will drop exponentially. Since the time constant of the circuit is short, the capacitor is fully charged (to +100 v) before the end of the half-cycle. The current and the voltage across the resistor will drop to zero for the remainder of the half-cycle.

3. At point B, the potential of the circuit reverses. The circuit conditions at this instant are shown in Fig. 9-9b. The applied voltage and the voltage across the capacitor are now additive. At this instant, the circuit voltage is 200 v. The current will reverse sharply and E_R will rise to a negative maximum of double the value at A. The voltage drop across the resistor (E_R) will be −200 v!

4. During the time period B to C, the capacitor discharges exponentially. The net circuit voltage is decreasing; the current and E_R will decrease. When the capacitor is completely discharged, it begins to charge with reversed polarity and opposes the line voltage, causing the current and E_R to drop further. Again, since the time constant is short, the capacitor charges completely; current drops to zero; E_R becomes zero before the second half cycle is completed.

5. At time C, the applied voltage suddenly reverses. But, due to the reversed charge on the capacitor, supply voltage and capacitor voltage are again additive. The current will reverse sharply and rise to a positive maximum. The voltage across the resistor (E_R) will rise to +200 v.

6. For time period C to D, the capacitor discharges and then recharges with opposite polarity, reducing the net circuit voltage. The current and E_R drop exponentially to zero.

In our explanation, the values (E_R, I, E_c) for the first half cycle differ in magnitude or slope from the curves shown for the remainder of the wave. This first half cycle should be ignored. It is a transient condition that occurs only at the closing of the circuit. From then on, all the cycles will be identical. The output of the differentiator circuit E_R is of special interest. Notice that:

1. The waveshape is very peaked. Such a circuit is often called a *peaker* or *peaking circuit.*
2. The amplitude of the output voltage is twice the input amplitude!

In the above circuit, the time constant was such that the capacitor was charged completely in less than one-half cycle of the square-wave input. This resulted in highly distorted output from the

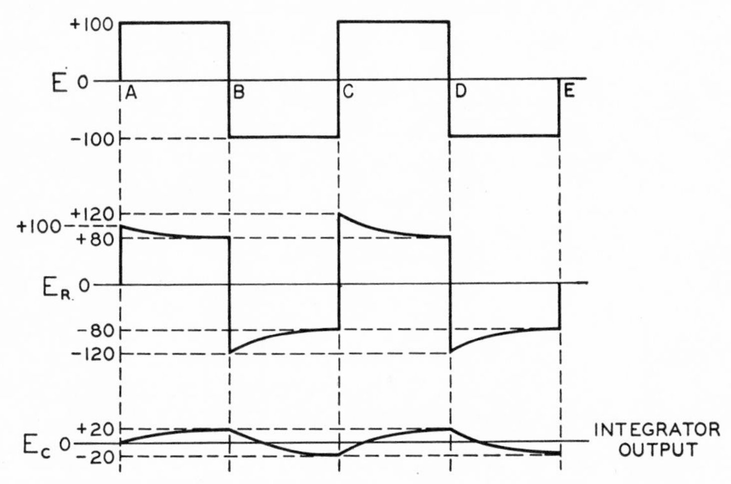

Fig. 9-10. Effect of long time constant on integrator output.

differentiator circuit. Meanwhile, the voltage across the capacitor (E_c) approaches the original square wave. Suppose now that the circuit constants are increased—either the capacitor or the resistor value or both are made larger. The time constant of the circuit is increased. This will result in good integrator action. It will take longer for the capacitor to charge. Let us see how the output wave shapes will look if the time constant of the circuit is increased to a point that the capacitor will charge to only 20% of the supply voltage in one-half cycle. The curves for this condition are shown in Fig. 9-10.

1. When the circuit is closed at A, the supply voltage rises immediately to its maximum value (100 v). Since the capacitor is not charged, the only opposition to current flow is the resistance

value. The current rises immediately to its Ohm's law value, and $E_R = IR = E$.

2. As the capacitor charges (A to B), the net voltage in the circuit is decreasing, and the current drops. But due to the long time constant, the charge on the capacitor, at B, is low (20 v). Therefore the drop in current is slight, and E_R will be reduced only a small amount ($E_R = 80$ v). Meanwhile, since the capacitor charges to such a small percentage of the supply voltage, the charging curve of E_c will be practically a straight line.

3. At point B, the supply voltage reverses. The charge on the capacitor aids the supply voltage. But since the capacitor charge is low, the net circuit voltage is only slightly greater than the supply voltage (120 v). The current will reverse sharply and rise to a negative maximum slightly greater than in (1) above. E_R will be a negative maximum slightly greater than the supply voltage (-120 v).

4. From B to C, the capacitor discharges and starts to charge with opposite polarity. The net circuit voltage decreases; the current drops; E_R drops. Again the capacitor will reach only a partial charge (20 v). The drop in current and E_R will be slight ($E_R = 80$ v).

5. At C the supply voltage again reverses; the capacitor voltage aids the supply voltage; the current reverses and rises immediately to positive maximum value greater than in (1); E_R will rise to a positive maximum greater than the supply voltage ($+120$ v).

From here on, the wave shape of E_R and E_c should be obvious. Again the transient values obtained in the first half cycle are slightly lower in value than the rest of the cycles and should be ignored in analyzing the action of the circuit. Notice that the voltage E_R across the resistor approaches the original square-wave input. Differentiator action is practically lost due to the long circuit time constant. On the other hand, good integrating action is obtained. Notice also that the voltage E_c across the capacitor looks like a triangular wave. Here the amplitude of the integrator output is low.

As the time constant of the circuit is made longer and longer, the capacitor will charge to a lesser and lesser degree. The current in the circuit will hardly drop. E_R will remain more nearly constant. At the points where the supply voltage reverses (B, C), the capacitor adds little to the net circuit voltage. The current will rise very little above its first maximum value. E_R will hardly exceed the supply voltage. The voltage E_R across the resistor is almost identical to the square-wave input. Meanwhile, since the capacitor charges very little, the integrator output is very low—approaching zero—and the wave shape approaches a perfect triangular wave.

What is the effect of an *R-C* circuit with some other complex wave input? Let us consider a saw tooth input applied to a circuit with very short time constant. Figure 9-11 shows the resulting wave shapes.

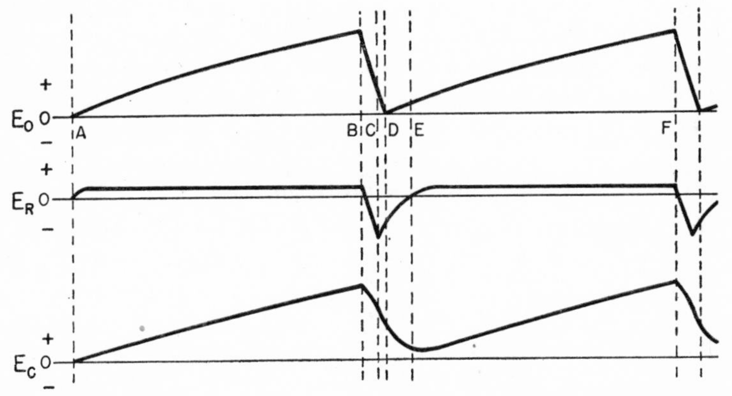

Fig. 9-11. Differentiator output from a saw tooth input wave.

1. At *A* the supply voltage is zero and the current must be zero. As the voltage starts to rise, the current tends to rise to a high value. But since the time constant of the circuit is short, the capacitor charges quickly, and the capacitor voltage follows the input voltage closely. The countervoltage of the capacitor will prevent the current from rising to a high value. Since the supply voltage increases at a constant rate from *A* to *B*, the charging current in the circuit will be constant. E_R will rise quickly to some low value and then remain constant for the remainder of the time *A* to *B*.

2. At *B* the supply voltage begins to drop to zero. But the capacitor is charged to the full supply voltage. A high current, in the opposite direction, will flow as the capacitor starts to discharge

rapidly. This produces a high negative voltage across the resistor. This condition prevails during the interval B to C.

3. At C, the capacitor has discharged sufficiently to reduce the current flow. The negative voltage across the resistor starts to decrease.

4. At D, the line voltage once again begins to rise in a positive direction, but the rate of rise in supply voltage is low. Meanwhile, the capacitor voltage is still higher than the supply voltage and the capacitor still continues to discharge, but at a slower rate. The voltage drop across the resistor is still negative.

5. Finally at E, the line voltage is now higher than the capacitor voltage. The direction of current flow reverses, the capacitor once again begins to charge, and the voltage across the resistor is now of positive polarity. From there on, the operation repeats as above. The differentiator circuit output is of special interest. It produces sharp negative *pips* that are often used for timing, trigger, or synchronizing pulses in special electronic circuits.

Review Problems

1. A capacitor of 0.002 μf is connected in series with a coil of 0.25 h. Find:

(a) The resonant frequency.
(b) The total circuit impedance at resonance.

2. A 200-μh coil, a 320-μμf capacitor, and a 200-ohm resistor are connected in series across a 50-v, 1990-kc supply source. Is this circuit in resonance? Explain the reason for your answer.

3. In Problem (2) the capacitor is reduced to one tenth of its previous capacitance. Is the circuit now resonant? Explain.

4. In Problem (2) at what frequency would the circuit become resonant if the capacitance is not changed?

5. In Problem (2) what value of inductance would produce resonance if the frequency and capacitance are unchanged?

6. Using the values of Problem 5 find:

(a) Line current.
(b) Voltage across each component.
(c) Circuit phase angle.

7. A capacitor of 1.0 μf is connected in series with a variable resistor. The input frequency is 100 cycles. Find the phase shift between E_{Line} and E_R for the following values of resistance:

(a) 250 ohms.
(b) 2500 ohms.
(c) 5000 ohms.
(d) 15,000 ohms.

8. Repeat Problem 7 for the phase angles between E_{Line} and E_c.

9. Draw the circuit diagram and determine the capacitance value for an R-C circuit that will cause the output voltage across a 600-ohm resistive load to lead the input voltage by 40 degrees at 2000 cycles. Draw the vector diagram.

10. Draw a circuit diagram suitable for coupling in an R-C coupled amplifier. Indicate the input and output voltage connections.

11. In the circuit of Problem 10, the coupling capacitor is 0.01 μf, and the grid resistor is 0.25 megohm. Find the phase shift between the input and output voltage:

(a) At 100 cycles.
(b) At 100,000 cycles.
(c) If the grid resistor is not changed, how can the phase shift at 100 cycles be reduced to 5 degrees?

12. In Problem 11 the input voltage is 10 v. Find the output voltage:

(a) At 100 cycles.
(b) At 10,000 cycles.
(c) Repeat (a), using a coupling capacitor of 0.1 μf.
(d) Repeat (b) for the 0.1 μf capacitor.

13. By means of circuit diagrams and supporting vector diagrams, show two ways by which the output voltage can be made to lag the input voltage.

14. A frequency attenuating circuit consists of a 0.001-μf capacitor in series with a 200,000-ohm resistor. The applied voltage of 10 v is varied in frequency from 50 to 10,000 cycles. Plot the output voltage across the resistor for this range of frequency. (Start at 50 cycles and double. This plot should be made on semilog paper.)

15. When is an R-C series circuit called

(a) An integrating circuit? (b) A differentiating circuit?

16. (a) Draw a circuit diagram showing an R-C circuit connected for differentiating action.

(b) Repeat for integrator action.

17. Find the time constant of the following R-C series circuits:

(a) R = 2 megohms, C = 2 μf.
(b) R = 0.5 megohm, C = 0.05 μf.
(c) R = 0.1 megohm, C = 200 $\mu\mu$f.
(d) R = 50,000 ohms, C = 40 $\mu\mu$f.

18. For a frequency of 15,000 cycles what values of time constants in (17) would be considered:

(a) Long? (b) Short?

19. At what frequencies would the R-C circuit of Problem 17(c) become a long time constant?

20. A square wave having a frequency of 200 cycles is fed to an R-C series circuit having a resistance of 100,000 ohms. What value of capacitor would be required for:

(a) Long time constant? (b) Short time constant?

21. A pulse wave has an amplitude of 10 v. The pulse duration is 50 μs and the pulse repetition rate is 2000. Find:

(a) The maximum time for a short time constant.
(b) The minimum time for a long time constant.
(c) The maximum value of resistance that would still produce a short time constant if $C = 0.005\ \mu$f.

22. The pulse wave of Problem 21 is fed to an integrating circuit consisting of $R = 250{,}000$ ohms and $C = 0.001\ \mu$f. To what value will the capacitor charge during the first pulse?

23. The pulse wave of Problem 21 is fed to a differentiating circuit consisting of $R = 50{,}000$ ohms and $C = 250\ \mu\mu$f. To what value will the capacitor charge during the first pulse?

24. Figure 9-12a shows a typical pulse wave used for horizontal synchronization in a television receiver. Draw the output wave shape that would be obtained from:

(a) Very short time constant differentiating circuit.
(b) Long time constant integrator circuit.

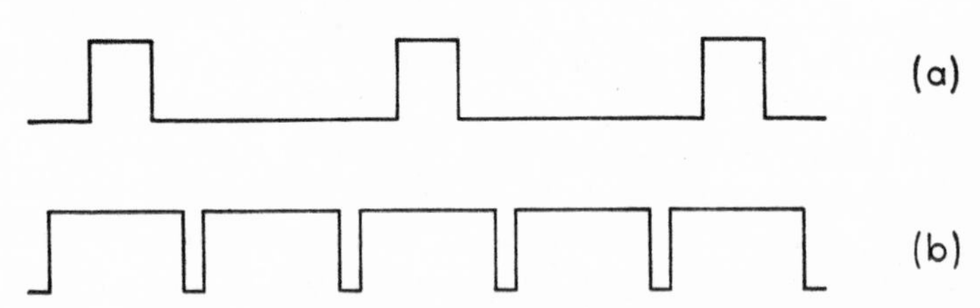

Fig. 9-12. Typical T.V. synchronizing signals. (a) Horizontal sync pulses. (b) Serrated vertical sync pulse.

25. Repeat Problem 24 for the vertical synchronizing signal shown in Fig. 9-12b.

CHAPTER 10

Parallel Circuits

PARALLEL CIRCUITS ARE ENCOUNTERED quite frequently in all phases of electronic work. A very common example is the tuning circuits in your home receiver. Whenever you change the dial setting of your receiver, you are actually changing the circuit constants in several parallel circuits. By-pass capacitors used in many portions of your receiver form parallel circuits. Filter networks and coupling circuits between stages of electronic units are further examples of parallel circuits. Sometimes the branches of these parallel circuits are pure components, that is, resistance alone, capacitance alone, or inductance alone. Such circuits are easily handled. But more often any branch of the parallel circuit may contain more than one circuit element. Actually, these circuits are not more difficult, but they are more laborious to solve. In order to understand the role of such circuits in electronic work, we must learn how to analyze and solve these circuits.

Rules for parallel circuits. All the principles we learned for handling D.C. parallel circuits apply equally well to A.C. circuits. However, now we must take phase angles into consideration. Let us summarize these principles with due respect to phase relations:

1. The voltage is the same across each branch of the parallel circuit. Since the voltage is common to all the branches, it is used as the reference value for vector diagrams.
2. The current in any branch can be found from the voltage across the branch and the impedance of the branch.
   (a) If the branch contains resistance only, the branch current is in phase with the applied voltage.
   (b) If the branch contains capacitance only, the branch current will lead the applied voltage by 90 degrees.
   (c) If the branch contains pure inductance only, the branch current will lag the applied voltage by 90 degrees.
   (d) If the branch contains a combination of circuit elements,

not only must we calculate the impedance and current for the branch, but we must also find the phase angle of that current with respect to the applied voltage. We can get this phase angle from the ratio of reactance (X_0) to resistance (R) for the branch.

3. Once the individual branch currents and their phase angles have been found, we can get the total line current by adding the branch currents. *This must be a vector addition.* The addition may be made graphically or mathematically from trigonometric relations.

4. The total impedance can be found from the total current and the supply voltage:

$$Z_T = \frac{E_T}{I_T}$$

When the voltage across the parallel circuit is not known, it is sometimes easier to assume a voltage and solve for the parallel circuit impedance, and then continue with the rest of the problem.

In studying direct current, we learned that

$$\frac{1}{R_T} = \frac{1}{R_1} + \frac{1}{R_2} + \frac{1}{R_3} \cdots \qquad \text{and} \qquad R_T = \frac{R_1R_2}{R_1 + R_2}$$

We used these relations to find the total resistance of a parallel circuit, the second formula being used when only two branches were involved. A similar statement can be made for A.C. parallel circuits:

$$\frac{1}{Z_T} = \frac{1}{Z_1} + \frac{1}{Z_2} + \frac{1}{Z_3} \cdots \qquad \text{and} \qquad Z_T = \frac{Z_1Z_2}{Z_1 + Z_2}$$

However, since impedances have phase angles, the solution to the above equations must be done by vector algebra. This method is shown in the next chapter.

We also learned, in D.C. theory, that the total resistance was less than the smallest branch resistance. *Due to phase angles of impedance, such a general statement cannot be made for A.C. circuits:*

1. If the parallel circuit contains resistive and inductive branches only, the total circuit impedance will be less than the smallest branch resistance.

2. The above statement will also be true when the branches are resistive and capacitive.

3. When a parallel circuit contains resistive, inductive, and capacitive branches, the total impedance will be greater than if the capacitive or inductive branches were disconnected. That sounds a little confusing—we add a branch, and the total impedance is higher! Yet a little thought will make it clear. Currents in inductive and capacitive branches are 180 degrees out of phase (with respect to each other). When we add these two currents, their 'sum' is less than either component. Lower current means higher impedance.

Equivalent series circuit. In series-parallel circuits (D.C.), we often replaced parallel networks by one resistance of equivalent value. Very often in electronics it is also easier to analyze a circuit by replacing parallel networks by their *equivalent series circuits.* This is not difficult. As far as the supply source is concerned, if the magnitude of the current being delivered and the phase angle between that current and the supply voltage are unchanged—it makes no difference whether the load is a parallel or series circuit.

We have already discussed how to find the line current, phase angle between this current and supply voltage, and the total impedance of a parallel circuit. Let us suppose that a parallel circuit has a total impedance of 50 ohms, and that the line current leads the supply voltage by 30 degrees. Can a series circuit produce the same results? Certainly, the current is leading by an angle of less than 90 degrees. A series R-C circuit would cause the current to lead by some such angle. The proper ratio of R to C would cause current to lead by 30 degrees. Also the proper choice of R and C in series could have an impedance of 50 ohms. From the impedance triangle for a series circuit we know that

$$\sin\theta = \frac{X}{Z} \qquad \text{and} \qquad \cos\theta = \frac{R}{Z}$$

But we already know θ (30 degrees) and Z (50 ohms). From the above relations we can, therefore, solve for X and R of the equivalent series circuit. Since the current is leading, the reactance (X) is capacitive. Using the relation $X_c = \frac{1}{2\pi fC}$, we can solve for the capacitance value.

That is just about all there is to parallel circuits. There are numerous variations for the application of these principles. It would be impossible to illustrate each. Yet a few problems now to 'clinch' the foregoing principles are in order. From there on, it is up to you to think each new problem through and apply the above principles to any variation.

Resistance and inductance in parallel. When a resistor and an inductance are connected in parallel, the line current consists of two components:

1. The current through the resistor—in phase with the line voltage.
2. The current through the inductance—lagging the voltage by 90 degrees.

EXAMPLE 1

A resistor of 100 ohms is connected in parallel with an inductance of 0.5 h across a 60-cycle, 120-v line. Find:

(a) Line current.
(b) Circuit phase angle.
(c) Total circuit impedance.
(d) Power dissipated.
(e) Equivalent series circuit.

SOLUTION

1. $X_L = 2\pi fL = 6.28 \times 60 \times 0.5 = 189$ ohms.

2. $I_L = \frac{E_L}{X_L} = \frac{120}{189} = 0.635$ amp, lagging by 90°.

3. $I_R = \frac{E_R}{R} = \frac{120}{100} = 1.20$ amps, in phase.

4. $I_T = \dot{I}_L + \dot{I}_R$ (the dots indicate a *vector* addition).

The addition can be made graphically, or trigonometrically. Using the mathematical solution, since the two currents are at right angles:

$$I_T = \sqrt{(I_R)^2 + (I_L)^2} = \sqrt{(1.20)^2 + (0.635)^2} = \mathbf{1.36} \text{ amps.}$$

5. Circuit phase angle

$$\theta = \text{arc tan } -\frac{I_L}{I_R} = \text{arc tan } -\frac{0.635}{1.20}; \qquad \theta = \mathbf{-27.9°}.$$

6. Total circuit impedance

$$Z_T = \frac{E_T}{I_T} = \frac{120}{1.36} = \mathbf{88.2} \text{ ohms.}$$

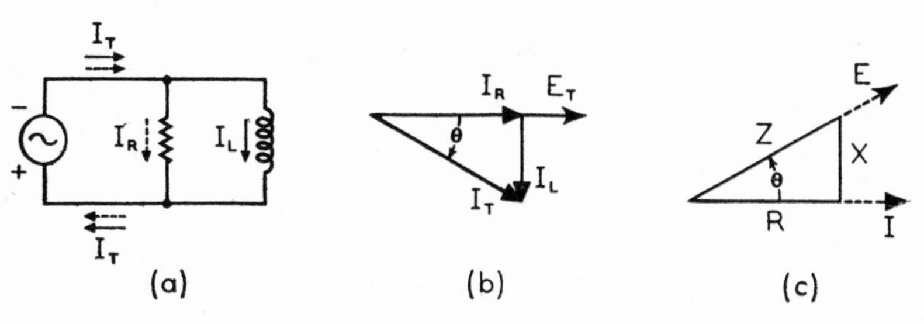

Fig. 10-1. *R-L* parallel circuit.

7. Power dissipated equals

$$EI \cos \theta = 120 \times 1.36 \times 0.884 = \mathbf{144} \text{ watts.}$$

But we also know that a pure inductance does not dissipate power. In this circuit the power dissipated is in the resistive branch alone, or

$$P = EI_R = 120 \times 1.20 = 144 \text{ watts.}$$

8. The total circuit has an impedance of 88.2 ohms, and the current lags by 27.9 degrees. *A series circuit would produce the same effect if it also had an impedance of 88.2 ohms—and the impedance triangle had a circuit phase angle of 27.9 degrees.* Such an impedance is shown in Fig. 10-1c. Therefore, the equivalent series circuit would be:

$$R = Z \cos \theta = 88.2 \times 0.884 = \mathbf{77.9} \text{ ohms.}$$

$$X_L = Z \sin \theta = 88.2 \times 0.468 = 41.3 \text{ ohms.}$$

$$L = \frac{X_L}{2\pi f} = \frac{41.3}{6.28 \times 60} = \mathbf{0.109} \text{ h.}$$

The above problem was simple because the two branch currents were at right angles. If either branch contained more than one type of circuit element, the current in that branch would have a phase angle less than 90 degrees. This makes the solution more laborious, but the method is still the same. A coil having resistance in parallel with a resistor would represent such a case.

Example 2

A coil (resistance 60 ohms, inductance 0.05 h) is connected in parallel with a resistor of 500 ohms across a 20-v, 1000-cycle supply. Find:

(a) Line current.
(b) Circuit phase angle.
(c) Power dissipated.

(d) Total circuit impedance.
(e) Equivalent series circuit.

SOLUTION

1. $X_L = 2\pi fL = 6.28 \times 1000 \times 0.05 = 314$ ohms.
2. $Z_L = \sqrt{R_L^2 + X_L^2} = \sqrt{(60)^2 + (314)^2} = 320$ ohms.
3. Coil phase angle $(\theta_L) = \text{arc tan } \frac{X_L}{R_L} = \text{arc tan } \frac{314}{60} = 79.2°$.
4. $I_L = \frac{E_L}{Z_L} = \frac{20}{320} = 0.0625$ amp $= 62.5$ ma.

This current lags the line voltage by 79.2 degrees.

5. $I_R = \frac{E_R}{R} = \frac{20}{500} = 40$ ma, in phase with the line voltage.

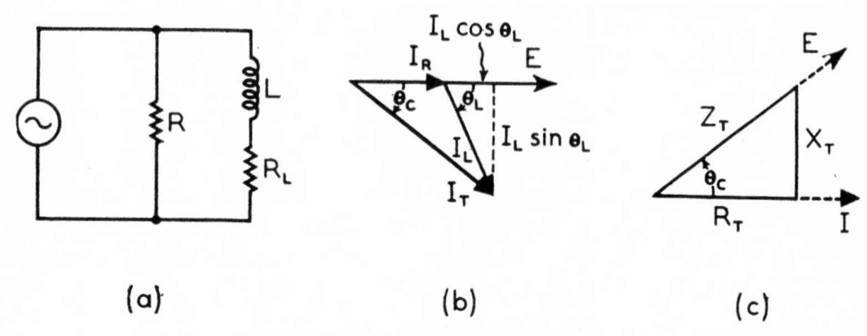

Fig. 10-2. Series-parallel *R-L* circuit.

6. $I_T = \dot{I}_R + \dot{I}_L$. The graphical solution for the line current is simple enough. Merely draw the diagram 10-2b to scale. Notice in this diagram that the total current is the hypotenuse of a right triangle, with one side equal to $I_L \sin \theta_L$, and the other side equal to $I_R + I_L \cos \theta_L$. This shows us how we can solve for the line current mathematically. The first step is to break down the current in the inductive branch into the *in-phase* component and the *out-of-phase* or *quadrature* component.

(a) In-phase component equals

$$I_L \cos \theta_L = 62.5 \times 0.187 = 11.7 \text{ ma.}$$

(b) Quadrature component equals

$$I_L \sin \theta_L = 62.5 \times 0.982 = 61.4 \text{ ma at } 90°.$$

(c) $I_R + I_L \cos \theta_L = 40 + 11.7 = 51.7$ ma at 0°.

(d) $I_T = \sqrt{(51.7)^2 + (61.4)^2} = \mathbf{80.4}$ ma.

7. Again from the vector diagram, we can see that the tangent of the

circuit phase angle is the ratio of the quadrature component of current ($I_L \sin \theta_L$) and the total in-phase component ($I_R + I_L \cos \theta_L$):

$$\theta_c = \text{arc tan } \frac{61.4}{51.7} = 49.9°.$$

The line current lags the line voltage by 49.9 degrees.

8. $P = EI \cos \theta = 20 \times (80.4 \times 10^{-3}) \times 0.644 =$ **1.035** watts. But $I \cos \theta$ is the in-phase component of the total current or $I_R + I_L \cos \theta_L$. Therefore, the power dissipated in any circuit is the product of the voltage and in-phase component of the current, or:

$$P = 20 \times 51.7 \times 10^{-3} = 1.034 \text{ watts.}$$

9. $Z_T = \dfrac{E_T}{I_T} = \dfrac{20}{80.4 \times 10^{-3}} = 249$ ohms.

10. The equivalent series circuit must have an impedance, Z_T, of 249 ohms. Also the reactance, X_T, and resistance, R_T, must be such as to produce a circuit phase angle of 49.9 degrees. This is shown in Fig. 10-2c. From the diagram, it is obvious that:

$$R_T = Z_T \cos \theta_c = 249 \times 0.644 = \mathbf{160} \text{ ohms.}$$
$$X_T = Z_T \sin \theta_c = 249 \times 0.765 = 190 \text{ ohms.}$$

Since the line current lags the line voltage, this reactance must be inductive.

$$L = \frac{X_L}{2\pi f} = \frac{190}{6.28 \times 1000} = 0.0302 \text{ h} = \mathbf{30.2} \text{ mh.}$$

Resistance and capacitance in parallel. Solution of R-C parallel circuits should present no difficulty at this time. The procedure is similar to the method discussed for R-L circuits above. The only change is that now the line current leads the line voltage by some angle less than 90 degrees.

EXAMPLE 3

A parallel circuit contains three branches as follows: a 350-μμf capacitor, a 500-ohm resistor, and a 100-μμf capacitor. The supply source is 40 v, 2000 kc. Find:

(a) Line current.
(b) Circuit phase angle.
(c) Power dissipated.
(d) Total circuit impedance.
(e) Equivalent series circuit.

SOLUTION

1. $X_{c_1} = \dfrac{1}{2\pi f C_1} = \dfrac{0.159 \times 10^{12}}{2000 \times 10^3 \times 350} = 227$ ohms.

2. $I_1 = \dfrac{E_1}{X_{c1}} = \dfrac{40}{227} = 0.176$ amps, leading by 90°.

3. $I_2 = \dfrac{E_2}{R} = \dfrac{40}{500} = 0.08$ amp, in phase.

4. $X_{c2} = \dfrac{1}{2\pi f C_2} = \dfrac{0.159 \times 10^{12}}{2000 \times 10^3 \times 100} = 795$ ohms.

5. $I_3 = \dfrac{E_3}{X_{c2}} = \dfrac{40}{795} = 0.0503$ amp, leading by 90°.

6. $I_T = \dot{I}_1 + \dot{I}_2 + \dot{I}_3$.

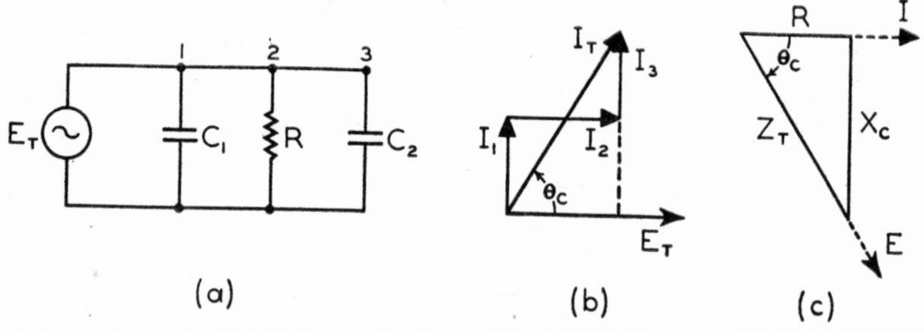

Fig. 10-3. *R-C* parallel circuit.

From the vector diagram, Fig. 10-3b, we can see that the line current is the hypotenuse of a right triangle. One side of this triangle (in-phase component) is equal to I_2, the resistive branch current; and the other side (quadrature component) is equal to the sum of I_1 and I_3, the capacitive branch currents. Therefore:

$$I_T = \sqrt{(I_2)^2 + (I_1 + I_3)^2} = \sqrt{(0.08)^2 + (0.226)^2} = \mathbf{0.239} \text{ amp.}$$

7. We can also see from the vector diagram, that the tangent of the circuit phase angle is the ratio of the quadrature to the in-phase components of the line current, or

$$\theta_c = \text{arc tan } \frac{0.226}{.08} = \mathbf{70.5°}.$$

The line current leads the supply voltage by 70.5 degrees.

8. $P = EI \cos \theta$, but $I \cos \theta = I_2$, the resistive branch current. So we can also use the relation:

$$P = E \times I_R = 40 \times 0.08 = \mathbf{3.20} \text{ v.}$$

9. $Z_T = \dfrac{E_T}{I_T} = \dfrac{40}{0.239} = \mathbf{167}$ ohms.

10. The equivalent series circuit must have an impedance of 167 ohms and a phase angle of 70.5 degrees:

$$R = Z_T \cos \theta_c = 167 \times 0.334 = \mathbf{55.9} \text{ ohms.}$$
$$X_c = Z_T \sin \theta_c = 167 \times 0.943 = \mathbf{157.5} \text{ ohms.}$$
$$C = \frac{1}{2\pi f X_c} = \frac{0.159 \times 10^{12}}{2000 \times 10^3 \times 157.5} = \mathbf{505}\ \mu\mu\text{f.}$$

In this problem, since the individual branch currents were not required, we could have combined branch one and branch three into one branch of capacitance equal to $C_1 + C_2$ and solved the problem as a two-branch circuit (R and C_T). The method used above, although it is a little longer, does show the steps more clearly.

Division of current: *R-C* parallel circuit. There are times when we do not know the voltage across a parallel circuit, but we do know the current flowing into the circuit. The method just shown cannot be used. Still, the principles developed can be applied in some other order. Figure 10-4 shows the phase relations in an R-C parallel circuit.

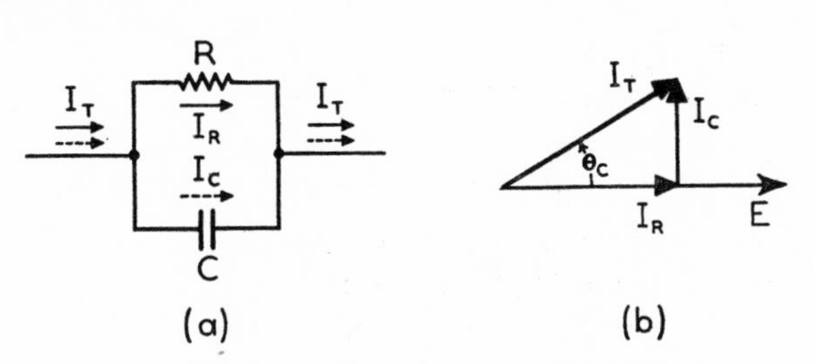

Fig. 10-4. R-C parallel-circuit phase relations.

Let us assume that we know the value of the resistance, R; the value of reactance, X_c; and the total current, I_T. How can we proceed to find the current in each branch?

1. We know that the current divides into two components: I_R in phase with the voltage developed across the circuit, and I_c leading the voltage by 90 degrees. But we do not know this voltage, so we cannot use Ohm's law.

2. We do not know the impedance, Z_T, so we cannot find this voltage by $E_T = I_T Z_T$. Nor do we know how to find the total impedance of a parallel circuit.

3. We know that $I_R = I_T \cos \theta$, but we do not know the circuit phase angle.

4. From Fig. 10-4b we see that the tangent of the circuit phase

angle is equal to the ratio of I_c to I_R. There is our clue! The ratio of currents must bear a definite relation to the ratio of oppositions, and we know both R and X_c. Since the units are in parallel, the voltage across each branch is the same, or

$$I_c X_c = I_R R \qquad \text{and} \qquad \frac{I_c}{I_R} = \frac{R}{X_c}$$

Since the tangent of the circuit phase angle is I_c/I_R, it is also equal to the *inverse* opposition ratio R/X_c. From this, we can get the circuit phase angle. Then, using the right-triangle relations, we solve for I_c and I_R.

EXAMPLE 4

A current of 50 ma, 400 cycles flows through the parallel circuit shown in Fig. 10-4a. The circuit values are 6000-ohm resistance and 0.05 μf capacitance. Find:

(a) The current through each component.
(b) The voltage across the circuit.

SOLUTION

1. $X_c = \frac{1}{2\pi fC} = \frac{0.159 \times 10^6}{400 \times 0.05} = 7950$ ohms.

2. $\tan \theta_c = \frac{R}{X_c} = \frac{6000}{7950}; \qquad \theta = 37.1°.$

3. $I_R = I_T \times \cos \theta = 50 \times 0.798 =$ **39.9** ma.
   $I_c = I_T \times \sin \theta = 50 \times 0.603 =$ **30.2** ma.

4. $E_R = I_R \times R = 39.9 \times 10^{-3} \times 6000 =$ **240** v
   $E_c = I_c \times X_c = 30.2 \times 10^{-3} \times 7950 =$ **240** v (check).

In the above example, what would be the effect of using a larger capacitor? The capacitive reactance would decrease; a greater portion of the current would flow through the capacitive branch; the total impedance would decrease; and the voltage developed across the circuit would drop.

EXAMPLE 5

In Example 4, find the current division and voltage across the circuit if the capacitance is 5 μf.

SOLUTION

1. $X_c = \frac{1}{2\pi fC} = \frac{0.159 \times 10^6}{400 \times 5} = 79.5$ ohms.

2. $\tan \theta = \frac{R}{X_c} = \frac{6000}{79.5} = 75.5, \qquad \theta = 89.2°.$

3. $I_R = I_T \cos\theta = 50 \times 0.014 = 0.7$ ma
$I_c = I_T \sin\theta = 50 \times 0.9999 = 50$ ma
4. $E_c = I_c \times X_c = 50 \times 10^{-3} \times 79.5 = 3.98$ v.

Notice that practically no current flows through the resistor, and that the voltage drop across the circuit was reduced from 240 v to less than 4 v!

By-pass capacitors. In general, electronic circuits carry currents that are complex waves, containing a D.C. component and several sine wave components of various frequencies. Very often these currents are passed through a resistance to produce a *D.C. voltage drop* across the resistor. If the A.C. components of the complex waves are also allowed to flow through the resistor, the voltage will vary depending on the magnitude and frequency of these components. To prevent these voltage variations, the resistor is shunted by a suitable capacitor. This capacitor is called a *by-pass capacitor.* From Example 5 it is obvious that if a capacitor value is selected so that its reactance (compared to the resistance it is shunting) is low *for the lowest frequency component* of the complex wave, then these sine waves will pass through the capacitor, instead of the resistor. Due to the low reactance of the capacitor, the A.C. voltage across the parallel circuit will be negligible. Common practice dictates that the capacitor reactance must be less than one-tenth of the resistance value at the lowest frequency. Actually, the greater the capacitance, the better the by-passing action. A typical example of such a circuit is the by-pass capacitor shunted across the resistor used in series with the cathode of a tube for bias.

Another illustration of the use of a by-pass capacitor is in the separation of the audio waves from a modulated carrier. From Chapter 1 we know that the modulated carrier contains the carrier frequency and audio intelligence. When this modulated carrier is put through a 'detector', sum and difference frequencies are created. The difference frequency is the desired audio signal. This complex wave of current can be passed through a resistor shunted by a suitable capacitor. This time the size of capacitor is selected so that its reactance is:

1. *High at the audio frequencies.* In this way, the audio currents pass through the resistor creating audio voltage drops. Since X_c is high at these frequencies, it does not by-pass these frequencies, and the audio voltages developed across the resistor are high.

2. *Low at the R.F. frequencies* (carrier, sidebands and sum frequencies). These frequencies are by-passed through the capacitor and negligible R.F. voltages are developed across the *R-C* parallel circuit.

Resistance, inductance, and capacitance in parallel. In the previous cases we have used only two types of circuit elements at a time, *R-L* or *R-C*. Since none of these circuits contained inductance in one branch and capacitance in another, we noticed that the total impedance was less than the smallest branch impedance. Now we will find that, due to the combined effect of inductive and capacitive branches, the total impedance of a circuit may become quite high. The solution of such circuits does not differ from the methods already discussed. For comparison purposes the illustrative problem used will employ the same values for *R*, *L*, and supply voltage as Example 1 (page 152).

Example 6

An inductance of 0.5 h, a resistor of 100 ohms, and a capacitor of 25 μf are connected in parallel across a 60-cycle, 120-v line. Find:

(a) Line current.
(b) Circuit phase angle.
(c) Power dissipated.
(d) Total circuit impedance.
(e) Equivalent series circuit.

Solution

1. $X_L = 2\pi fL = 6.28 \times 60 \times 0.5 = 189$ ohms.

2. $I_L = \dfrac{E_L}{X_L} = \dfrac{120}{189} = 0.635$ amp, lagging by 90°.

3. $I_R = \dfrac{E_R}{R} = \dfrac{120}{100} = 1.20$ amps, in phase.

4. $X_c = \dfrac{1}{2\pi fC} = \dfrac{0.159 \times 10^6}{60 \times 25} = 106$ ohms.

5. $I_c = \dfrac{E}{X_c} = \dfrac{120}{106} = 1.13$ amps, leading by 90°.

6. $I_T = \dot{I}_L + \dot{I}_R + \dot{I}_c$. Since I_L and I_c are exactly 180 degrees apart, the net reactive current is the difference between these two currents.

$$I_X = I_c - I_L = 0.495 \text{ amp, leading by } 90°.$$

From the vector diagram, Fig. 10-5b, it is obvious that

$$I_T = \sqrt{I_R^2 + I_X^2} = \sqrt{(1.20)^2 + (0.495)^2} = 1.30 \text{ amps.}$$

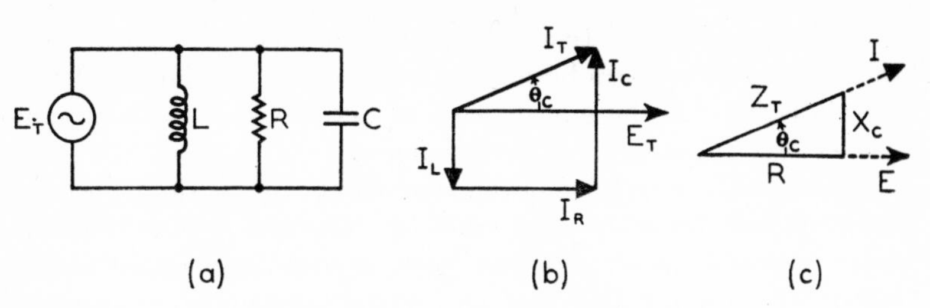

Fig. 10-5. *L-C-R* parallel circuit.

7. Circuit phase angle

$$\theta_c = \text{arc tan } \frac{I_X}{I_R} = \text{arc tan } \frac{0.495}{1.20} = 22.4°.$$

The current leads the voltage by 22.4 degrees.

8. Power dissipated equals

$$EI \cos \theta = EI_R = 120 \times 1.20 = \mathbf{144} \text{ watts.}$$

9. $Z_T = \dfrac{E_T}{I_T} = \dfrac{120}{1.30} = 92.3$ ohms.

10. Since the line current leads the line voltage by an angle less than 90 degrees, the circuit acts like an *R-C* series circuit. From the impedance diagram, 10-5c, it is obvious that the equivalent series circuit would be

(a) $Z_T = 92.3$ ohms.
(b) $R = Z_T \cos \theta = 92.3 \times 0.925 = \mathbf{85.3}$ ohms.
(c) $X_c = Z_T \sin \theta = 92.3 \times 0.381 = 35.1$ ohms.
(d) $C = \dfrac{1}{2\pi f X_c} = \dfrac{0.159 \times 10^6}{60 \times 35.1} = \mathbf{75.5}\ \mu\text{f}.$

A comparison of these results, and the results from Problem 1, reveals several interesting points:

1. The power dissipated (144 watts) is the same for each circuit. This should be obvious. The added capacitor dissipates no power!

2. By adding the capacitor in parallel, the line current dropped from 1.36 amps to 1.30 amps. Also, the current shifted from a lag of 27.9 degrees to a lead of 22.4 degrees! The capacitor not only completely counteracted the effect of the inductive branch, but made the circuit capacitive.

3. The circuit impedance is greater with the capacitor added (92.3 ohms) than it was for the *R-L* circuit (88.2 ohms). In this

problem it is still less than the smallest branch impedance. Yet, the addition of an extra branch *did increase* the impedance. Under certain conditions the impedance may actually increase to a value *much higher* than any branch impedance.

Mathematical solution of the above problem was simple because the reactance branches were taken as pure reactances. The currents I_L and I_c were, respectively, 90 degrees lagging and leading compared with the line voltage. These currents were therefore 180 degrees apart and we were able to subtract current values algebraically to find the net reactive current, or the quadrature component of the total current. For the same reason, the only in-phase component of the line current was the current through the resistive branch, I_R.

What would be the effect if one or both reactive branches had resistance as well as reactance? (An example of this would be if the coil had a low Q.) The phase shift of the reactive branch currents would not be exactly 90 degrees. Obviously we could not subtract I_L from I_c, algebraically, to get the quadrature component of the line current. It would be necessary to:

1. Find the magnitude and phase angle of each current.
2. Resolve each current into its in-phase and quadrature components.
3. Add all the in-phase components and add all the quadrature components, algebraically.
4. The line current $= \sqrt{\left(\begin{matrix}\text{in-phase}\\ \text{components}\end{matrix}\right)^2 + \left(\begin{matrix}\text{quadrature}\\ \text{components}\end{matrix}\right)^2}$
5. The phase angle of this current θ_c

$$= \text{arc tan } \frac{\text{quadrature components}}{\text{in-phase components}}$$

If you check back on Example 2 (page 148) you will notice that this method was used. It applies equally well to any number of branches and to C-R series branches as well as L-R series branches. The procedure is laborious and care must be used to label all values carefully in order to prevent accidental errors. An alternate method, using complex algebra, will be shown in the next chapter.

Parallel resonance. In Problem 6 (page 160), we added a capacitive branch to an R-L parallel circuit. The size of the capacitor added created a capacitive branch current that exceeded the inductive branch current and caused the line current to lead the line voltage. Suppose we had used a smaller capacitor—for example 14 μf. Then

$$X_c = \frac{1}{2\pi fC} = \frac{0.159 \times 10^6}{60 \times 14} = 189 \text{ ohms}$$

This would make the capacitive branch reactance exactly equal to the inductive branch reactance. Under such conditions

1. $X_c = X_L$.

2. I_T **is a minimum and the circuit impedance is a maximum.** The reason for this can be readily explained. Since $X_L = X_c$, the reactive branch currents I_L and I_c are also equal. But we also know that these currents are 180 degrees apart. Their vector sum is zero, and the line current would be equal to the resistive branch current alone. This is the minimum value of current and consequently the maximum value of parallel circuit impedance. It should be noted that if the circuit contained only the inductive branch and the capacitive branch—and both branches were pure reactances—the line current would be zero and the circuit impedance infinite!

3. The circuit acts as a pure resistive circuit (line current in phase with line voltage). This should be obvious, since the vector sum of the reactive branch current is zero. This condition is known as *parallel resonance.* In some texts, it is called *anti-resonance,* to distinguish from the series resonant condition. In the above illustration, parallel resonance was obtained by changing the capacitance value. As in the case of series circuits, resonance could also have been produced by varying the inductance value or the applied frequency. In any parallel circuit, regardless of the values of L and C, there is always some frequency at which the circuit will be resonant. *If the reactive branches contain pure reactances,* the three conditions above will occur simultaneously.

As the frequency is increased above the resonant value, the inductive branch reactance will increase in proportion and the inductive branch current will decrease. Meanwhile the capacitive branch reactance will decrease, increasing the current in this branch. The two branch currents are no longer equal—the total current has increased and is now capacitive. Obviously, the circuit acts as a capacitive circuit with the line current leading the line voltage. Since the line current has increased, the total impedance of the circuit has decreased. Similarly, if the frequency is reduced below resonance, the capacitive branch current decreases; the inductive branch current increases; and the line current increases. The circuit now acts as an inductive circuit with the line current lagging the line voltage. This again means that the total impedance has decreased. In other words, a parallel circuit offers a maximum impedance to currents at the resonant frequency. To all other frequency currents, the circuit offers less and less impedance, depending on how far these frequencies are removed (above or below) from the resonant frequency.

It is this characteristic of a parallel *L-C* circuit that provides us with a means of selecting one frequency from all others—as in the tuning circuit of your home receiver. Another application is found in the 'tank circuit' of a Class C amplifier in a transmitter. In this case the plate current is a complex wave containing a D.C. component, a fundamental frequency component, and many harmonic frequency components. By proper selection of *L-C* values we can make the parallel-tuned tank circuit resonant to the fundamental frequency component. The output will then be a pure sine wave of fundamental frequency. Or we can tune the tank circuit to the second or third harmonic frequency and operate this stage as a frequency doubler or tripler. Again the output will be a pure sine wave—but now at the higher frequency.

Parallel resonance with impedance branches. Although most cases of parallel resonance in electronic work are with circuits containing pure reactive branches, we are sometimes faced with circuits where either the inductive branch or capacitive branch also contains resistance. This is particularly true in the inductive branch if the coil used has a low Q. A typical illustration is the transmitter *tank circuit* (tuning circuit), where a low Q is often necessary. Instructions for tuning such a circuit to resonance often advise the operator to tune for minimum current and then tune just beyond that point. *The line current will not be a minimum.* But if one condition of resonance is minimum line current, why do we go beyond this point? The answer is that when a parallel circuit contains an impedance branch (instead of pure reactance), the three 'resonant' conditions described above *occur at three separate frequencies:*

1. The frequency at which $X_L = X_c$.
2. The frequency at which the line current is a minimum.
3. The frequency at which the parallel circuit acts as a pure resistance.

Condition (1) is the one that applies to series resonant circuits, regardless of the resistance of the coil. In parallel circuits, condition (3) is the most generally used resonant condition. However, when the Q of the coil is fairly high, the resistance in the inductive branch is negligible compared with the reactance, and all three conditions will occur at the same frequency. Since this is generally the case, resonance for the parallel circuit is usually considered as the frequency at which $X_L = X_c$. Still, this point must not be forgotten—*that if appreciable resistance is introduced into either reactive branch of a parallel resonant circuit, the circuit will be thrown out of resonance and must be retuned.* This point will be substantiated when you learn how to tune and load a transmitter.

For an exaggerated case, $Q = 1$, these three conditions are shown in Fig. 10-6.

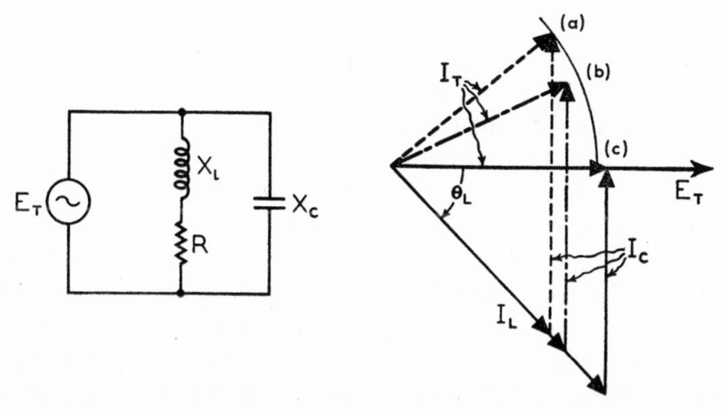

Fig. 10-6. Separation of resonant conditions in a low Q circuit due to coil resistance. (a) Frequency at which $X_L = X_c$. (b) Frequency for minimum line current. (c) Frequency for unity power factor.

(a) $X_L = X_c$.

At some frequency, X_L will equal X_c. Since this condition is similar to the one discussed for series circuits, the frequency at which this condition occurs is again $f_1 = \dfrac{1}{2\pi\sqrt{LC}}$. But, due to the resistance in the inductive branch, the impedance Z_L will be greater than X_c. Therefore, I_L will be smaller than I_c, and also it will be lagging by 45 degrees ($Q = 1$) instead of 90 degrees. Naturally, the quadrature components are not balanced, and the line current will lead the applied voltage. The circuit does not act as a resistive circuit, nor is the line current a minimum. Yet it does satisfy the condition $X_L = X_c$.

(b) ***Minimum Line Current.***

If the applied frequency is decreased, X_L and Z_L will decrease, and the current I_L will increase. The phase angle of this current was assumed to remain constant. (For a small change in frequency, and also considering the reduction of effective resistance of the coil, this assumption is permissible.) At the same time X_c will increase, thereby decreasing the capacitor branch current I_c. Both effects will cause the circuit phase angle to decrease toward zero. Meanwhile, the resultant line current will also decrease—up to a certain point. The minimum line current occurs at a frequency corresponding to

$$f_2 = \frac{1}{2\pi\sqrt{LC}}\left(\sqrt{1 - \frac{1}{4Q^2}}\right)$$

If the frequency is reduced further, the phase angle will continue to decrease, but the line current will once again start to increase. Condition (b) shows the situation for minimum line current.

(c) ***Circuit Acts as Pure Resistive Circuit.***

As the frequency is reduced further, I_L will continue to increase and I_c will continue to decrease. At some point the *quadrature* component of I_L will equal the magnitude of I_c. Since the reactive currents are balanced out, the line current is in phase with the line voltage. But now, due to the increase in I_L, the line current is no longer at its minimum value. The frequency at which this unity power factor occurs is given by

$$f_3 = \frac{1}{2\pi\sqrt{LC}}\left(\sqrt{\frac{Q^2}{Q^2 + 1}}\right)$$

or,

$$f_3 = \frac{1}{2\pi\sqrt{LC}}\left(\sqrt{1 - \frac{CR^2}{L}}\right)$$

These last two equations are identical—one is in terms of the coil

Q, the other in terms of inductance and resistance, where R, L, and Q are all at this frequency (f_3).

If the resistive component of the inductive branch were decreased (higher Q), the angle of lag of I_L would increase. Examine Fig. 10-6 again. It is obvious that as I_L approaches 90 degrees, the three I_c lines will fall into coincidence. Certainly for a coil Q of 20 ($\theta_L = 87°$) it would be impossible to distinguish the three separate conditions. With a Q of 20, also notice that the parenthetical expression in each of the above formulas becomes unity, and the equation for resonant frequency reduces to the familiar

$$f_0 = \frac{1}{2\pi \sqrt{LC}}$$

The proof of the above equations has been deliberately omitted because the mathematics does get rather involved.

In most electronic circuits, the Q of these circuits is usually high enough so that all three conditions will occur at the same frequency. For this reason the resonant frequency is generally calculated from the simplified formula $f_0 = \frac{1}{2\pi \sqrt{LC}}$. However it must be kept in mind that if sufficient resistance is introduced into a tank circuit (parallel-tuned circuit) and the Q drops to a low value, the resonant frequency may decrease. Remember this basic principle when you study oscillator stability or transmitter circuits. If these circuits are poorly designed and the resistance introduced into the tank circuit varies, the resonant frequency will change.

Resonant circuits, both series and parallel, will be treated in greater detail in a subsequent volume, just before we study circuits in which resonance is an important feature.

Review Problems

1. A coil of 20 h is connected in parallel with a resistor of 5000 ohms across a 400-v, 50-cycle supply. Find:

(a) Line current.
(b) Circuit phase angle.
(c) Power dissipated.
(d) Total impedance.
(e) Equivalent series circuit.

2. Repeat Problem 1 for L = 80 mh, R = 2000 ohms, and supply of 100 v, 5000 cycles.

3. Repeat Problem 1 for $L = 30$ μh, $R = 800$ ohms, and supply of 20 v, 2000 kc.

4. In each of the following cases, a commercial coil (coil has resistance) is connected in parallel with a resistor. Using a graphical method, find the coil phase angle and circuit phase angle if:

(a) $I_T = 1.2$ amps, $I_R = 0.8$ amp, $I_L = 0.7$ amp.
(b) $I_L = 200$ ma, $I_T = 450$ ma, $I_R = 300$ ma.
(c) $I_T = 5$ amps, $I_L = 3.5$ amps, $I_R = 2.5$ amps.

5. A coil of 5 h and 500-ohm resistance is connected in parallel with a 3500-ohm resistor across a 220-v, 60-cycle supply. Find:

(a) Line current.
(b) Circuit phase angle.
(c) Power dissipated.
(d) Total circuit impedance.
(e) Equivalent series circuit.

6. Repeat Problem 5 for a 60-mh, 150-ohm coil in parallel with a 240-ohm resistor across a 30-v, 2000-cycle supply.

7. A capacitor of 0.008 μf is connected in parallel with a 1000-ohm resistor across a 15-kc, 100-v supply. Find:

(a) Line current.
(b) Circuit phase angle.
(c) Power dissipated.
(d) Total circuit impedance.
(e) Equivalent series circuit.

8. Repeat Problem 7 for a 0.0001-μf capacitor shunted by a 10,000-ohm resistor across a 20-v, 500-kc supply.

9. A cathode bias circuit consists of a 2000-ohm resistor shunted by a 2-μf capacitor. If the A.C. component of the plate current is 10 ma at 100 cycles, find:

(a) Current through the resistor.
(b) Current through the capacitor.
(c) Voltage across the combination.

10. In an *R-C* coupled amplifier, the load resistance (R_L) is 250,000 ohms. The output capacitance (tube and circuit) shunting this resistor is 50 μμf. If the A.C. component of the plate current is 0.5 ma, find:

(a) Voltage across R_L at 15,000 cycles.
(b) Voltage across R_L at 100 cycles.
(c) What is the general effect of shunt capacity on the frequency response (voltage across R_L)?

11. A complex wave, due to demodulation, contains component frequencies of 1000 kc and 100 cycles. These components are fed to a parallel circuit consisting of a 0.5-megohm resistor and a 100-μμf capacitor. If the amplitude of the current for each frequency is 30 μa, find the rms voltage across the circuit:

(a) At the carrier frequency (1000 kc).
(b) At the audio frequency.

12. An impedance, Z, is connected in parallel with a capacitor of 16 μf, across an 80-v, 100-cycle supply. The line current is 2.1 amps, in phase with the supply voltage.

(a) Draw the vector diagram.
(b) Find the current through the impedance, Z.
(c) What are the components of this impedance?

13. A capacitor of 100 $\mu\mu$f is connected in parallel with an inductance of 80 μh and also in parallel with a resistor of 3000 ohms across a supply voltage of 40 v, 1000 kc. Find:

(a) Line current.
(b) Circuit phase angle.
(c) Total circuit impedance.
(d) Equivalent series circuit.

14. Repeat Problem 13, with the inductance raised to 0.4 mh.

15. What value of inductance in Problem 13 would give a 'resonant' condition ($X_L = X_c$)?

16. Using the inductance value of Problem 15, repeat Problem 13.

17. A capacitor of 0.1 μf is in parallel with a coil of 0.04 h and 200 ohms resistance (two branches). The supply voltage is 15 v, 2000 cycles. Find:

(a) Line current.
(b) Circuit phase angle.
(c) Total circuit impedance.
(d) Equivalent series circuit.

18. What value of capacitance would give $X_L = X_c$ in Problem 17?

19. Repeat Problem 17, using the value of capacitor found in Problem 18.

20. Repeat Problem 17, using the value of capacitor found in Problem 18, but dropping the applied frequency to 1840 cycles. Is this a resonant condition? Explain.

21. A coil of 10-mh inductance has a Q of 1.5. It is connected in parallel with a capacitor of 0.05 μf across a variable frequency source of 100 v. Find:

(a) The frequency at which the two reactances are equal.
(b) The line current and circuit phase angle at this frequency.
(c) The impedance of this tank circuit.

22. Using the values of Problem 21, find the frequency that results in minimum line current.

23. Using the values of Problem 21, find the frequency that makes the circuit act as a pure resistance.

24. A coil of 0.2 h is in series with 1000-ohm resistance. The combination is in parallel with a 0.1-μf capacitor.

(a) Find the resonant frequency. (Unity power-factor condition.)
(b) If the resistance is neglected, how much error would have been caused?

25. A transmitter tank circuit has a Q of 50 when unloaded. Due to improper loading, the Q drops to 3. What is the percentage change in the resonant frequency (condition for pure resistive load)?

CHAPTER 11

Vector Algebra for A.C. Circuits

IN D.C. CIRCUITS, since there were no phase angles involved, we were able to solve all problems using plain algebra and straight numerical solutions. However, in A.C. circuits, phase angles enter the picture to complicate the solutions. In the previous chapters we handled the situation by resorting to graphical and trigonometric methods. Graphical solutions, in general, are not too accurate. Trigonometric treatment is quite satisfactory when the values involved are either in phase (zero degrees) or at a 90-degree angle. But, as you have seen in the previous problems, this method is somewhat awkward when the values are at some angle other than zero or 90 degrees. Addition of vectors (between zero and 90-degrees lead or lag) required breaking down each vector into its in-phase and quadrature components; adding the components; and then solving by the square root of the sum of the squares of the in-phase and quadrature values. What makes this method awkward is not so much the procedure required but, rather, the terminology or 'bookkeeping' system.

By use of vector algebra the terminology is simplified, making the solution of such problems easier. Furthermore, by trigonometric means, we were unable to multiply or divide two vector quantities. Nor could we square or take the square root of a vector quantity. All these things are made possible by use of vector algebra. Problems that would be too tough to solve by trigonometry become mere routine by vector algebra. In addition, even if you never solve a problem by vector algebra, it is still important that you learn the notations used in this system and their meanings. Many articles and texts in the electronic field use these methods of notation. Understanding of this new 'language' will bring treasure chests of additional technical data within your reach.

Vector algebra systems. There are two systems of vector algebra in common use. Each method has its advantages. Each method has its limitations. The two systems are often used interchangeably. Very often we may start a problem in one system, continue it in the other, and later return to the first—using whichever system is simpler for the particular section of the problem on hand. One system uses *rectangular coordinates;* the other uses *polar coordinates.*

In the rectangular coordinate system, a vector is expressed in terms of its in-phase and quadrature components. This method makes addition and subtraction of vector quantities simple. Multiplication, division, and squaring of vectors can also be done, but somewhat more laboriously. However, it is impossible to find the square root of a vector quantity by this method.

On the other hand, the polar coordinate system makes multiplication, division, squaring, and taking the square root of vectors mere child's play. What are the limitations of this system? We cannot add or subtract vectors! It is necessary first to change the values from polar form to rectangular form; then to add (or subtract) the values while in rectangular coordinates; and finally convert the answer back to polar form. So you see why it is necessary to understand both forms of vector algebra notation.

Representation by rectangular coordinates. From your previous studies in mathematics, you are probably familiar with X and Y axes and how these axes divide an area into four quadrants. In the first quadrant, both X and Y values are positive; in the second quadrant, X values are negative, Y values are positive; in the third quadrant, both X and Y values are negative; in the fourth quadrant, X values are positive, but Y values are negative. This system of rectangular coordinates is shown in Fig. 11-1.

Using this system of coordinates, if we wish to represent a voltage at zero-degrees phase angle, it would be drawn from the origin (O) horizontally *to the right.* For example, 50 v at zero degrees is shown in Fig. 11-1b as E_1. A second voltage, displaced by 180 degrees, would be negative and would be drawn from the origin *to the left* (E_2). Since the first voltage is positive, this second voltage, rotated by 180 degrees, must be negative or -50. Vectorially, E_2 is similar to E_1 but *rotated through 180 degrees.* Mathematically, E_2 is the same as E_1 but *multiplied by* (-1). Therefore a rotation of 180 degrees corresponds to multiplying by an *operator* of (-1). Now suppose we wish to represent a voltage leading by

90 degrees. It would be drawn from the origin, *upward*. Since the operator for 180 degrees rotation is (-1), the operator to denote a counter-clockwise (leading) rotation of 90 degrees is taken as $\sqrt{-1}$. *This operator to indicate a 90 degree lead,* $(\sqrt{-1})$, *is*

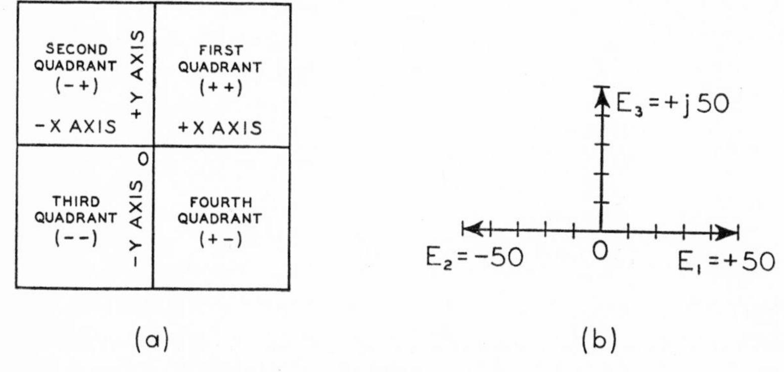

Fig. 11-1. Rectangular coordinate system.

designated by the symbol $+j$. Therefore E_3, 50 v leading by 90 degrees, is expressed as $+j50$. Using this system, a rotation of 90-degrees clockwise (lagging) would be denoted by the operator $-j$, $(-\sqrt{-1})$. The negative sign preceding the operator denotes a lagging angle. It must be clearly understood that the operator j, whether positive or negative, denotes a 90-degree rotation only. *There is no notation for any other angles of rotation.*

Well then, how do we represent a voltage leading or lagging by some angle other than 90 or 180 degrees? Very simple—resolve the voltage into two components, the in-phase and quadrature components, and specify this voltage in terms of these components. But isn't that exactly what we did in the trigonometric method? Sure—only now we have a simple way of expressing its components. The form used is

$$E = a \pm jb$$

where a is the in-phase component of the voltage, and b is the quadrature component. To evaluate these components we resort to trigonometry:

$$\text{in-phase component} = E \cos \theta = a$$
$$\text{quadrature component} = E \sin \theta = b$$

If the voltage is leading, the quadrature component is prefixed with $+j$. If the voltage is lagging, we use $-j$ for the prefix. When the voltage is in phase (or at 180 degrees), the quadrature component is zero. Therefore the j term becomes zero. Let us try a few illustrations.

Example 1

Draw a vector diagram, and express each of the following voltages in vector algebra notation.

(a) $E_1 = 100$ v at 0°.
(b) $E_2 = 80$ v leading by 30°.
(c) $E_3 = 60$ v leading by 90°.
(d) $E_4 = 50$ v at 180°.
(e) $E_5 = 75$ v lagging by 50°.

Solution

(a) E_1 being at zero degrees has no quadrature component, therefore:

$$E_1 = 100 + j0$$

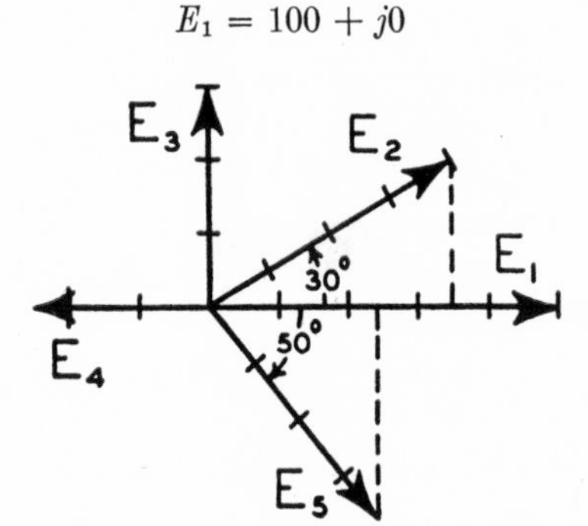

¼″ = 20 v

Fig. 11-2.

(b) E_2 at 30 degrees has both in-phase and quadrature components, as follows:

$$\text{in-phase} = E \cos \theta = 80 \times 0.866 = 64.3 \text{ v}$$
$$\text{quadrature} = E \sin \theta = 80 \times 0.500 = 40 \text{ v}$$

therefore $$E_2 = 64.3 + j40$$

(c) E_3 is at 90 degrees. It has no in-phase component.

therefore $$E_3 = 0 + j60$$

(d) E_4 at 180 degrees has no quadrature component. In addition, the voltage is opposite or negative compared to E_1. Therefore

$$E_4 = -50 + j0$$

(e) E_5 is lagging by 50 degrees. Since the angle is not zero, 90, or 180 degrees, this voltage has both in-phase and quadrature components:

$$\text{in-phase} = E \cos \theta = 75 \times 0.643 = 48.3 \text{ v}$$
$$\text{quadrature} = E \sin \theta = 75 \times 0.766 = 57.4 \text{ v}$$

Remembering that the voltage is lagging:

$$E_5 = 48.3 - j57.4$$

So far we have been discussing how to represent voltages at various angles in the vocabulary of vector algebra. The same procedure applies equally well to currents at any angle of lead or lag. Merely express them in terms of their horizontal (in-phase) and vertical (quadrature) components, exactly as we did for the voltages in the above illustrations.

Can we express impedances by vector algebra? We pointed out in an earlier chapter that an impedance, reactance, or resistance is not a vector. True enough. Yet these circuit constants do affect the phase angles of currents or voltages in the circuit. They must therefore be treated as vectors. In Chapter 8 we saw that, when a resistance and reactance are connected in series, the impedance of the combination is given by:

$$Z = \sqrt{R^2 + X^2}$$

We also saw that the impedance triangle is a right triangle with R as the horizontal component and X as the vertical or quadrature component. Furthermore, if the reactance was inductive, it was drawn upward (positive direction), whereas for a capacitive reactance, X_c was drawn downward (negative direction). Since an impedance has both an in-phase component (R), and a quadrature component (X), it can be expressed in vector algebra notation.

EXAMPLE 2

Express each of the following oppositions in vector algebra notation:

(a) Resistor of 1200 ohms.
(b) Capacitor of 750 ohms reactance.
(c) Coil of 6240 ohms reactance.
(d) (a) and (b) in series.

(e) (a) and (c) in series.
(f) A coil of 5 h and 500 ohms at 100 cycles.
(g) A coil of 12,000-ohms impedance and a Q of 8.

SOLUTION

(a) $Z = 1200 + j0.$
(b) $Z = 0 - j750.$
(c) $Z = 0 + j6240.$
(d) $Z = 1200 - j750.$
(e) $Z = 1200 + j6240.$
(f) $X_L = 2\pi fL = 6.28 \times 100 \times 5 = 3140$ ohms.
$Z = 500 + j3140.$
(g) $Q = \frac{X_L}{R} = \text{arc tan } \theta_L = 8.$
$\theta = 82.9°.$
$R = Z \cos \theta = 12{,}000 \times 0.124 = 1490$ ohms.
$X_L = Z \sin \theta = 12{,}000 \times 0.992 = 11{,}900$ ohms.
$Z = 1490 + j11{,}900.$

Representation by polar coordinates. We mentioned earlier in this chapter that any vector (or impedance) is expressed in polar coordinates by its magnitude and phase angle, and that is all there is to it! For example, 50 ma leading by 20 degrees is written as $50\underline{/20°}$; or 150 v in phase would be $150\underline{/0°}$. Could anything be simpler? When the vector is lagging, we merely put a minus sign in front of the degree value. For example, a capacitor having a reactance of 240 ohms would be $240\underline{/-90°}$; or 80 v lagging by 70 degrees would be $80\underline{/-70°}$. In some texts or articles, when the vector is lagging, instead of using the minus sign notation, the angle sign is reversed. For example, a current of 1.35 amps lagging by 38 degrees would be $1.35\ \overline{\backslash 38°}$.

Conversion between systems. Many times it is necessary, or convenient, to change from one system of notation to the other before continuing the solution of a problem. It is therefore important that we understand how to convert from polar to rectangular form and vice-versa. The method has already been discussed. In polar form we know the magnitude and phase angle of the vector quantity. To change to rectangular form we merely solve for the in-phase component, (magnitude $\times \cos \theta$) and the quadrature component (magnitude $\times \sin \theta$). If the phase angle is positive, the quadrature or j component is also positive. When the phase angle is negative, the j component is also negative.

Example 3

Convert the following polar vectors into rectangular form:

(a) $E = 83\underline{/72°}$ v.

(b) $I = 125\underline{/-43°}$ ma.

(c) $Z = 2160\underline{/23°}$ ohms.

Solution

(a) $E = 83 \cos \theta + j83 \sin \theta = 24 + j78.9$ v.

(b) $I = 125 \cos \theta - j125 \sin \theta = 91.7 - j85.2$ ma.

(c) $Z = 2160 \cos \theta + j2160 \sin \theta = 1985 + j845$ ohms.

To convert from rectangular to polar coordinates takes two steps:

1. Find the magnitude from the square root of the sum of the squares of the components:

$$\text{magnitude} = \sqrt{a^2 + b^2}$$

2. Find the phase angle from the ratio of the component values:

$$\theta = \text{arc tan } \frac{b}{a}$$

The angle is leading if the j term is positive, and lagging if the j term is negative.

Example 4

Convert the following values from rectangular to polar form.

(a) $Z = 75 - j140$ ohms.

(b) $E = 24 - j86$ v.

(c) $I = 1.7 + j0.6$ amp.

Solution

(a) $Z = \sqrt{(75)^2 + (140)^2} = 159$ ohms.

$\theta = \text{arc tan } \frac{140}{75} = 61.8°.$

$Z = 159\underline{/-61.8°}$ ohms.

(b) $E = \sqrt{(24)^2 + (86)^2} = 89.5$ v.

$\theta = \text{arc tan } \frac{86}{24} = 74.4°.$

$E = 89.5\underline{/-74.4°}$ v.

(c) $I = \sqrt{(1.7)^2 + (0.6)^2} = 1.8$ amps.

$$\theta = \text{arc tan}\ \frac{0.6}{1.7} = 20.7°.$$

$$I = 1.8\underline{/20.7°}\ \text{amps.}$$

Addition and subtraction by vector algebra. In series circuits, it is often necessary to add (or subtract) the voltages across the various units. Also, we can add the impedances of the various units. Similarly, in a parallel circuit, we have to add or subtract currents to find the total current or branch currents. Vector quantities expressed in rectangular form may be added or subtracted by treating them as ordinary binomials. Merely add all a terms, then all b terms *algebraically*. *Vector quantities in polar form cannot be added or subtracted directly.* First, you must convert the values to rectangular form. Then add them. Finally convert the sum back to polar form.

EXAMPLE 5

A resistor, capacitor, and commercial coil are connected in series. The voltage across each unit is

$$E_R = 50 + j0.$$
$$E_c = 0 - j120.$$
$$E_L = 27 + j36.$$

Find the supply voltage (magnitude and phase angle) and express in polar form.

SOLUTION

(a) $E_T = \dot{E}_R + \dot{E}_c + \dot{E}_L$, or:

$$\begin{array}{r} 50 + j0 \\ 0 - j120 \\ 27 + j36 \\ \hline 77 - j84 \end{array}$$

(b) $E_T = \sqrt{(77)^2 + (84)^2} = 114$ v.

$\theta = \text{arc tan}\ \frac{84}{77} = 47.5°$ lagging.

(c) $E_T = 114\underline{/-47.5°}$ v.

EXAMPLE 6

The line current in a parallel circuit is $I_T = 2.6\underline{/15°}$. The current in branch 1 is $I_1 = 1.8\underline{/-65°}$. Find the current in branch 2.

SOLUTION

(a) $I_T = 2.6 \cos 15° + j2.6 \sin 15° = 2.51 + j0.67.$

(b) $I_1 = 1.8 \cos 65° - j1.8 \sin 65° = 0.76 - j1.63.$

(c) and since $I_2 = \dot{I}_T - \dot{I}_1$:

$$\begin{array}{r} 2.51 + j0.671 \\ - \quad + \quad \\ \oplus\, 0.76 \ominus j1.63 \\ \hline I_2 = 1.75 + j2.30 \end{array} = 2.89\underline{/52.7°}$$

Multiplication: rectangular form. Vectors expressed in rectangular form were treated as ordinary binomials for the purpose of addition or subtraction. It is therefore not surprising to learn that they can also be multiplied or divided in exactly the same manner that you treated binomials in your study of algebra. Such a situation arises whenever you have to apply Ohm's law to the solution of an A.C. circuit. Since the values, current, voltage, and impedance are all treated as vector quantities, the solution by vector algebra is applicable.

There is one point to remember—since $j = \sqrt{-1}$, then $j^2 = -1$; the j^2 term appearing in the product can be simplified in this manner.

EXAMPLE 7

Multiply $9 + j5$ by $12 + j4$, and express the answer in polar form.

SOLUTION

$$\begin{array}{r} 9 + j5 \quad\quad\quad \\ 12 + j4 \quad\quad\quad \\ \hline 108 + j60 \quad\quad\quad \\ + j36 + j^2 20 \\ \hline 108 + j96 + j^2 20 \end{array}$$

replacing j^2 by -1: $108 + j96 - 20 = 88 + j96.$

in polar form $= 130\underline{/47.5°}.$

EXAMPLE 8

A current of 1.25 amps flows in a series circuit containing 40-ohms resistance and 70-ohms capacitive reactance. Using vector algebra, solve for the voltage applied to the circuit.

SOLUTION

1. Using current as the reference vector:

$$
\begin{array}{lrl}
 & I = & 1.25 + j0 \\
2. & Z = & 40 - j70 \quad \text{by multiplication we get:} \\
\hline
 & & 50 + j0 \\
 & & \quad - j87.5 - j^2 0 \\
\hline
 & E = IZ = & 50 - j87.5
\end{array}
$$

in polar form $E = 94.6\underline{/-60.3^\circ}$ v.

The line voltage is 94.6 v and lags the current by 60.3 degrees.

Division: rectangular form. Division of vectors expressed in rectangular form is accomplished by multiplying both the numerator and denominator by the *conjugate* of the denominator. This rationalizes the denominator: The j term is eliminated and we can simplify the answer.

Example 9

Divide $40 + j25$ by $6 + j4$, and express the answer in polar form.

Solution

$$\frac{40 + j25}{6 + j4} \times \frac{6 - j4}{6 - j4} = \frac{240 - j10 - j^2 100}{36 - j^2 16}$$

simplifying the j^2 term: $\dfrac{340 - j10}{52} = 6.53 - j0.192.$

in polar form: $6.57\underline{/-1.7^\circ}$.

Example 10

A resistor of 60 ohms is connected in series to an inductance of 90-ohms reactance across a 50-v supply. Using vector algebra, solve for the magnitude and phase angle of the current in the circuit.

Solution

1. Using the supply voltage as the reference vector

$$E = 50 + j0.$$

2. $$Z = 60 + j90.$$

3. $$I = \frac{E}{Z} = \frac{50 + j0}{60 + j90} \times \frac{60 - j90}{60 - j90} = \frac{3000 - j4500}{3600 - j^2 8100}$$

$$= \frac{3000 - j4500}{11{,}700} = 0.256 - j0.384 \text{ amps.}$$

in polar form, $I = 0.463\underline{/-56.3^\circ}$ amps. The current is 0.463 amps lagging the line voltage by 56.3 degrees.

Multiplication and division: polar form. When vectors are expressed in rectangular form, multiplication or division of these vector quantities is somewhat laborious. The polar form is much easier to handle.

1. *To multiply in polar form, multiply the magnitudes, and add the angles algebraically.*
2. *To divide in polar form, divide the magnitudes, and subtract the angles algebraically.*

Even when the vector quantities are expressed in rectangular coordinates, it is often more convenient to change to polar form and then multiply or divide as required.

EXAMPLE 11

Multiply $50\underline{/20^\circ}$ by $32\underline{/-40^\circ}$.

SOLUTION

1. $50 \times 32 = 1600$.
2. $20^\circ + (-40^\circ) = -20^\circ$.
3. $1600\underline{/-20^\circ}$

EXAMPLE 12

Divide $147\underline{/64^\circ}$ by $840\underline{/35^\circ}$.

SOLUTION

1. $147 \div 840 = 0.175$.
2. $64^\circ - 35^\circ = 29^\circ$.
3. $0.175\underline{/29^\circ}$.

Squares and square roots by vector algebra. Vector quantities can be squared, using either the rectangular or polar systems. Since squaring means multiplying by itself, merely follow the methods shown above for the multiplication of vector quantities. In polar form this becomes very simple—square the magnitude and double the angle.

We pointed out earlier in this chapter that it was impossible to find the square root of a vector quantity, using the rectangular coordinate system. The polar system makes this operation very simple:

1. Take the square root of the magnitude
2. Divide the angle by 2.

If a vector is expressed in rectangular form, we must first change to polar form before extracting the square root.

EXAMPLE 13

Square $75 + j50$.

SOLUTION

$$\begin{array}{r} 75 + j50 \\ 75 + j50 \\ \hline 5625 + j3750 \qquad\quad \\ + j3750 + j^2 2500 \\ \hline 5625 + j7500 + j^2 2500 \end{array} = 3125 + j7500$$

EXAMPLE 14

Find the square root of $3125 + j7500$.

SOLUTION

1. $3125 + j7500 = 8120\underline{/67.4^\circ}$.
2. $\sqrt{8120\underline{/67.4^\circ}} = 90.3\underline{/33.7^\circ}$; converting back to rectangular form:
3. $75 + j50$; this checks with Example 13.

Vector algebra in series circuits. We have covered all the elements of vector algebra. Let us now apply all these principles to the solution of a circuit.

EXAMPLE 15

A capacitor of 0.02 μf, a resistor of 4,000 ohms, and a commercial coil of 1.0 h and 1800-ohm resistance are connected in series across a 120 v, 1000-cycle supply. Find the magnitude of the line current and its phase relation to the supply voltage.

SOLUTION

1. $X_c = \dfrac{1}{2\pi fC} = \dfrac{0.159 \times 10^6}{1000 \times 0.02} = 7{,}950$ ohms.

   $X_c = 0 - j7950$.
2. $R = 4000 + j0$.
3. $X_L = 2\pi fL = 6.28 \times 1000 \times 1 = 6280$ ohms.

   $Z_L = 1800 + j6280$.
4. $Z_T = 5800 - j1670 = 6040\underline{/-16^\circ}$.
5. $E = 120\underline{/0^\circ}$ (reference vector).
6. $I = \dfrac{E}{Z} = \dfrac{120\underline{/0^\circ}}{6040\underline{/-16^\circ}} = 0.0198\underline{/16^\circ}$.

   $I = 19.8$ ma leading by 16°.

Vector algebra in parallel circuits. Series circuits can be solved almost as readily by trigonometric methods as by vector algebra. This is also true for parallel circuits if the branches are pure reactances. But when one or more branches of a parallel circuit contain impedances, the vector algebra solution is far superior. Let us try a problem of that type.

EXAMPLE 16

Find the magnitude and phase angle of the line current for the circuit shown in Fig. 11-3. Also find the voltage across the capacitor.

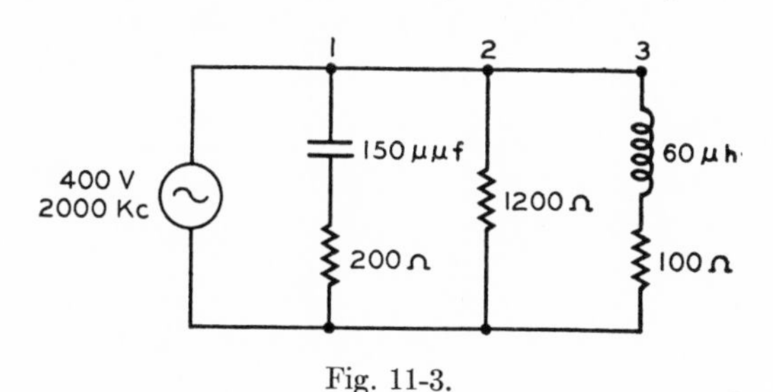

Fig. 11-3.

SOLUTION

1. $X_c = \dfrac{1}{2\pi fC} = \dfrac{0.159 \times 10^{12}}{2 \times 10^6 \times 150} = 530$ ohms.

   $Z_1 = 200 - j530.$

2. Taking the supply voltage as the reference vector:

$$E = 400 + j0.$$

3. $I_1 = \dfrac{E}{Z_1} = \dfrac{400 + j0}{200 - j530} \cdot \dfrac{200 + j530}{200 + j530} = \dfrac{8 \times 10^4 + j21.6 \times 10^4}{4 \times 10^4 - j^2 27.6 \times 10^4}$

   $= \dfrac{8 \times 10^4 + j21.6 \times 10^4}{31.6 \times 10^4} = 0.253 + j0.683$ amp.

4. $Z_2 = 1200 + j0.$

   $I_2 = \dfrac{E}{Z_2} = \dfrac{400 + j0}{1200 + j0} = 0.333 + j0$ amp.

5. $X_L = 2\pi fL = 6.28 \times 2 \times 10^6 \times 60 \times 10^{-6} = 754$ ohms.

   $Z_3 = 100 + j754.$

6. $I_3 = \dfrac{E}{Z_3} = \dfrac{400 + j0}{100 + j754} \cdot \dfrac{100 - j754}{100 - j754}$

   $= \dfrac{4 \times 10^4 - j30.2 \times 10^4}{57.8 \times 10^4} = 0.0692 - j0.522$ amp.

7. $I_T = \dot{I}_1 + \dot{I}_2 + \dot{I}_3$ (dots signify *vector* addition).

$$\begin{array}{rl} & 0.253 \;\; + j0.683 \\ & 0.333 \;\; + j0 \\ & 0.0692 - j0.522 \\ \hline = & 0.655 \;\; + j0.161 \\ = & 0.675\underline{/13.3^\circ} \text{ amps.} \end{array}$$

The line current is 0.675 amp and leads the line voltage by 13.3 degrees.

8. $I_1 = 0.253 + j0.683 = 0.729\underline{/69.7^\circ}$ amps.

$X_c = 0 - j530 = 530\underline{/-90^\circ}$ ohms.

$E_c = IX_c = 0.729\underline{/69.7^\circ} \times 530\underline{/-90^\circ} = 386\underline{/-20.3^\circ}$ v.

The voltage across the capacitor is 386 v and lags the line voltage by 20.3 degrees.

You may be wondering why the rectangular form was used to solve for I_1, I_2 and I_3. We could have converted impedances to polar form. This would have made the division process easier. But then the currents would have been expressed in polar form also. Before we could add these branch currents, it would have been necessary to convert the current values back to rectangular form. Under the circumstances, it seems more sensible to solve for branch currents in the rectangular form.

Parallel circuit impedance. In the previous chapter on parallel circuits, we were unable to find the impedance of the circuit directly. Instead, using the voltage across the circuit (given or assumed value), and the impedance of each branch, we:

1. Solved for each branch current.
2. Added the branch currents vectorially.
3. Solved for Z_T by Ohm's law ($Z_T = E_T/I_T$).

We also saw that

$$\frac{1}{Z_T} = \frac{1}{Z_1} + \frac{1}{Z_2} + \frac{1}{Z_3} \cdots$$

This equation could not be solved by our former trigonometric methods. Now, using vector algebra, we can do it. The procedure involves the use of polar and rectangular forms.

1. Express each branch impedance in polar form.
2. Solve for the reciprocals, and convert to rectangular form.
3. Add these values while in rectangular form, and convert the sum back to polar form.
4. Z_T is the reciprocal of the value found in (3).

The method, though simple, is laborious. Luckily, most electronic circuit problems contain only two branches, or can be simplified into only two branches. We can therefore use the simplified formula for two branches:

$$Z \text{ parallel } = \frac{Z_1 \times Z_2}{Z_1 + Z_2}$$

EXAMPLE 17

Find the parallel impedance of the circuit shown in Fig. 11-4, and solve for the equivalent series circuit.

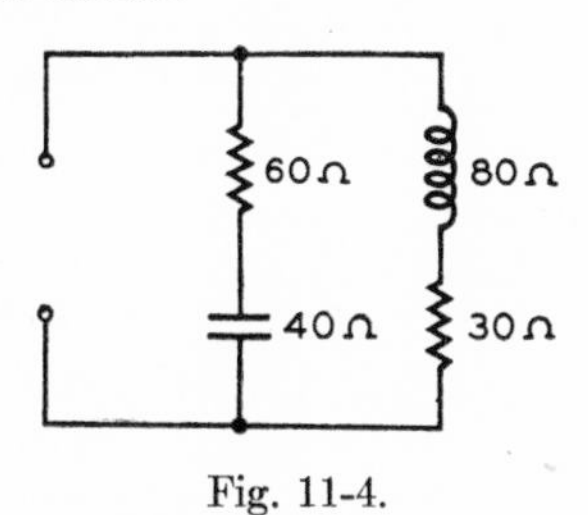

Fig. 11-4.

SOLUTION

1. $Z_1 = 60 - j40 = 72.2\underline{/-33.7°}$.
2. $Z_2 = 30 + j80 = 85.5\underline{/69.4°}$.
3. $Z_1 + Z_2 = 90 + j40 = 98.6\underline{/24°}$.
4. $Z_T = \dfrac{Z_1Z_2}{Z_1 + Z_2} = \dfrac{6170\underline{/35.7°}}{98.6\underline{/24°}} = 62.6\underline{/11.7°}$ ohms.

In the equivalent series circuit

5. $R = 62.6 \cos 11.7° = 62.6 \times 0.98 = 61.3$ ohms.
   $X_L = 62.6 \sin 11.7° = 62.6 \times 0.203 = 12.7$ ohms.

The equivalent series circuit consists of a resistor of 61.3 ohms in series with an inductance of 12.7 ohms. This method is definitely easier than solving for branch currents, total current and total impedance by Ohm's law.

For comparison purposes let us solve Problem 2 of Chapter 10 (page 148) by the vector algebra method.

EXAMPLE 18

A coil (resistance 60 ohms, inductance 0.05 h) is connected in parallel with a resistor of 500 ohms, across a 20-v, 1000-cycle supply. Find:

(a) Line current.
(b) Circuit phase angle.

(c) Total circuit impedance.
(d) Power dissipated.
(e) Equivalent series circuit.

SOLUTION

1. $X_L = 2\pi fL = 6.28 \times 1000 \times 0.05 = 314$ ohms.
2. $Z_L = R + jX = 60 + j314 = 320\underline{/79.2°}$.
3. $Z_R = 500 + j0 = 500\underline{/0°}$.
4. $Z_R + Z_L = 560 + j314 = 642\underline{/29.3°}$.
5. $Z_T = \dfrac{Z_R Z_L}{Z_R + Z_L} = \dfrac{500\underline{/0°} \times 320\underline{/79.2°}}{642\underline{/29.3°}} = 249\underline{/49.9°}$ ohms (checks).
6. $I_T = \dfrac{E_T}{Z_T} = \dfrac{20\underline{/0°}}{249\underline{/49.9°}} = 0.0804\underline{/-49.9°}$ amps.

   $I_T = 80.4$ ma lagging by 49.9° (checks).
7. $P = EI \cos \theta = 20 \times 0.0804 \times 0.644 = 1.035$ watts (checks).
8. Equivalent series circuit $= Z_T \cos \theta + jZ_T \sin \theta$

   $Z_T \cos \theta = 249 \times 0.644 = 160$ ohms.

   $Z_T \sin \theta = 249 \times 0.765 = 190$ ohms.

   Z equiv. $= 160 + j190$ ohms (checks).

   $$L = \frac{X_L}{2\pi f} = \frac{190}{6.28 \times 1000} = 0.0302 = 30.2 \text{ mh.}$$

Notice how much more direct, and how much simpler this method is in comparison to the trigonometric solution.

Series-parallel circuit impedance. Series-parallel circuits may be quite difficult to solve by trigonometric methods. For example, how would you proceed to solve for the line current (magnitude and phase angle), in the circuit shown in Fig. 11-5? Since the only voltage given is the line voltage, we must find the total impedance. But we could not find Z_T by trigonometric methods, unless we knew the current! The solution would require:

1. *Assume* a voltage across the parallel branches (R_2L_2 and CR_s).
2. Solve for the branch currents—*assumed values.*
3. Find the horizontal (in-phase) and vertical (quadrature components) of each branch current.
4. Find the total current—*again this is only an assumed value.*
5. From the assumed voltage and the resulting total current (Step 4), solve for Z_T of parallel branches.
6. Convert this impedance into the equivalent series impedance.

7. Add this value (Step 6) to the series impedance (R_1L_1). This is the total circuit impedance.
8. From the actual supply voltage and Z_T (Step 7), solve for the true line current.

You notice what a task this is—even to describe!

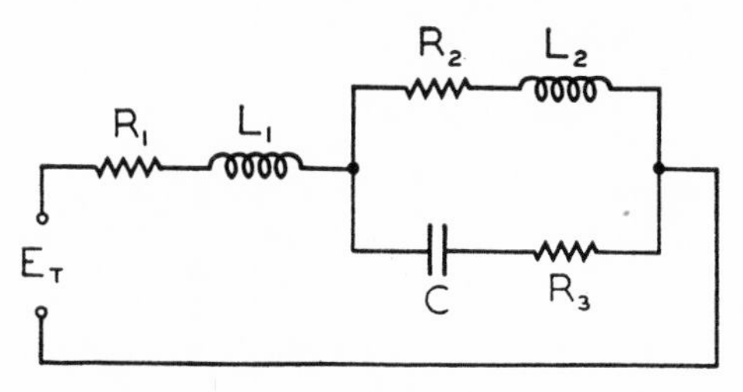

Fig. 11-5.

By vector algebra, the solution for this current is much simpler:

1. Find the equivalent impedance of the parallel branches.
2. Convert this value to rectangular form.
3. Add this value (Step 2) to the series impedances (R_1L_1). This is the total circuit impedances.
4. Convert Z_T to polar form and solve for I_T.

Equivalent π and *T* circuits. Many electronic circuits, particularly filter circuits, contain impedances connected to form a π (pi) or *T* network. Such circuits are shown in Fig. 11-6. In the 'power' field, loads of this type are known as *delta* (Δ) or *wye* (Y)

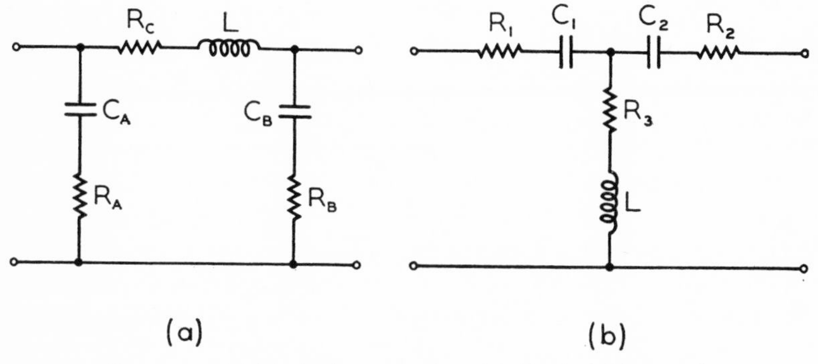

Fig. 11-6. (a) Typical π network. (b) Typical *T* network.

loads. The delta connection is equivalent to the π connection, but referring to Fig. 11-6a it is drawn schematically with the lower end of R_A and R_B coming to a common-point connection. The wye connection, which is the same as the T connection, is shown schematically with the horizontal arms drawn upward to simulate the letter Y. These circuits will be discussed in more detail in a later chapter. The impedances in these networks could be all resistors, all capacitors, all inductances, or any combination of *R-L-C*. By themselves, these circuits would not be difficult to handle. But many times the π or T circuit is only part of a more complex network. Quite often the solution of such networks can be simplified by converting the component π circuit into its equivalent T circuit, or vice-versa.

We shall not attempt to prove the equations for converting from one circuit to the other. Such a proof could be found in any good engineering text. Figure 11-7 shows a simplified form of the π and T networks.

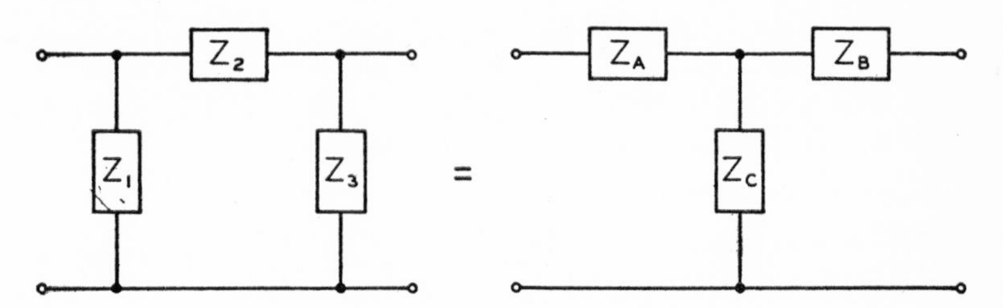

Fig. 11-7. Equivalent π and T networks.

1. *T to π (or Y to Δ) conversion:*

$$Z_1 = \frac{Z_A Z_B + Z_B Z_C + Z_A Z_C}{Z_B}$$

$$Z_2 = \frac{Z_A Z_B + Z_B Z_C + Z_A Z_C}{Z_C}$$

$$Z_3 = \frac{Z_A Z_B + Z_B Z_C + Z_A Z_C}{Z_A}$$

Notice that in each case the numerator is the same, while the denominator is the T impedance *which connects to the opposite line terminal.*

2. *π to T (or Δ to Y) conversion:*

$$Z_A = \frac{Z_1 Z_2}{Z_1 + Z_2 + Z_3}$$

$$Z_B = \frac{Z_2 Z_3}{Z_1 + Z_2 + Z_3}$$

$$Z_C = \frac{Z_1 Z_3}{Z_1 + Z_2 + Z_3}$$

This time, the denominators are all alike and the numerator is the *product of the two π impedances* that connect to the same terminal.

An application of the use of such conversions would apply to the solution of the A.C. bridge circuit shown in Fig. 11-8.

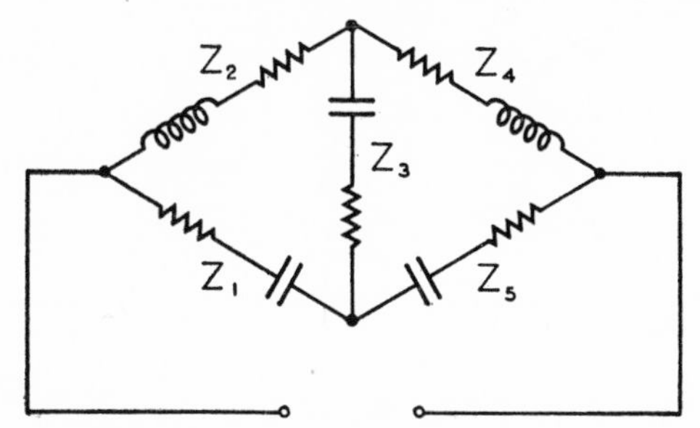

Fig. 11-8. Typical A.C bridge circuit.

The impedances Z_1, Z_2, Z_3 (or Z_3, Z_4, Z_5) are actually connected in a π network. It does not resemble the diagram shown in Fig. 11-7. You will recognize the circuit (Fig. 11-8) more readily if you separate any junction such as Z_1 and Z_3 and make the connection with a horizontal wire. Since Z_1, Z_2, Z_3 is a π network, it can be replaced by an equivalent T circuit (Z_A, Z_B, Z_C).

Figure 11-9 shows the equivalent circuit, redrawn.

Notice now that:

1. Z_B and Z_4 are in series.
2. Z_C and Z_5 are in series.
3. The combination of (1) and (2) are in parallel.
4. The equivalent impedance of (3) is in series with Z_A.

From this analysis you can see how to solve for the total impedance of such a circuit.

No illustrative problems have been given for series-parallel circuits or for π to T conversion. The omission was quite deliberate.

The average technician will probably never have to solve problems of this type. However, he should know that such problems can be handled by vector algebra. As an incentive to the student who

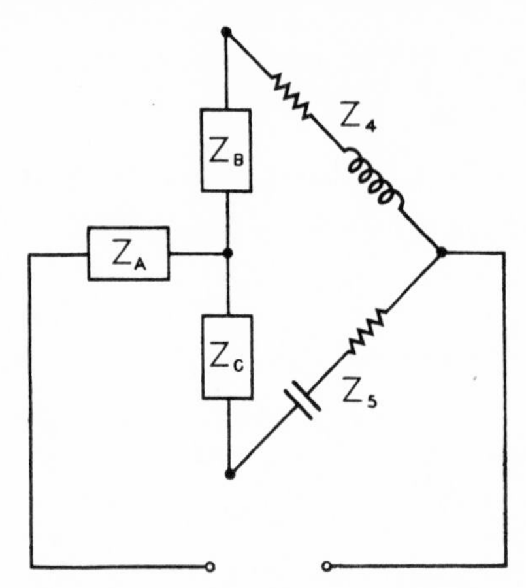

Fig. 11-9. Equivalent of bridge circuit (Fig. 11-8).

wishes to test his complete mastery of vector algebra, several more difficult problems are included in the assignments.

Review Problems

1. (a) Name two systems of vector algebra.

(b) What mathematical operations can be performed by each system?

(c) What are the limitations of each system?

2. Describe briefly the method used for representing a vector quantity by each system.

3. Explain the meaning and use of the j operator.

4. (a) What is the general form for expressing a vector quantity in rectangular coordinates?

(b) When is the j term made positive or negative?

5. Express each of the following in rectangular form:

(a) E = 145 v at 30-degree lead.

(b) I = 37.6 amps at 180 degrees.

(c) E = 25 v at 48-degree lag.

(d) I = 85 ma at 90-degree lag.

(e) I = 4.3 amps at zero degrees.

(f) Capacitive reactance of 1200 ohms.
(g) Inductive reactance of 850 ohms.
(h) Resistance of 600 ohms.
(i) (f) and (g) in series.
(j) (f) and (h) in series.
(k) (g) and (h) in series.
(l) (f), (g), and (h) in series.

6. Express each of the values in Problem 5 in polar form.

7. Convert each of the following from polar to rectangular form:
(a) $E = 80\underline{/30^\circ}$ v.
(b) $I = 65\underline{/-20^\circ}$ ma.
(c) $Z = 380\underline{/65^\circ}$ ohms.
(d) $I = 3.5\underline{/80^\circ}$ amps.

8. Convert each of the following from rectangular to polar form:
(a) $I = 50 + j30$ ma.
(b) $E = 10 - j45$ v.
(c) $Z = 120 + j200$ ohms.
(d) $Z = 15 - j8$ ohms.

9. Add the following values and express the sum in polar form:
(a) $I_1 = 15 + j7$, $I_2 = 8 - j5$, $I_3 = 4 + j2$.
(b) $E_1 = 140 - j60$, $E_2 = 30 + j80$, $E_3 = 20 - j50$.
(c) $Z_1 = 25 + j70$, $Z_2 = 18 - j30$, $Z_3 = 10 + j15$.
(d) $E_1 = 40\underline{/30^\circ}$, $E_2 = 25\underline{/-48^\circ}$, $E_3 = 60\underline{/0^\circ}$.

10. Find the missing values and express in polar form:
(a) $E_T = 80\underline{/0^\circ}$, $E_1 = 75\underline{/40^\circ}$, $E_2 = ?$
(b) $I_T = 30 + j25$, $I_1 = 15 - j20$, $I_3 = 4 + j30$, $I_2 = ?$
(c) Series circuit $Z_T = 120 - j85$, $Z_1 = 70 - j100$,
$Z_2 = 20 + j15$, $Z_3 = ?$

11. A parallel circuit is connected across a 200-v, 5000-cycle supply. The branches are: 1. A capacitor of 0.1 μf. 2. A resistor of 500 ohms. 3. A coil of 20 mh, and a resistor of 200 ohms. Using the rectangular coordinate method, find the line current and express the answer in polar form. Draw the vector diagram.

12. In Fig. 11-3, the circuit values are:
(a) Supply voltage 100 v, 400 kc.
(b) Branch 1: 0.0005 μf and 600 ohms.
(c) Branch 2: 1200 ohms.
(d) Branch 3: 1.2 mh and 300 ohms.

Using vector algebra (either form), solve for:

(a) Branch currents.
(b) Line current (express in polar form).
(c) Voltage across the coil and its phase relation to the supply voltage.
(d) Voltage across the resistor (branch 3) and its phase relation to the supply voltage.
(e) Draw the vector diagram.

13. In Problem 12, if the voltage across the capacitor is 50 v, find:

(a) Supply voltage (frequency as in Problem 12).
(b) Current in each branch.
(c) Total current.
(d) Draw the vector diagram.

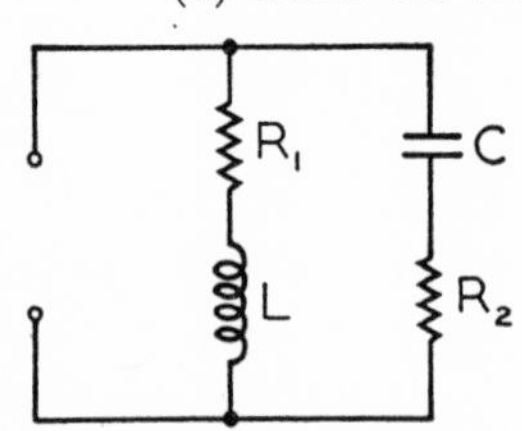

14. Find the total impedance of the circuit shown at left if $R_1 = 1500$ ohms, $X_L = 800$ ohms, $X_C = 2000$ ohms, and $R_2 = 500$ ohms.

15. In Problem (14), if the line current is 80 ma, find the current in each branch.

16. In Fig. 11-5, the supply voltage is 3000 v, 50 kc. The circuit constants are:

$R_1 = 5000$ ohms.	$R_2 = 5000$ ohms.	$R_3 = 5000$ ohms.
$L_1 = 50$ mh.	$L_2 = 5$ mh.	$C = 600\ \mu\mu f$.

Find:

(a) Total impedance.
(b) Line current.
(c) Voltage across the parallel circuit.
(d) Current through each branch of the parallel circuit.
(e) Draw the vector diagram.

17. In Fig. 11-6b the values are

$R_1 = 500$ ohms.	$X_{c1} = 300$ ohms.
$R_2 = 800$ ohms.	$X_{c2} = 1000$ ohms.
$R_3 = 1000$ ohms.	$X_L = 3000$ ohms.

Find the circuit values for the equivalent π circuit.

18. In Fig. 11-8 find the total impedance if

$Z_1 = 300 - j400$	$Z_4 = 200 + j400$
$Z_2 = 100 + j80$	$Z_5 = 400 - j300$
$Z_3 = 600 - j500$	

CHAPTER 12

Three-Phase Systems

In Chapter 2, we saw how a sine wave of voltage was produced when a coil was rotated in a uniform magnetic field. Such a single-phase voltage source was used in the chapters that followed. Now let us suppose that our simple generator of Chapter 2 has two coils rotating in the same magnetic field. This was done in Chapter 3 (page 31) when discussing phase and time relations. Each coil produced its own sine-wave voltage. When the two coils were displaced by 90 degrees we had two voltages 90 degrees apart (see Fig. 3-3). Such a source would constitute a two-phase system. This is the simplest polyphase system. Since two-phase supplies are not generally used, they will not be discussed. However, the same principle can be extended to include more coils, symmetrically spaced, producing other polyphase systems. The most common of these is the three-phase system.

Generation of three-phase supply. The generator shown in Fig. 12-1 has three coils (aa', bb', and cc') spaced 120 degrees apart. Each of these coils generates a sine-wave voltage as explained in Chapter 2. At the instant shown, coil aa' is not cutting any lines. The voltage $a'a$ is zero. During the next half turn, terminal a will be moving down, electrons will be pulled away from this end, leaving it positive. At the same time terminal a' will be negative. So the voltage across this coil is starting at zero and going positive. This waveshape is shown as the solid curve in Fig. 12-1b. Meanwhile terminal b of the second coil is moving up through the magnetic field. At this instant it is negative and approaching its maximum value. Again, as the coil rotates, it will produce a sine-wave voltage, but due to its space location this wave lags the previous coil's voltage by 120 degrees. Voltage $b'b$ is shown as the dot-dash curve. Similarly voltage $c'c$, shown as the dotted curve, lags voltage $a'a$ by 240 degrees, (or leads by 120 degrees). At the instant shown in Fig. 12-1a, terminal *c* is moving down; its potential is positive but approaching zero.

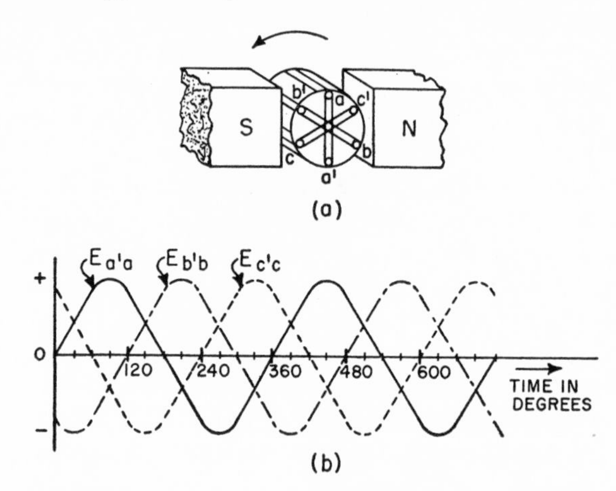

Fig. 12-1. Generation of three-phase voltage supply.

The three voltages generated constitute a three-phase supply. The phase relations between these voltages are shown by vector diagram in Fig. 12-2.

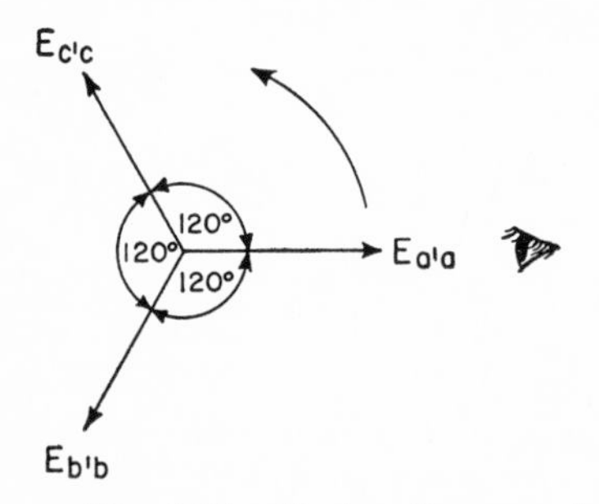

Fig. 12-2. Vector diagram of a three-phase voltage supply. (Note that as the vectors rotate counterclockwise they will be "seen" in the sequence $E_{a'a}$, $E_{b'b}$, $E_{c'c}$.)

Alternating-current generators are known as *alternators.* Their construction differs from the simple diagram shown in Fig. 12-1a. The major difference is that the generating coils are stationary and the field structure revolves. For a three-phase supply, three generating coils or *stator* windings are used. The windings are wound on the frame of the machine and are spaced 120 *electrical* degrees apart. The field structure is an electromagnet and is mounted on the rotating shaft of the machine. It may be a two-pole structure or it may have any even number of poles. Where more than two poles are used, one revolution produces one cycle (360 electrical degrees) for each pair of poles. This, however, does not alter the above discussion. Details of the alternators will be left to texts on machinery.

Phase sequence. Due to the space location of the coils in a polyphase system, each coil reaches its positive maximum value at a different time. In our machine of Fig. 12-1a, starting with coil $a'a$, the next coil to reach maximum value is $b'b$, then comes $c'c$, and then $a'a$ again. This is known as the *phase sequence* of this three-phase system. If the direction of rotation of our machine were reversed, the phase sequence would have been $a'a$, $c'c$, $b'b$. No other phase sequence is possible with this machine. Instead of the positive maximum value, any other instantaneous value could be used to determine phase sequence. In general, the phase sequence of any polyphase system can be stated as the order in which the phase voltages reach a specific instantaneous value.

Double subscript notation. In the above diagrams and discussion you may have noticed the three voltages referred to by double subscripts, $a'a$, $b'b$, and $c'c$. As you will see later, the three phases of the alternator will be interconnected. Vector addition of these voltages will be necessary. If a coil's connections are reversed with respect to another coil or a load, its instantaneous polarity is also reversed (180 degrees phase difference). The vector representing this coil's voltage should be shown 180 degrees out of phase in contrast to its original direction. Some method must be used to distinguish between these two conditions. In addition, polyphase circuits generally involve several voltages and currents. When tracing through such circuits, it is important to know the instantaneous polarity of the voltages and the direction of flow of the currents encountered. Double subscript notation will solve our problem. An illustration will show the value of this system of notation. Figure 12-3 (a and b) shows two coils of a generator, spaced 60 degrees apart, and the vector relation between the voltages generated in their windings. If we connect these two coils in series, we have four possible output voltages, depending on which end of each coil is tied together. Using 100 volts as the effective value of each coil voltage and $E_{a'a}$ as reference, let us find the output voltage for each of the four connections.

1. *Tie a and b' together* (Fig. 12-3c).

$$E_R = E_{a'a} + E_{b'b} = E_{a'b}$$

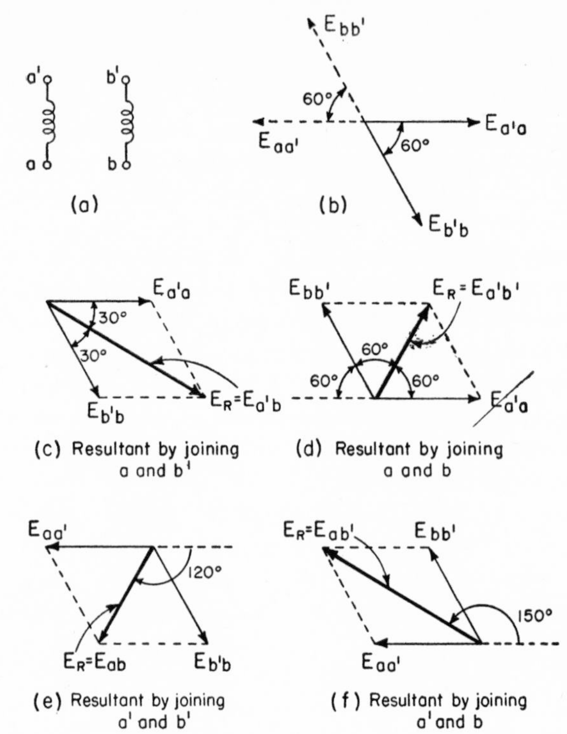

Fig. 12-3. Vector addition, showing use of double subscript notation.

By vector algebra

$$\begin{aligned} E_{a'a} &= 100 + j0 \\ E_{b'b} &= 50 - j86.6 \\ \hline E_R &= 150 - j86.6 = 173\angle -30^\circ \end{aligned}$$

2. *Tie a and b together* (Fig. 12-3d).

$$E_R = E_{a'a} + E_{bb'} = E_{a'b'}$$

$$\begin{aligned} E_{a'a} &= 100 + j0 \\ E_{bb'} &= -50 + j86.6 \\ \hline E_R &= 50 + j86.6 = 100\angle 60^\circ \end{aligned}$$

3. *Tie a′ and b′ together* (Fig. 12-3e).

$$E_R = E_{aa'} + E_{b'b} = E_{ab}$$

$$\begin{aligned} E_{aa'} &= -100 + j0 \\ E_{b'b} &= 50 - j86.6 \\ \hline E_R &= -50 - j86.6 = 100\angle -120^\circ \end{aligned}$$

4. *Tie a′ and b together* (Fig. 12-3f).

$$E_R = E_{aa'} + E_{bb'} = E_{ab'}$$

$$E_{aa'} = -100 + j0$$

$$E_{bb'} = -50 + j86.6$$

$$E_R = -150 + j86.6 = 173\underline{/150°}$$

You can notice from the above that the direction in which a coil is connected can make appreciable difference not only in the magnitude but also in the phase of the resultant voltage. The double subscript notation made our circuit evaluation simple. This system of notation will be used throughout our discussion of polyphase systems.

Three-phase delta (Δ) connection. A three-phase alternator has three sets of coils and therefore six output terminals. If six

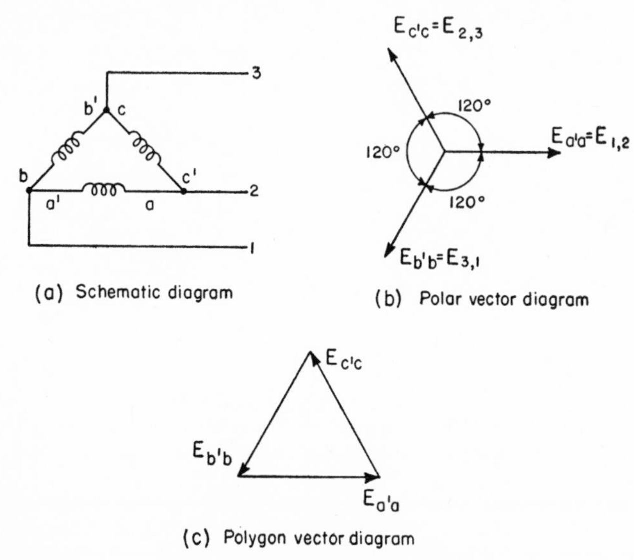

Fig. 12-4. Connections and voltage relations in a 3ϕ delta system.

lines were used to connect between supply source and load, it would result in an inefficient distribution system because of the amount of copper required. To reduce the number of lines, the coils are interconnected at the alternator. One such method is known as the *delta (or mesh)* connection. This method is shown in Fig. 12-4a.

Coil end a is connected to coil end c'; coil ends c to b' and b to a', to form a closed circuit. Each junction is brought out, resulting in a three-wire distribution system. But doesn't this interconnection short-circuit the alternator? It could—if the connections were improperly phased! Let us examine the vector diagrams for the connections we are using. Figure 12-4b shows the phase relations among the three coil voltages. Since this is a three-phase system, these voltages are 120 degrees apart. When we connect coil end a with coil end c', we are adding $E_{c'c}$ to $E_{a'a}$. Then when we connect coil end b' to coil end c we are adding $E_{b'b}$ to the previous two voltages. This vector addition of the three coil voltages is shown in Fig. 12-4c. *Notice that the resultant is zero!* Therefore we were able to close the circuit by connecting coil end b to coil end a' without creating a short circuit and without causing any current to flow in the delta loop.

By definition, in any polyphase circuit the voltage across an individual coil is known as the *phase* voltage, while the voltage between any two lines is called the *line* voltage. Examination of Fig. 12-4 shows that the voltage between lines 1 and 2 equals $E_{a'a}$; between lines 2 and 3 equals $E_{c'c}$; and between lines 3 and 1 equals $E_{b'b}$. In other words *in any delta system, the line voltage equals the phase voltage*, or

$$E_L = E_p \qquad \text{(delta circuit)}$$

EXAMPLE 1

A voltmeter connected across lines 1 and 2 of a three-phase delta supply (Fig. 12-4) indicates 100 volts. The phase sequence is known to be $E_{a'a}$, $E_{b'b}$, $E_{c'c}$. (a) Write the equation for each line voltage, using $E_{1,2}$ as reference. (b) Express each voltage in polar form and in complex form.

SOLUTION

1. $E_{\max} = \dfrac{E}{0.707} = \dfrac{100}{0.707} = 141$ v.

2. $E_{1,2} = E_{\max} \sin (\omega t + 0°) = 141 \sin \omega t$

$E_{3,1} = E_{\max} \sin (\omega t - 120°) = 141 \sin (\omega t - 120°)$

$E_{2,3} = E_{\max} \sin (\omega t + 120°) = 141 \sin (\omega t + 120°)$

3. $E_{1,2} = E\underline{/0°} = 100\underline{/0°} = 100 + j0$

$E_{3,1} = E\underline{/-120°} = 100\underline{/-120°} = -50 - j86.6$

$E_{2,3} = E\underline{/+120°} = 100\underline{/+120°} = -50 + j86.6$

Earlier in this discussion, we mentioned that proper phasing must be used when connecting the coils in delta. Our connections were correct, but what would happen if the terminals of one coil were reversed? Suppose we had connected coil end c to b' as before, but we now connect coil end a to coil end b. Referring to the vector diagram (Fig. 12-4c), $E_{c'c} + E_{b'b}$ would still be as shown. Now however, when we add $E_{aa'}$, this voltage is the reverse (180 degrees) of $E_{a'a}$ and it would extend to the left. *The resultant voltage (see Fig. 12-5) is not zero, but would equal twice the phase*

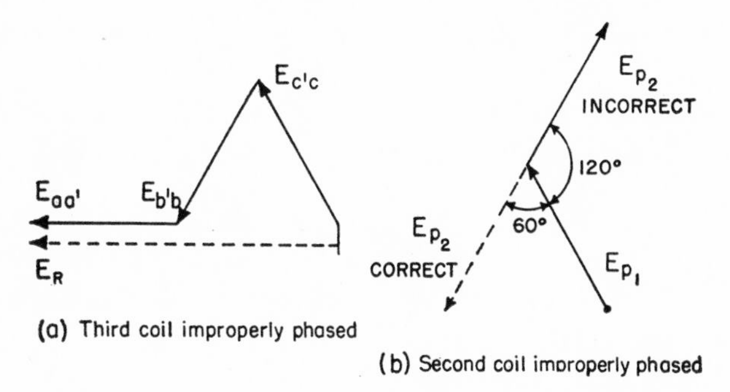

Fig. 12-5. Effect of improper coil phasing in a delta system.

voltage. Coil end a' should not be connected to coil end c' as this would cause a short circuit. The circulating current within the delta may burn out the windings.

In a commercial machine, if the two leads from each winding are brought out without any phasing identification, how can we tell if we are making the correct connections? A simple voltmeter check will solve the problem.

1. Measure the phase voltage across any one coil.
2. Connect any two coils in series and measure the voltage across their free ends. If this voltage is still equal to the phase voltage the phasing is correct; if the new reading is almost double the phase voltage ($1.73E_p$), the connection is incorrect. This effect is shown in Fig. 12-5b. To correct this situation, merely reverse *either* coil.
3. Connect the third coil in series, and again measure the voltage across the free ends. This voltage may be zero or twice the phase voltage. If it is zero, fine—connect the

free ends together and our delta is completed. On the other hand, if the voltage is double the phase voltage, reverse the *third* coil and now complete the delta.

Three-phase wye (Y) connection. Another system for interconnecting the three coils of a three-phase supply is to tie one end of each coil together and bring out the three free ends as the three

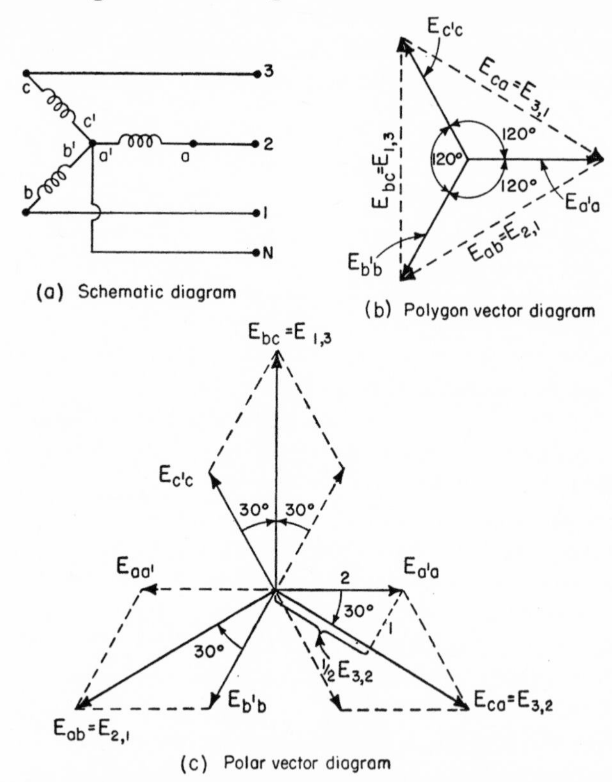

Fig. 12-6. Voltage relations in a 3ϕ wye system.

line wires to form a three-phase, 3-wire system. This type of connection is known as the *wye* (Y) *or star* system. In addition, a fourth line—*the neutral*—is usually also brought out from the junction of the three coils. We now have a three-phase, four-wire system. This is shown in Fig. 12-6. For convenience of comparison with the previous delta system, the wye has been drawn sideways so as to keep the individual coil voltages at the same phase angles in both cases. Let us examine the voltage relations, for a phase sequence of $E_{a'a}$, $E_{b'b}$, $E_{c'c}$.

The three phase voltages, as before, are 120 degrees apart. But what about the line voltages? Inspection of the circuit interconnections in Fig. 12-6a shows that the voltage between any two lines is the vector sum of two of the phase voltages. For example, the potential of line 3 with respect to line 2 ($E_{3,2}$ or E_{ca}) is the vector sum of $E_{cc'}$ ($E_{c'c}$ reversed) and $E_{a'a}$. In a similar manner we can find the remaining line voltages.

$$E_{ca} = E_{3,2} = E_{cc'} + E_{a'a}$$
$$E_{ab} = E_{2,1} = E_{aa'} + E_{b'b}$$
$$E_{bc} = E_{1,3} = E_{bb'} + E_{c'c}$$

These phase and line voltage relations are shown vectorially by the polygon diagram and polar diagram of Fig. 12-6b and c. Notice that the phase voltage $E_{a'a}$ **leads** the line voltage E_{ca} (the line voltage with the same second subscript) by 30 degrees. Similarly notice that $E_{b'b}$ and $E_{c'c}$ also lead their *respective* line voltages E_{ab} and E_{bc} by 30 degrees. This 30-degree phase shift between phase and line voltages is characteristic of any three-phase, four-wire wye system or of any *balanced* three-phase, three-wire wye system.

Let us backtrack for a moment. We obtained the above line voltages by taking the potential of line 3 with respect to line 2. Then we followed in rotation with line 2 to line 1 and line 1 back to line 3. Referring to the polygon diagram, Fig. 12-6b, we went from $E_{c'c}$ to $E_{a'a}$, $E_{a'a}$ to $E_{b'b}$, $E_{b'b}$ to $E_{c'c}$. This is the same order in which we would 'see' our phase voltages.

Now there is no reason why we could not have taken our line voltages in the opposite order, that is from line 1 to line 2 to line 3. We would then get line voltages $E_{1,2}$, $E_{2,3}$, and $E_{3,1}$. For example, $E_{1,2}$ would be E_{ba} and would equal

$$E_{ba} = E_{1,2} = E_{bb'} + E_{a'a}$$

This line voltage is shown in Fig. 12-7. In our previous analysis of line voltages, we had

$$E_{ab} = E_{2,1} = E_{aa'} + E_{b'b}$$

This line voltage is also shown in Fig. 12-7.

Notice that these voltages are 180 degrees apart. The explanation is simple. *They are the same voltage seen one-half cycle later.* After all, we know that any alternating voltage varies from a positive maximum to a negative maximum. In one case (E_{ab}) we took the *instantaneous* polarity of our component phase voltages as $E_{aa'}$ and $E_{b'b}$. In the second case (E_{ba}) we reversed the instantaneous polarity of our phases and used $E_{a'a}$ and $E_{bb'}$. Either analysis is correct, as long as we are consistent throughout the circuit. To avoid possibility of confusion, we will use the first method (i.e., take our line voltages in the same order as our phase sequences) throughout this text.

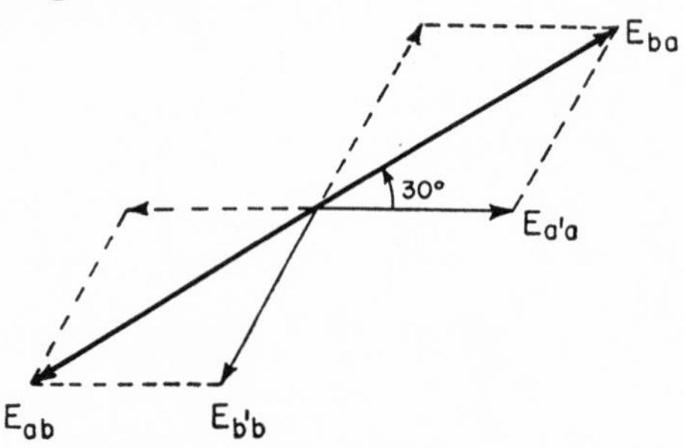

Fig. 12-7. Comparison of voltage between lines 1 and 2 taken with opposite instantaneous phase polarities.

Returning to our vector diagram of Fig. 12-6, we have seen how to show the phase relation between phase and line voltages. But what is the magnitude of the line voltage? By inspection it is obviously greater than the phase voltage. How much greater? To find this relation, notice again that each phase voltage leads its corresponding line voltage (line voltage with the same second subscript) by 30 degrees. Now let us drop a perpendicular from the end of $E_{a'a}$ to $E_{3,2}$, forming a 30, 60, 90 triangle, and cutting $E_{3,2}$ in half. This is shown in Fig. 12-6c. Notice that $E_{a'a}$ forms the hypotenuse of this triangle. Now in such a triangle we know that the side opposite the 30° angle is one-half the hypotenuse. Therefore if we assign a value of 1 to the side opposite the 30° angle, the hypotenuse ($E_{a'a}$) is 2 and by right triangle theorem the side adjacent ($\frac{1}{2}E_{3,2}$) is $\sqrt{2^2-1^2}$, or $\sqrt{3}$. But $E_{3,2}$ is twice this value or $2\sqrt{3}$.

Then $$\frac{E_{3,2}}{E_{a'a}} = \frac{2\sqrt{3}}{2} \quad \text{and} \quad E_{3,2} = \sqrt{3}\,E_{a'a}$$

By inspection of the other line and phase voltages it is obvious that the same relationship holds true. We can therefore generalize and say that *in a wye-connected system the line voltage leads or lags its component phase voltages by* 30 *degrees and exceeds the phase voltage by* $\sqrt{3}$, or

$$E_L = \sqrt{3}\, E_p \qquad \text{(wye circuit)}$$

EXAMPLE 2

Using the phase voltage values found in Example 1 (for delta connection) and $E_{a'a}$ again as the reference vector, write the equation for each line voltage and express each in polar and complex form.

SOLUTION

1. From Example 1, we found that

$$E_{a'a} = 141 \sin \omega t = 100\underline{/0^\circ} = 100 + j0$$
$$E_{b'b} = 141 \sin (\omega t - 120^\circ) = 100\underline{/-120^\circ} = -50 - j86.6$$
$$E_{c'c} = 141 \sin (\omega t + 120^\circ) = 100\underline{/120^\circ} = -50 + j86.6$$

2. Each line voltage $= \sqrt{3}\, E$ phase and lags 30 degrees behind the adjacent phase voltage. Therefore

(a) $E_{3,2} = \sqrt{3}\, E_{a'a}$ delayed $30^\circ = 244 \sin (\omega t - 30^\circ)$
(b) $E_{2,1} = \sqrt{3}\, E_{b'b}$ delayed $30^\circ = 244 \sin (\omega t - 150^\circ)$
(c) $E_{1,3} = \sqrt{3}\, E_{c'c}$ delayed $30^\circ = 244 \sin (\omega t + 90^\circ)$

3. Converting to effective values and expressing in vector algebra,

$$E_{3,2} = 173\underline{/-30^\circ} = 150 - j86.6$$
$$E_{2,1} = 173\underline{/-150^\circ} = -150 - j86.6$$
$$E_{1,3} = 173\underline{/90^\circ} = 0 + j173$$

In a wye system, the alternator coils do not form a closed loop. Therefore is it necessary to consider which end of each coil is connected to the neutral or common junction? Definitely yes! If we reverse any coil, the line voltages will not be 120 degrees apart nor will this voltage equal $\sqrt{3}\, E_p$. Again a voltmeter can be used to check proper phasing.

1. Connect two coils in series and measure the voltage across the free ends. This voltage should be $\sqrt{3}\, E_p$. If it is less, reverse one coil.

2. Now connect one end of the third coil to the common junction. Again, the voltage from the free end of this coil to the free end of each of the other two coils should be $\sqrt{3}\,E_p$. If this voltage value is not obtained, reverse the third coil connections.

Loading of a three-phase system. We have seen so far that a three-phase alternator can be connected in delta or wye to supply a three-wire distribution or load system. (Discussion of the four-wire wye system will be considered later.) The question now is, how is the load applied? A load can be applied across any one pair of lines to form a single-phase load, or more than one load can be connected across any combination of pairs of lines to form a polyphase load. The loads can be pure resistive, pure reactive, or any combination of resistance and reactance. The simplest type of load to analyze (and the most efficient) is the *balanced load. Such a load is achieved when all line currents are equal and have the same phase angle with respect to the line voltages.* This is the only type of load that will be discussed in this chapter.

Current relations in a balanced wye-connected load. One method of obtaining a balanced load is to connect three identical loads in wye. Such a load circuit is shown in Fig. 12-8. The load is a pure resistive load. It is evident from the circuit diagram that the line current I_1 flows through resistor R_1 and must be the same current as the phase current I_{01}. Similarly I_2 and I_3 equal respectively I_{02} and I_{03}. From this we can conclude that in a wye-connected load, the line current is the same as the phase current.

$$I_L = I_p \qquad \text{(wye circuit)}$$

Another thought may occur to you as you look at the circuit diagram. If these three line currents are feeding into the free end of the wye-connected resistors, what happens to these currents at the neutral, or junction point of the resistors? Current cannot pile up at a point! True enough, but we have not yet considered their phase relations. Let us do that now. From our knowledge of voltage relations in a wye circuit, we can draw the vector diagram for the phase and line voltages. We also know that in any resistive circuit, the current through the resistor is in phase with the voltage across it. But the voltage across each resistor is the phase voltage. Therefore our line currents (which are the same as the phase currents) are in phase with the phase voltages, and are 120 degrees apart. As can be seen in Fig. 12-8c the sum of these line currents is zero, and so there is no pile-up at the junction.

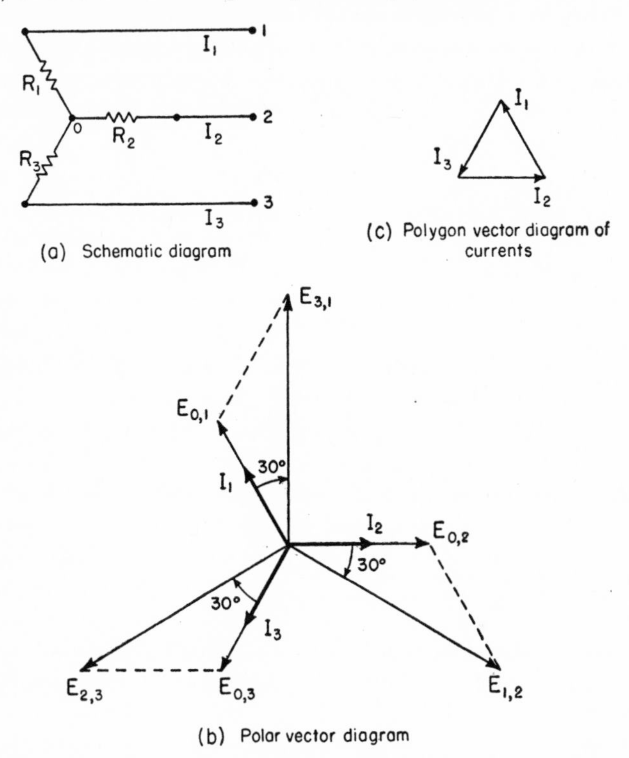

Fig. 12-8. Current and voltage relations in a 3ϕ wye resistive load.

Phase angle in a three-phase circuit. When we studied single-phase circuits we learned that in a resistive circuit, the circuit phase angle between line voltage and line current was zero. Now examine the vector diagram, Fig. 12-8b. This represents a resistive circuit. What is the phase angle between line voltage and line current? That is a problem—which line current to which line voltage? Between I_1 and $E_{3,1}$, current leads by 30 degrees; between I_1 and $E_{1,2}$ current leads by 150 degrees. Shall we make it more confusing? Between I_1 and $E_{2,1}$ the current lags by 30 degrees. Obviously we can no longer speak of circuit phase angle as the angle between line current and line voltage. Now examine the phase relation between phase current and *its* phase voltage. They are in phase, and this is a resistive circuit. Now phase angle makes sense again. So in polyphase circuits *reference to phase angle, unless otherwise specified, means the angle between* **phase** *voltage and the corresponding* **phase** *current. In a balanced load this phase angle is the same for all three phases.*

EXAMPLE 3

Three 20-ohm resistors are connected in wye across a 220-v 3-phase supply. Find the line current and circuit phase angle.

SOLUTION

1. Since the resistors are connected in wye, the voltage across each resistor is the phase voltage. In a wye system the phase voltage is *less* than the line voltage.

$$E_p = \frac{E_L}{\sqrt{3}} = \frac{220}{\sqrt{3}} = 127 \text{ v.}$$

2. $I_p = I_L \text{ (wye)} = \frac{E_p}{R_p} = \frac{127}{20} =$ **6.35 amps.**

3. Since the circuit is resistive, I_p is in phase with E_p, and the phase angle is **zero.**

EXAMPLE 4

Three impedances, each having a resistance of 30 ohms and an inductive reactance of 40 ohms, are connected in wye across a three-phase 208-v system. Find the line current and phase angle.

SOLUTION

1. $Z_p = \sqrt{R_p^2 + X_p^2} = \sqrt{(30)^2 + (40)^2} = 50$ ohms.

2. $E_p = \frac{E_L}{\sqrt{3}} = \frac{208}{\sqrt{3}} = 120$ v.

3. $I_p = I_L \text{ (wye)} = \frac{120}{50} =$ **2.40 amps.**

4. $\theta_p = \text{arc tan } \frac{X_p}{R_p} = \text{arc tan } \frac{40}{30} =$ **53.1°.**

Let us consider now the effect of a reactive load on the vector diagram for a wye system. The phase voltage and line voltage relations are unchanged. But the current vectors will be shifted. Referring to Fig. 12-8, an inductive load will cause the currents I_1, I_2, and I_3 to lag their respective phase voltages by some angle θ, the value of which depends on the ratio of inductive reactance to resistance of the load. Conversely, a capacitive load will cause the line currents to lead their respective phase voltages.

EXAMPLE 5

Using a line voltage phase sequence of $E_{1,2}$, $E_{2,3}$, $E_{3,1}$, and $E_{1,2}$ as the reference, draw the vector diagram for the currents and voltages of Example 4. Express each current in polar form.

SOLUTION

1. Line voltages. Since the line voltages are 120 degrees apart and $E_{1,2}$ is the reference voltage, $E_{2,3}$ lags by 120 degrees and $E_{3,1}$ lags by 240 degrees (or leads by 120 degrees). Draw these vectors (see Fig. 12-9).

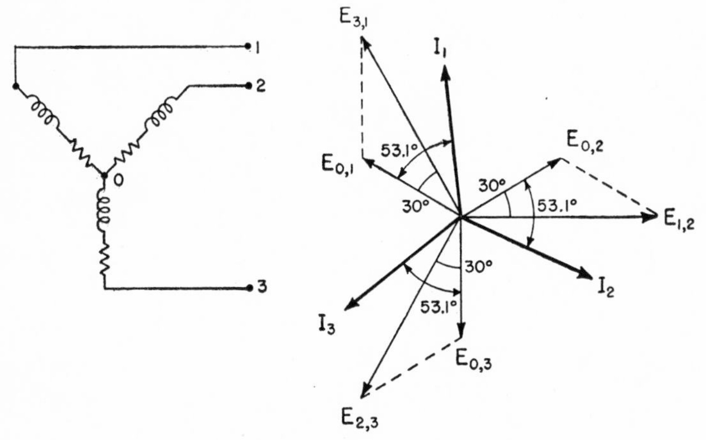

Fig. 12-9. Current and voltage relations in a 3ϕ wye inductive load.

2. Phase voltages. Let us call the phase voltages $E_{0,1}$, $E_{0,2}$, and $E_{0,3}$. These phase voltages must be 120 degrees apart, in the phase sequence as listed, and leading their respective line voltages (the line voltage with the same second subscript) by 30 degrees. In addition, from the designation of the line voltages,

$$E_{1,2} = E_{1,0} + E_{0,2}$$
$$E_{2,3} = E_{2,0} + E_{0,3}$$
$$E_{3,1} = E_{3,0} + E_{0,1}$$

This locates our phase voltages with respect to the line voltages. Add these voltages to the vector diagram, Fig. 12-9.

3. Line currents. In Example 4, the phase angle of the load was found to be 53.1 degrees, and the load was inductive. Since the line current is also the phase current (wye load), this places each line current 53.1 degrees

lagging with respect to the *phase* voltage. Add these currents to the vector diagram.

4. To express the currents in polar form we must know their magnitude and direction. From Example 4, we found the magnitude to be 2.40 amps. Now let us use the vector diagram (Fig. 12-9) to establish their direction.

(a) I_2 lags $E_{0,2}$ by 53.1 degrees and therefore lags the reference vector ($E_{1,2}$) by 23.1 degrees.

$$I_2 = 2.40\underline{/-23.1^\circ}$$

(b) I_3 lags I_2 by 120 degrees.

$$I_3 = 2.40\underline{/-143.1^\circ}$$

(c) I_1 leads I_2 by 120 degrees.

$$I_1 = 2.40\underline{/96.9^\circ}$$

EXAMPLE 6

Solve Example 4, using vector algebra and using a phase sequence of $E_{1,2}$, $E_{2,3}$, $E_{3,1}$, and $E_{1,2}$ as reference vector.

SOLUTION

1. To solve for currents by using vector algebra, we must express all voltages and impedances in vector form. We will start with line voltages.

(a) $E_{1,2} = 208\underline{/0^\circ}$

(b) $E_{2,3} = 208\underline{/-120^\circ}$

(c) $E_{3,1} = 208\underline{/+120^\circ}$

2. Phase voltages. Remembering that the phase voltages $= E_L/\sqrt{3}$ in magnitude and lead their respective line voltages by 30 degrees,

(a) $E_{0,1}$ (leading $E_{3,1}$ by 30 degrees) $= 120\underline{/+150^\circ}$

(b) $E_{0,2}$ (leading $E_{1,2}$ by 30 degrees) $= 120\underline{/+30^\circ}$

(c) $E_{0,3}$ (leading $E_{2,3}$ by 30 degrees) $= 120\underline{/-90^\circ}$

3. Load impedances. From Example 4, the load impedance was found to be 50 ohms and the phase angle 53.1°. Since the load is inductive, this makes the impedances

$$Z = 50\underline{/53.1^\circ}$$

4. Line currents.

(a) $I_1 = \dfrac{E_{0,1}}{Z_1} = \dfrac{120\underline{/150}}{50\underline{/53.1}} = 2.40\underline{/96.9^\circ}$

(b) $I_2 = \frac{E_{0,2}}{Z_2} = \frac{120/\underline{30}}{50/\underline{53.1}} = 2.40/\underline{-23.1°}$

(c) $I_3 = \frac{E_{0,3}}{Z_3} = \frac{120/\underline{-90}}{50/\underline{53.1}} = 2.40/\underline{-143.1°}$

These currents check with our vector analysis of Example 5.

Current relations in a balanced delta-connected load. Just as alternator coils can be connected in wye or delta, so can loads. If the impedance of each 'leg' of the delta loads is the same, we will again have a balanced load. A balanced resistive delta-connected load is shown in Fig. 12-10a. Since the load is resistive, the phase

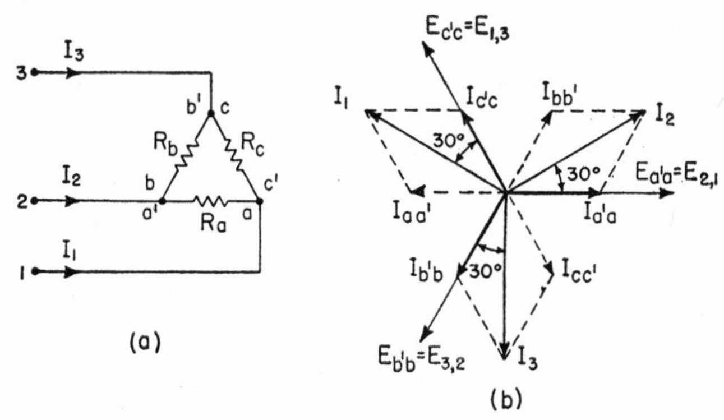

Fig. 12-10. Current and voltage relations in a 3ϕ delta resistive load.

currents must be in phase with their phase voltages. But in a delta circuit, we already know that phase voltages are identical with line voltages. These phase relations are shown in Fig. 12-10b. Now let us examine the line currents.

$$I_1 = I_{c'c} + I_{aa'}$$
$$I_2 = I_{a'a} + I_{bb'}$$
$$I_3 = I_{b'b} + I_{cc'}$$

The line currents are greater than the phase currents, and these current vectors are similar to the voltage vectors for the wye circuit. The same method of analysis can be used to prove that

$$I_L = \sqrt{3}\, I_p \qquad \text{(delta)}$$

EXAMPLE 7

The three resistors of Example 3 (20 ohms each) are reconnected in delta to the same supply line (220-v, 3-phase). Find the line current and the circuit phase angle.

SOLUTION

1. $E_L = E_p = 200$ v (delta)

2. $I_p = \dfrac{E_p}{R_p} = \dfrac{220}{20} = 11.0$ amps

3. $I_L = \sqrt{3}\, I_p = 11\sqrt{3} = 19.0$ amps

4. Since the circuit is resistive, I_p is in phase with E_p and the phase angle is **zero.**

From a comparison of Examples 3 and 7, notice that for the same supply voltage and the same resistance values, the line current in the delta load is three times the line current for the wye load.

Three-phase four-wire distribution system. Earlier in this chapter we learned that the coils of a three-phase alternator could be connected in delta or in wye. The delta connection resulted in a three-wire distribution system. The wye connection could be used as a three-wire system, or by bringing out the neutral (common terminal of the wye-connected phases), a four-wire distribution system could be obtained. This latter system (3Φ, 4-wire) has definite advantages and is in common use. To explain why this is so leads us into a discussion on the selection of a suitable line voltage as related to efficiency and safety.

Power delivered to (or taken by) a load is dependent on voltage and current. For a given amount of power, the higher the line voltage, the lower the line current. From the standpoint of transmission-line efficiency, the lower the line currents, the better. The copper losses (I^2R) in the transmission lines and in the equipment itself will be reduced; or the size of wire used in the lines or equipment can be made smaller, for the same power loss; or the lines and equipment can be used at a higher power rating. On the other hand, from the standpoint of safety, it is obvious that the lower the line voltage, the less the possibility of lethal or serious shocks. As a compromise between safety and efficiency the local distribution line voltages commonly used are 120 volts (approximately) for lighting and low-power equipment such as fractional horsepower motors, and 220 volts (approximately) for higher power loads. Of course the power company can (and does) use much higher voltages (23,000 to 150,000 v) at its power stations and long-distance transmission lines, and then step down (by transformers) to the consumer voltage level at local distribution areas.

With a three-wire distribution system, if the line voltage is 220 volts, additional transformers will be needed, or the main distribution transformers must be center-tapped in order to supply the lower voltage needed for lighting loads or low power appliances. This in turn means at least three more wires for the local distribution system. On the other hand, the four-wire distribution system, with a slight compromise, can furnish the proper voltage to either type of load. The line voltage used is 208 volts. Since it is a wye-connected system, the phase voltage between any line and the neutral is 120 volts.

$$E_p = \frac{E_L}{\sqrt{3}} = \frac{208}{\sqrt{3}} = 120 \text{ volts}$$

Notice the flexibility available. This four-wire system can be used to supply a three-phase 208-v load by connecting the load to the three line wire; it can be used to supply single-phase 208-v loads by connecting the loads to any pair of lines; and it can be used to supply single-phase 120-v loads by connecting the loads between any line and the neutral.

Review Problems

1. What is an alternator?

2. Two coils of an alternator each generate 120 v, but the phase relation between these coils is such that E_{cd} of coil 2 lags E_{ab} of coil 1 by 90 degrees. Find the magnitude and phase angle of the four possible resultant voltages when these coils are connected in series.

3. Repeat Problem 2 for a generated voltage of 80 v per coil and E_{cd} leading E_{ab} by 70 degrees.

4. Repeat Problem 2 for a generated voltage of 120 v and E_{cd} lagging E_{ab} by 120 degrees.

5. What is the relation between phase voltages and line voltages in a three-phase delta system?

6. (a) Draw a vector diagram for the voltages in a three-phase delta system for a phase sequence of $E_{1,2}$, $E_{2,3}$, $E_{3,1}$, and starting with $E_{1,2}$ at 90 degrees leading.

(b) For a generated voltage of 220 v, express each line voltage in polar and rectangular form.

7. Repeat Problem 6 for a generated voltage of 200 v, phase sequence of $E_{1,2}$, $E_{3,1}$, $E_{2,3}$, and starting with $E_{1,2}$ at zero degrees.

8. Repeat Problem 6 for a generated voltage of 100 v, phase sequence of $E_{1,2}$, $E_{2,3}$, $E_{3,1}$, and starting with $E_{1,2}$ at 90 degrees lagging.

9. The three phases of an alternator are to be connected in delta. The generated voltage per phase is 200 v. Describe a procedure, and give values, for obtaining the proper connections.

10. What is the relation between phase and line voltages in a three-phase, four-wire wye system.

11. (a) Draw a vector diagram for the phase and line voltages in a three-phase, 4-wire wye system, for a phase sequence of $E_{a'a}$, $E_{b'b}$, $E_{c'c}$, and starting with $E_{a'a}$ at 90 degrees lagging.

(b) For a generated voltage per phase of 120 v, express each voltage in polar and rectangular form.

12. Repeat Problem 11 for a generated phase voltage of 100 v, phase sequence of $E_{a'a}$, $E_{c'c}$, $E_{b'b}$, and starting with $E_{a'a}$ at zero degrees.

13. The three phases of an alternator are to be connected in wye. The generated voltage per phase is 120 v. Describe a procedure, and give values, for obtaining the proper connections.

14. Three 50-ohm resistors are connected in wye across a 60-cycle 220-v three-phase supply. Find the line current and circuit phase angle.

15. Repeat Problem 14 for three 0.2-henry inductors.

16. Three loads, each consisting of 20 ohms resistance and 30 ohms capacitive reactance, are connected in wye across a 60-cycle, 208-v three-phase four-wire supply. Find the line current and circuit phase angle.

17. Repeat Problem 14 for the loads connected in delta.

18. Repeat Problem 15 for the loads connected in delta.

19. Repeat Problem 16 for the loads connected in delta.

20. (a) What is the advantage of a three-phase, four-wire distribution system over a three-wire system?

(b) Can a four-wire distribution system be used with a delta supply? Explain.

CHAPTER 13

Power in Three-Phase Systems

IN THE discussion of single-phase A.C. circuits, it was shown that the power dissipated in such a circuit could be found from

$$P = EI \cos \theta$$

In a three-phase circuit, this same equation can be used to find the power dissipated in each phase. To keep our 'bookkeeping' correct, the equation should now be rewritten as

$$P_p = E_p I_p \cos \theta_p$$

where the subscript p is used to denote phase values.

This subscript is often omitted from the $\cos \theta$ term. But you will recall that unless otherwise stated, θ refers to the phase angle between I_p and E_p. Therefore the meaning of the equation is unchanged.

In a polyphase circuit, each phase is dissipating power (load) or delivering power (alternator). The total power for the circuit must then be the sum of the individual phase powers.

$$P_T = P_1 + P_2 + P_3 + \ . \ . \ .$$

where P_1, P_2, P_3 represent the respective phase powers. This equation applies to any polyphase circuit whether balanced or unbalanced. For a *balanced* three-phase system, since each phase power is equal, we can simplify the above equation by

$$P_T = 3P_p$$

Replacing P_p by its equivalent $E_p I_p \cos \theta$,

$$P_T = 3E_p I_p \cos \theta$$

But in a delta system $E_p = E_L$ and $I_p = I_L/\sqrt{3}$. Substituting line values for phase values,

$$P_T = 3E_L \frac{I_L}{\sqrt{3}} \cos \theta = \sqrt{3}\, E_L I_L \cos \theta$$

Similarly in a wye system, $E_p = E_L/\sqrt{3}$ and $I_p = I_L$. Substituting these line values for the original phase values,

$$P_T = 3 \frac{E_L}{\sqrt{3}} I_L \cos \theta = \sqrt{3}\, E_L I_L \cos \theta$$

Notice that in *either* case, wye or delta, *for a balanced load* the equation for total power in terms of line current and line voltage is the same:

$$P_T = \sqrt{3}\, E_L I_L \cos \theta$$

Does the $\cos \theta$ term refer to the angle between the line current and line voltage? No. Remember that there are many phase angles among the three line currents and line voltages; θ refers to the angle between phase current and phase voltage *of the same phase.* In a balanced circuit, this angle is the same for all three phases.

EXAMPLE 1

A wye-connected 3-phase balanced load when connected to 220-v 3-phase supply draws a line current of 50 amps. The power factor of the load (phase value) is 0.8 lagging. Find the total power drawn by the load.

SOLUTION

1. Since line current and voltage are known, it makes no difference whether the load is delta- or wye-connected.
2. $P_T = \sqrt{3}\, E_L I_L \cos \theta = \sqrt{3} \times 220 \times 50 \times 0.8 = 15.25$ kw

EXAMPLE 2

A delta-connected load has an impedance per phase of 20 ohms resistance and 40 ohms inductance. It is connected to a 440-v 3-phase supply. Find the power taken by the load.

SOLUTION

1. $Z_p = \sqrt{R_p^2 + X_p^2} = \sqrt{(20)^2 + (40)^2} = 44.8$ ohms
2. $\cos \theta_p = \dfrac{R_p}{Z_p} = \dfrac{20}{44.8} = 0.447$
3. $E_p = E_L = 440$ (delta)

4. $I_p = \frac{E_p}{Z_p} = \frac{440}{44.8} = 9.82$ amps

5. $I_L = \sqrt{3}\, I_p = 9.82\sqrt{3} = 17.05$ amps

6A. $P_T = \sqrt{3}\, E_L I_L \cos\theta = \sqrt{3} \times 440 \times 17.05 \times 0.447$
$= \mathbf{5.81\ kw}$

or 6B. $P_T = 3P_p = 3E_p I_p \cos\theta$
$= 3 \times 440 \times 9.83 \times 0.447 = \mathbf{5.81\ kw}$

Measurement of power. We have seen that power in a balanced three-phase circuit can be calculated readily from line or phase values. However, if the load is not balanced the calculations are much more involved. In commercial applications, since the loads are often unbalanced, it is therefore desirable to measure power directly. We know how to use a wattmeter to measure power in a single-phase load (see p. 70). The same method could be used to measure the power in each phase. The current coil of the wattmeter should be in series with each phase, and the potential coil should be connected across each phase. In a four-wire wye system this can be done readily. Since the phase current is the same as the line current, each wattmeter current coil is connected in series with each line before tying the line to the load. Each wattmeter potential coil is connected with one end to its own current coil line terminal and the other end to the neutral, since this is its phase voltage. But in a three-phase balanced wye load, such as a three-phase oven, the neutral is not brought out. That does create a problem. The wattmeter connections described above become impractical if not absolutely impossible. With a delta load, the situation is even worse. Line currents and phase currents are not equal. It would be necessary to open each delta junction and insert each wattmeter current coil in series with each phase *inside* the delta junctions. This is definitely impractical. Luckily there are other techniques for measuring power in a three-phase circuit.

The three-wattmeter method. Here again, we are using three wattmeters, but regardless of whether the load is delta or wye connected, each current coil is connected in series with a *line* lead. The potential coils are connected at one end to their own current coil line and at the other end to a common junction (see Fig. 13-1). The potential coils actually form a wye-connected load. If the load itself were also a balanced wye-connected load, the load phase voltage would be identical with the potential coil voltage. Also in any wye load the line current and phase current are identical. Therefore each wattmeter indicates the phase power, and the sum of the three wattmeter readings is the total power. If the power factor of the load is changed, the phase voltage and the voltage across the potential coils are not affected. The angle of the phase current, and therefore line current, will shift with respect to phase voltage. The wattmeter readings will change, but all three wattmeter readings will still be identical. However, if the load is unbalanced, the 'neutral' of the load will not correspond to the

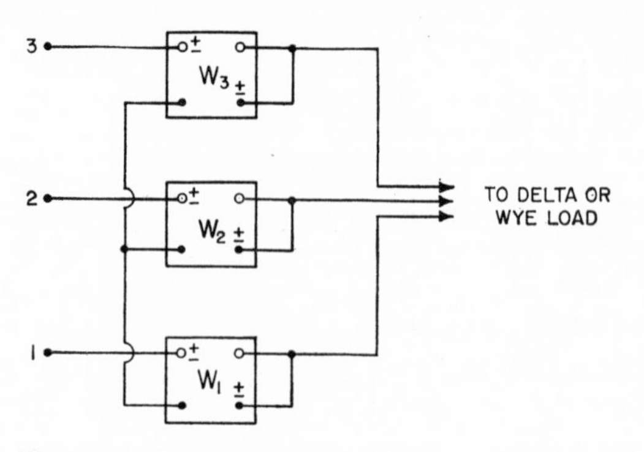

Fig. 13-1. The 3-wattmeter method for measuring power.

'neutral' of the potential coils. The three wattmeter readings will not be identical, but the sum of the three will still be the true total power. The same effect, unequal wattmeter readings, will also be produced if the three wattmeter potential coils do not have identical impedances, but again the correct total power will be the sum of the three wattmeter readings. Since unbalanced circuit analysis has not been covered, the proof for the effect of unbalanced loads or unbalanced potential coils cannot be given here.

If the load is a delta load, will the wattmeter connections of Fig. 13-1 give the correct power indication? To answer this we will have to use a vector diagram. Figure 13-2a shows a three-phase delta resistive load being metered by the three-wattmeter method. Since the potential coils of the wattmeters form a wye load, they have been shown diagrammatically as a wye within the delta. The delta configuration and nomenclature used are the same as were used in Fig. 12-10. Therefore the same vector diagram can be repeated here to show current and line voltage relations. If our wattmeters were 'properly' connected, each should be recording phase power E_pI_p. (We have simplified the problem by using resistive load which makes $\cos \theta = 1$.) For example, one meter should deflect due to the phase current $I_{a'a}$ and line voltage $E_{2,1}$. (Remember that with a delta load the line voltage is also the phase voltage.) But no wattmeter has the full delta voltage across its potential coil. Let us find these voltages. Since the potential coils are wye-connected, three *wye-phase voltages*, 120

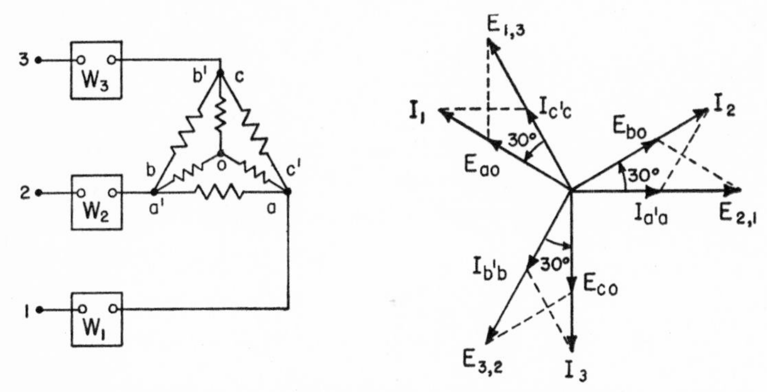

Fig. 13-2. The 3-wattmeter method of measuring power used with delta load.

degrees apart, will be developed across the potential circuits. These voltages are E_{ao}, E_{bo}, and E_{co}, 30 degrees away from the line voltages and such that

$$E_{bo} + E_{oa} = E_{2,1}$$
$$E_{co} + E_{ob} = E_{3,2}$$
$$E_{ao} + E_{oc} = E_{1,3}$$

This places E_{ao}, E_{bo}, and E_{co} in phase with the line currents I_1, I_2, and I_3, respectively. The deflection of the wattmeter in line 1 is due to line current I_1 and the wye phase voltage E_{ao}. As far as magnitudes are concerned, $I_1 = \sqrt{3}\, I_p$ and $E_{ao} = E_p/\sqrt{3}$, and the product $I_1 \times E_{ao} = I_p \times E_p$. As far as phase angles are concerned, I_1 and E_{ao} are in phase and so are E_p and I_p for each phase. In other words, the power indicated by the wattmeter in line 1 is equal to the actual phase power. Similarly, the power indicated by each of the wattmeters in lines 2 and 3 is also the phase power. Therefore the connections shown, although seemingly incorrect, will still give true power indication with a three-phase delta load.

For loads of other than unity power factor the phase currents will shift with respect to their phase voltages. For example, $I_{a'a}$ will either lead or lag $E_{2,1}$ by some angle, θ, causing I_2 to shift away from E_{bo} *by the same amount.* The product $E_{2,1} \times I_{a'a} \cos \theta$ will still equal $E_{bo} \times I_2 \cos \theta$, and each wattmeter will still indicate the phase power. As for a wye load, if the load is unbalanced (or if the potential coils are not of identical impedance), the wattmeter readings will not be alike, but their sum will still give the true total power.

The one-wattmeter method. It was pointed out in the above discussion, that *when the load is balanced and the three wattmeter potential coils have identical impedances,* each wattmeter reading is alike. Each meter indicates phase power, and the total power can be obtained by multiplying any one meter reading by three. Then why use three meters? But if we remove the other two wattmeters,

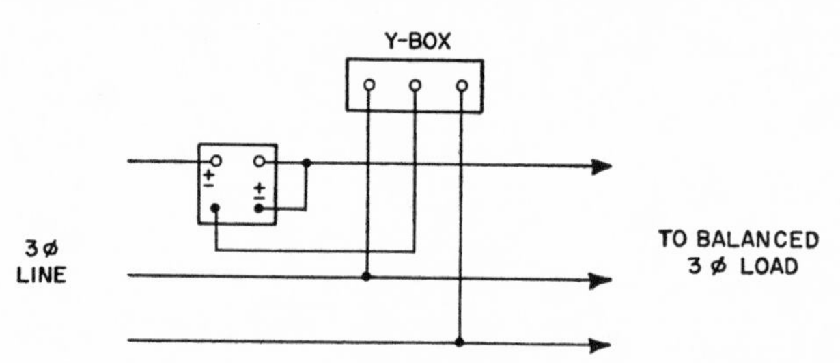

Fig. 13-3. The 1-wattmeter method of measuring power using a Y-box.

the potential circuit wye-connection is broken! This can be remedied by using two impedances each equal in value (*magnitude and phase*) to the impedance of the remaining wattmeter potential coil. Commercial units for this purpose are known as '*Y-boxes.*' They are available to duplicate the potential coils of various models of wattmeters. A Y-box for one type of meter cannot be used with a different model instrument unless the potential coil impedances are identical. The one-wattmeter method, employing a Y-box, is shown in Fig. 13-3.

Remember that this system can be used only with balanced loads.

The two-wattmeter method. In discussing the three-wattmeter method for measuring power, it was stated that when the potential coils do not have identical impedances, the three meters do not have equal readings, but their sum is still equal to the total power. Let us carry this idea to the extreme and make the impedance of one potential circuit equal zero. For example, suppose the potential coil of W_1 in Fig. 13-1 is short-circuited. This is the same as connecting the common junction of the wattmeters to line 1. Since there is no voltage across its potential coil, wattmeter 1 will read zero. It can therefore be removed from the circuit. This results in the two-wattmeter method for measuring power.

Figure 13-4 shows the two-wattmeter method for measuring the power taken by a balanced wye load of power factor θ. The phase

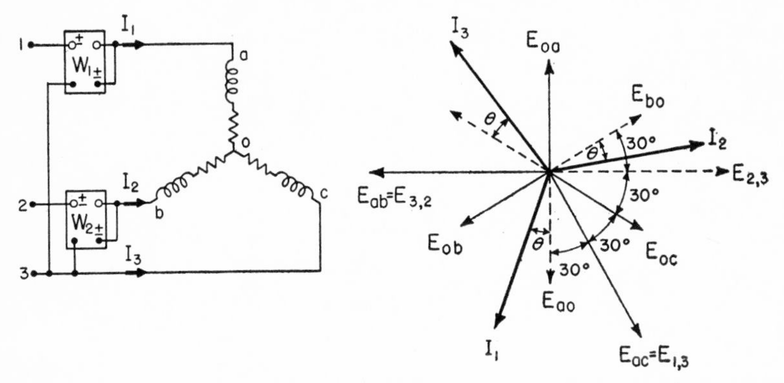

Fig. 13-4. The 2-wattmeter method of measuring power in a wye-load.

and line voltage relations are shown in the usual manner, with the phase voltages leading the respective line voltages by 30 degrees. The line currents I_1 and I_2 lag their respective phase voltages by the power factor, angle θ. The power indicated by wattmeter W_1 must be due to the torque that is produced by the current I_1 through its current coil and the voltage $E_{1,3}$ across its potential coil, with due consideration to their instantaneous values or time phase relations. In other words,

$$P_1 = E_{1,3} \times I_1 \times \cos \left. \frac{E_{1,3}}{I_1} \right]$$

The symbol $\cos \left.\frac{E_{1,3}}{I_1}\right]$ is used to indicate the cosine of the angle between $E_{1,3}$ and I_1. From the vector diagram it is obvious that this angle is $(30 + \theta)$ degrees. Also $E_{1,3}$ and I_1 are the line voltage and line current, respectively. Therefore

$$P_1 = E_L I_L \cos (30 + \theta)$$

Similarly, the power indicated by the meter W_2 is

$$P_2 = E_{2,3} \times I_2 \times \cos \left.\frac{E_{2,3}}{I_2}\right]$$

From the vector diagram this phase angle is seen to be $(30° - \theta)$. Again, since $E_{2,3}$ and I_2 are line values,

$$P_2 = E_L I_L \cos (30 - \theta)$$

In trigonometry it has been proved that the cosine of the sum of two angles α and β can be expressed as: $\cos (\alpha + \beta) = \cos \alpha \cos \beta - \sin \alpha \sin \beta$. Also the cosine of the difference between these two angles is: $\cos (\alpha - \beta) = \cos \alpha \cos \beta + \sin \alpha \sin \beta$. Now, if we add the two wattmeter readings, meanwhile replacing our cosine terms by their trigonometric equivalents, we get

$$P_T = P_1 + P_2 = E_L I_L(\cos 30 \cos \theta - \sin 30 \sin \theta) + E_L I_L(\cos 30 \cos \theta + \sin 30 \sin \theta)$$

Factoring out $E_L I_L$ and simplifying,

$$P_T = E_L I_L(2 \cos 30 \cos \theta)$$

But $\cos 30° = 0.866$ and $2 \cos 30° = 1.732 = \sqrt{3}$. Therefore

$$P_T = \sqrt{3}\, E_L I_L \cos \theta$$

But this is the equation for total power. In other words, the two-wattmeter method will give the true total power taken by the wye load.

Will this method measure total power in a delta-connected load? The answer is yes, it will. Analysis of a vector diagram for a delta load will reveal that the power indicated by each wattmeter will still be $E_L I_L \cos (30 + \theta)$ for one meter and $W_2 = E_L I_L \cos (30 - \theta)$ for the other. (The proof of this will be left as a student problem at the end of the chapter.) As was shown above, the sum of these two values equals the total power.

If the load is unbalanced, will the two-wattmeter method still measure the total power? The answer is again yes. The currents in the lines will change and the phase angles between line voltages and these currents will also change. These changes will affect the wattmeter indications and their sum will still be the total power.

Effect of power factor on the two-wattmeter readings. From the circuit shown in Fig. 13-4, our wattmeter indication for W_1 was $P_1 = E_L I_L \cos (30 + \theta)$, and for W_2 was $P_2 = E_L I_L \cos (30 - \theta)$. Had we used a leading power factor load, each current would have led its phase voltage by θ degrees, and the phase angles between line current and wattmeter potential coils would have been reversed. The reading for wattmeter W_1 would have been proportional to $\cos (30 - \theta)$, and that for wattmeter W_2 would have been proportional to $\cos (30 + \theta)$. Even with a lagging power-factor load—had we put the second wattmeter (W_2) into line 3, and used line 2 as the common junction point of the wattmeter potential coils—the cosine functions would have been reversed, and again the wattmeter indications would have been W_1 proportional to $\cos (30 - \theta)$ and W_2 proportional to $\cos (30 + \theta)$. The important point is that in any case one wattmeter reading is $E_L I_L \cos (30 - \theta)$ and the other is $E_L I_L \cos (30 + \theta)$.

Now let us examine the effect of the power factor angle on the relative wattmeter readings.

1. At unity power factor, $\theta = 0°$ and the two cosine functions reduce to $\cos 30°$. Both wattmeters read alike, each indicating one-half the power taken by the load.

2. For power factor angles between 0° and 30°:

(a) $(30 + \theta)$ approaches 60 degrees. This wattmeter reading decreases.

(b) $(30 - \theta)$ approaches zero degrees. This wattmeter reading increases. It is the higher reading wattmeter.

3. For power factor angles between 30° and 60°:

(a) $(30 + \theta)$ approaches 90 degrees. This wattmeter reading approaches zero.

(b) $(30 - \theta)$ increases from 0° to $-30°$. This wattmeter reading drops, but it is still the higher reading wattmeter.

4. For power factor angles between 60° and 90°:

(a) $(30 + \theta)$ increases from 90° to 120°. The numerical value of the cosine function increases, but it is now negative. The wattmeter reading begins to increase again, *but now its indication is negative* and must be subtracted from the indication of the other wattmeter to get the total power. (It will be necessary to reverse the current coil connections in order for the meter to indicate upscale.)

(b) $(30 - \theta)$ increases from $-30°$ to $-60°$. This wattmeter reading drops, but (except at a power factor angle of 90°) it is still the higher reading wattmeter.

5. At zero power factor, $\theta = 90°$; $(30 + \theta)$ is 120°; $(30 - \theta)$ is $-60°$; the two cosine values are equal in magnitude, and once more the two wattmeter readings are alike. However, since the $\cos(30 + \theta)$ is negative, the total power indication is zero. Such a condition, power factor angle of 90 degrees, can be obtained only with a pure reactive load and we know that in such a case no power is consumed by the load.

To summarize the above discussion, let us first recall that the power factor of a load is generally expressed as the cosine of the phase angle θ, (either as a decimal or a percentage) rather than as the angle itself. For example, when the phase angle θ is 60 degrees, the load has a power factor ($\cos\theta$) of 0.5 or 50%. With this in mind:

1. The wattmeter whose deflection is proportional to $(30 - \theta)$ is always positive and (except for unity or zero power factor) is always the higher-reading wattmeter.
2. The wattmeter whose deflection is proportional to $(30 + \theta)$ is positive only for power factors above 0.5, and is negative for power factors below 0.5. For a power factor of exactly 50% this wattmeter indication is zero.

Power factor from the two-wattmeter method. In the above discussion we saw that some idea of the power factor of the load could be obtained from the relative deflections of our two wattmeters. There are two methods by which this power factor can be determined accurately. One method is to take the ratio of the two wattmeter readings.

$$\frac{\text{lower WM reading}}{\text{higher WM reading}} = \frac{E_L I_L \cos(30 + \theta)}{E_L I_L \cos(30 - \theta)} = \frac{\cos(30 + \theta)}{\cos(30 - \theta)}$$

If we evaluate the ratio $\cos(30 + \theta)/\cos(30 - \theta)$ for several values of θ between 0 and 90 degrees and the corresponding power factor ($\cos \theta$) for each of these values of θ, we can plot a curve of wattmeter ratio versus power factor. Such a curve is shown in Fig. 13-5. Notice that this ratio is 1.0 at unity power factor since the wattmeter readings are equal; the ratio is zero at 0.5 power factor, since the lower-reading wattmeter indicates zero; that the ratios are negative for all lower power factors; and that the ratio is -1.0

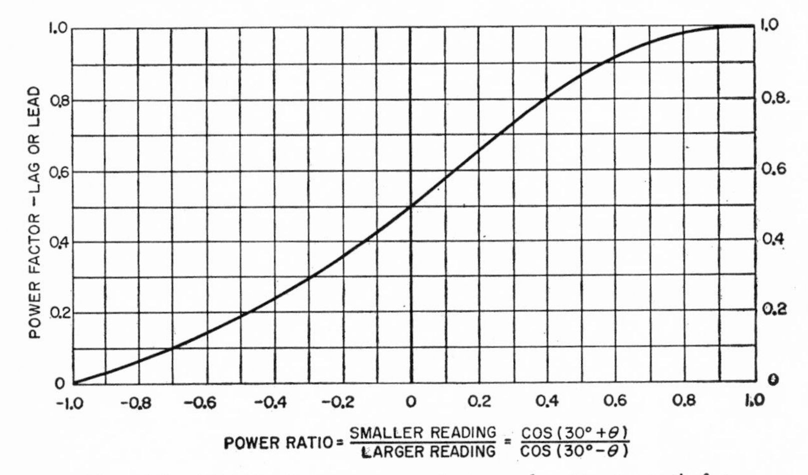

Fig. 13-5. Relation between power factor and wattmeter ratio for balanced 3ϕ loads.

at zero power factor since the wattmeter readings are again equal but the lower reading wattmeter gives reverse indication. From this curve it is a simple matter to find the power factor of a load when we know the individual wattmeter readings. Remember however, that this curve is applicable only for *balanced* loads when metered by the two-wattmeter method.

Such a curve as shown in Fig. 13-5 may not be available when needed. The power factor of the load can still be found mathematically. We have already shown that the sum of the two wattmeter readings is

$$P_1 + P_2 = \sqrt{3}\, E_L I_L \cos \theta$$

Now let us take the difference between the two readings, *subtracting the smaller reading from the larger.* Calling P_2 the higher wattmeter reading we get

$$P_2 - P_1 = E_L I_L \cos(30 - \theta) - E_L I_L \cos(30 + \theta)$$

Expanding by trigonometry,

$$P_2 - P_1 = E_L I_L(\cos 30 \cos\theta + \sin 30 \sin\theta) - E_L I_L(\cos 30 \cos\theta - \sin 30 \sin\theta)$$

Factoring out $E_L I_L$ and simplifying,

$$P_2 - P_1 = E_L I_L(2 \sin 30 \sin\theta)$$

But $\sin 30° = 0.5$ and $2 \sin 30° = 1.0$. Therefore

$$P_2 - P_1 = E_L I_L \sin\theta$$

Now let us take the ratio of the difference between wattmeter readings over sum of wattmeter readings.

$$\frac{P_2 - P_1}{P_2 + P_1} = \frac{E_L I_L \sin\theta}{\sqrt{3}\, E_L I_L \cos\theta} = \frac{\tan\theta}{\sqrt{3}}$$

$$\tan\theta = \sqrt{3}\,\frac{P_2 - P_1}{P_2 + P_1}$$

or

$$\theta = \text{arc tan } \sqrt{3}\,\frac{\text{algebraic difference between WM readings}}{\text{algebraic sum of WM readings}}$$

Example 3

A three-phase balanced load is metered by the two-wattmeter method. The wattmeter readings are 4.80 kw and −1.60 kw (meter current coil reversed). Find the power factor of the load.

Solution

1. $\theta = \text{arc tan } \sqrt{3}\,\dfrac{\text{algebraic difference between WM readings}}{\text{algebraic sum of WM readings}}$

$$= \text{arc tan } \sqrt{3}\,\frac{4.80 - (-1.60)}{4.80 + (-1.60)}$$

$$= \text{arc tan } \sqrt{3}\,\frac{6.40}{3.20} = \text{arc tan } 3.46 = 73.9°$$

2. $\text{PF} = \cos\theta = \cos 73.9° = 0.277$

Wattmeter connections: polarity marks. With single-phase loads, a wattmeter will deflect backward only if it is improperly connected. This is also true when the three-wattmeter method is used to measure power in a three-phase circuit. But in the discussion above on the two-wattmeter method of measuring power, we saw that the lower-reading wattmeter will reverse its deflection if the load power factor is less than 50%. So when a wattmeter gives a reverse indication, is it because of improper connection or low power factor? To avoid this ambiguity it is necessary to pay careful attention to the polarity marks ($\pm$) on the wattmeter terminals. The procedure recommended for connecting the wattmeters for the two-wattmeter method is as follows:

1. Connect each wattmeter in the proper manner, that is, the $\pm$ terminal of the current coil on the *line* side of the line lead, and the $\pm$ terminal of the potential coil to the same line as its own current coil.

2. Now if either wattmeter deflection is backward, it is an indication of low power factor. Therefore reverse its *current* coil connections and consider this reading a negative value.

Volt-amperes and reactive volt-amperes. Earlier in this text, when studying single-phase circuits we saw that, due to the power factor of the load, the product of voltage and current was not the true power of the circuit (except in the special case of a pure resistive load.) This product was therefore called the *volt-amperes* (va) of the circuit. Naturally, when either or both current and voltage are high in value, the larger unit kilovolt-amperes (kva) is used. Can we apply this same term to a three-phase load? *Yes, but only if it is a balanced load.* Since the power in such a load is $P = \sqrt{3}\, E_L I_L \cos\theta$, if we remove the power factor term, we are left with the volt-amperes of the circuit.

$$\text{va} = \sqrt{3}\, E_L I_L = \frac{\text{watts}}{\cos\theta}$$

Again, using the single-phase circuit for comparison, since the reactive volt-amperes (var or kvar) was the product of voltage, current, and the *sine* of the phase angle, for the balanced three-phase circuit we have

$$\text{var} = \sqrt{3}\, E_L I_L \sin\theta$$

EXAMPLE 4

A balanced load draws 48 amps from a 440-v line at 80% power factor. Find the power, volt-amperes, and reactive volt-amperes of the load.

SOLUTION

1. $P = \sqrt{3}\, E_L I_L \cos\theta = \sqrt{3} \times 440 \times 48 \times 0.8 = 29.3$ kw
2. Volt-amperes $= \sqrt{3}\, E_L I_L = \sqrt{3} \times 440 \times 48 = 36.7$ kva

or 2A. Volt-amperes $= \dfrac{\text{watts}}{\cos\theta} = \dfrac{29.3 \text{ kw}}{0.8} = 36.7$ kva

3. $\cos\theta = 0.8$, $\theta = 36.9°$, and $\sin\theta = 0.6$
4. Reactive volt-amperes = volt-amperes $\times \sin\theta$
$= 36.7 \times 0.6 = 22.0$ kvar

Advantages of the three-phase system. By now you may be wondering why all this fuss over a three-phase distribution system? If a dual voltage system is needed, why not use a single-phase three-wire system such as a 240/120-v three-wire supply? Offhand it might seem that the single-phase system requiring one less wire (two wires for single supply voltage or three wires for dual supply voltage, as compared with three-phase three-wire or three-phase four-wire) would be better. But let us examine these two systems from their relative power and current relations.

$$\text{power (single-phase)} = E_L I_L \cos\theta$$
$$\text{power (three-phase)} = \sqrt{3}\, E_L I_L \cos\theta$$

For the same line voltage and line current, the three-phase system will deliver 1.73, or $\sqrt{3}$ times as much power. Therefore with only one extra wire the transmission lines can deliver almost double the power. Another way of looking at this is that for a given total load, since the line current is lower, smaller wires can be used in a three-phase system. To transmit a given amount of power with equal line loss, (over a fixed distance and with equal line voltage) the three-phase system requires only 75 per cent as much copper as a single-phase system.

Another advantage of the three-phase distribution system becomes of major importance when large motors are needed. Three-phase motors are easier to start, are simpler in construction, have higher efficiencies, require less maintenance, and have smoother torque characteristics than single-phase machines. (Discussion of machine characteristics will be left to texts on machinery.) Although a single-phase motor can be used directly on a three-phase system, the converse cannot be done without expensive conversion equipment.

Review Problems

1. A balanced three-phase delta load draws 120 amps from a 240-v three-phase supply, at a power factor of 0.74 leading. Find the power taken by the load.

2. Repeat Problem 1, if the phase current is 120 amps.

3. Find the power taken by a balanced three-phase wye-connected load if the line current is 85 amps, line voltage is 220 v, and the power factor of the load is 0.68 lagging.

4. Three loads, each having a resistance of 40 ohms and an inductive reactance of 30 ohms, are connected in wye across a 230-v, three-phase, 60-cycle supply. Find the power taken by the load.

5. Repeat Problem 4 for the loads connected in delta.

6. A balanced three-phase delta load draws 300 amps from a 440-v three-phase supply. If the power taken by the load is 200 kw, find the power factor of the load.

7. A 150-hp three-phase induction motor draws 126 amps from a 660-v three-phase supply at a power factor of 0.85 when operating at full load. Find the efficiency of the motor.

8. A three-phase alternator has the following rating per phase: current 60 amps, voltage 230 v. Find the rated line current, line voltage, and power output at 80% power factor for

(a) Delta connection. (b) Wye connection.

9. The nameplate on a three-phase alternator gives the following ratings: phase—3; cycles—60; volts—2200; amperes—(defaced); speed—1200 rpm; kw—400; power factor—0.8. Find the current rating for this machine.

10. A balanced three-phase load draws 60 amps from a 440-v three-phase supply. The phase angle between line current and line voltage is 30 degrees. Find the power taken by the load. (Give two possible answers.)

11. Can the equation $P_T = \sqrt{3}\, E_L I_L \cos\theta$ be used to find the power taken by an unbalanced load? Give two reasons to support your answer.

12. Draw a schematic diagram showing the use of three wattmeters to measure the power taken by a three-phase load. Indicate wattmeter terminal polarity marks.

13. Draw the vector diagram for current and voltage relations in a balanced three-phase delta load, for a power factor angle of θ degrees, (current) leading. Prove that the power measured by any one wattmeter is the phase power.

14. (a) Draw a schematic diagram showing the one-wattmeter method of measuring power taken by a three-phase load.

(b) Can this method be used for unbalanced loads? Explain.

(c) Can a Y-box be used with any wattmeter? Explain.

15. Draw a schematic diagram showing the two-wattmeter method for measuring power in a three-phase load.

16. (a) Draw the vector diagram for current and voltage relations in a balanced delta load for a power factor angle of θ degrees, lagging.

(b) Prove that the two-wattmeter method will measure the total power taken by the load.

17. The power taken by a three-phase induction motor (delta-connected, balanced load) is checked using the two-wattmeter method. The wattmeter readings are 8.8 kw and 4.0 kw. The supply is three-phase 230-v.

(a) Calculate the power factor of the load.

(b) Check by finding the power factor from the curve in Fig. 13-5.

(c) Find the line and phase current values.

18. A three-phase induction motor draws a line current of 50 amps from a 220-v line at 40% power factor while starting. The two-wattmeter method is used to measure the power taken by the motor. Find the reading indicated by each wattmeter.

19. A balanced three-phase wye-connected load is connected across a 208-v three-phase supply. The two wattmeters used to measure the power taken by the load indicate 4.6 kw and −2.4 kw.

(a) Find the power factor of the load.

(b) Find the current in each phase.

20. A balanced three-phase delta load draws a current of 95 amps from a 208-v, 60-cycle three-phase supply at a power factor of 0.8 lagging. Find (a) kva of the load; (b) power taken by the load; (c) kvar of the load.

21. Repeat Problem 20 for a load drawing 120 amps at a power factor of 70% lagging.

22. If the loads of Problems 20 and 21 are combined, find (a) total kva; (b) total power; (c) total kvar.

23. It is desired to raise the power factor of the load in Problem 22 to unity, by adding a three-phase delta-connected pure capacitive load.

(a) Find the reactive kva needed

(b) Find the capacitance value needed per phase.

24. Repeat Problem 23 if the power factor is raised only to 90%.

25. What are the advantages of a three-phase system over a single-phase system (a) to the utility company; (b) to the consumer?

CHAPTER 14

Unbalanced Three-Phase Loads

IN AN earlier chapter we saw that a three-phase system could be used to supply three-phase loads or individual single-phase loads. The discussions and problems so far have all been with respect to loads having identical impedance per phase. This resulted in balanced loads. What are the chances of such a condition occurring in actual practice? Three-phase equipment, such as motors, are balanced loads, but when we add lights, appliances, and other single-phase loads on the system, the balance is lost. Homes are generally supplied with single-phase service. The power company tries to obtain a balanced load by equalizing the number of homes on each phase of its three-phase supply. Industrial consumers are generally supplied with all three lines and neutral. The internal wiring is then planned to attempt to distribute the single-phase loads equally between neutral and each of the three lines. However, any such measures, no matter how carefully planned, can prevent only drastic unbalance. In dealing with unbalanced circuits, the same basic principles discussed in the previous chapters are employed. The problems are more tedious, and careful attention must be paid to phase relations.

Unbalanced delta loads. Whenever dissimilar loads are connected across the lines of a three-phase supply, an unbalanced delta load will result, with the phase currents as the individual load currents. Since the currents in each load are not equal in magnitude and/or phase, the three line currents will be unbalanced. Each load (phase) current can be found from the line (phase) voltage and load impedance. The line currents can then be found from the vector addition of the appropriate load currents.

EXAMPLE 1

Three loads Z_1 = 31 ohms resistance and 59 ohms inductive reactance, Z_2 = 30 ohms resistance and 40 ohms capacitive reactance, and Z_3 = 80 ohms resistance and 60 ohms inductive reactance are connected one each across the lines of a 200-v three-phase supply. Find the line current.

SOLUTION

1. Draw a diagram of the circuit and a vector diagram of the line voltages (see Fig. 14-1).

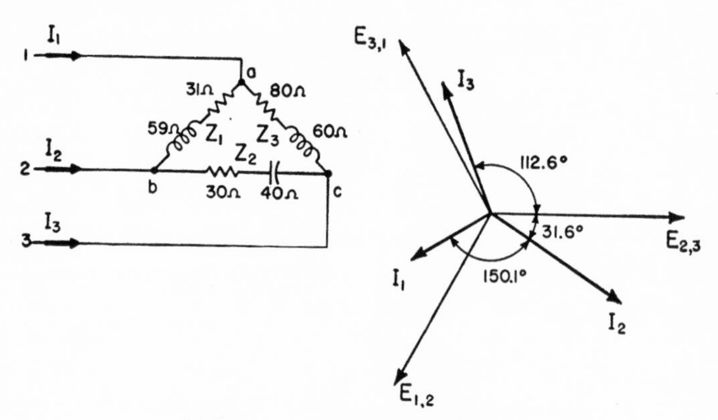

Fig. 14-1. Unbalanced delta load.

2. Express each voltage in vector form

(a) $E_{1,2} = 200\underline{/-120°}$

(b) $E_{2,3} = 200\underline{/0°}$

(c) $E_{3,1} = 200\underline{/120°}$

3. Express each impedance in vector form

(a) $Z_1 = 31 + j59 = 66.7\underline{/62.3°}$

(b) $Z_2 = 30 - j40 = 50.0\underline{/-53.1°}$

(c) $Z_3 = 80 + j60 = 100\underline{/36.9°}$

4. Solve for each phase current.

(a) $I_{ab} = \dfrac{E_{1,2}}{Z_1} = \dfrac{200\underline{/-120}}{66.7\underline{/62.3}} = 3.0\underline{/-182.3°}$

(b) $I_{bc} = \dfrac{E_{2,3}}{Z_2} = \dfrac{200\underline{/0}}{50.0\underline{/53.1}} = 4.0\underline{/-53.1°}$

(c) $I_{ca} = \dfrac{E_{3,1}}{Z_3} = \dfrac{200\underline{/120}}{100\underline{/36.9}} = 2.0\underline{/83.1°}$

5. Convert these current values to rectangular form.

(a) $3.0\underline{/-182.3°} = -3.0 \cos 2.3° + j3.0 \sin 2.3°$

$I_{ab} = -3.0 + j0.12$

(b) $4.0\underline{/-53.1^\circ} = 4.0 \cos 53.1^\circ - j4.0 \sin 53.1^\circ$

$$I_{bc} = 2.40 - j3.20$$

(c) $2.0\underline{/83.1^\circ} = 2.0 \cos 83.1^\circ + j2.0 \sin 83.1^\circ$

$$I_{ca} = 0.24 + j1.98$$

6. Find the line currents.

(a)
$$\begin{array}{rr} I_1 = I_{ab} - I_{ca} = & -3.0 \quad + j0.12 \\ & \overline{\oplus}0.24\ \overline{\oplus}\ j1.98 \\ \hline & -3.24 - j1.86 \end{array}$$

$$= 3.74\underline{/-150.1^\circ}$$

(b)
$$\begin{array}{rr} I_2 = I_{bc} - I_{ab} = & 2.40 - j3.20 \\ & \overset{+}{\ominus}3.0\ \overline{\oplus}\ j0.12 \\ \hline & 5.40 - j3.32 \end{array}$$

$$= 6.44\underline{/-31.6^\circ}$$

(c)
$$\begin{array}{rr} I_3 = I_{ca} - I_{bc} = & 0.24 + j1.98 \\ & \overline{\oplus}2.40\ \overline{\oplus}\ j3.20 \\ \hline & -2.16 + j5.18 \end{array}$$

$$= 5.60\underline{/112.6^\circ}$$

7. To complete the vector diagram, add these line currents to Fig. 14-1.

Unbalanced wye load, with neutral. In a three-phase four-wire distribution system, as described in a previous chapter, the line voltage commonly used is 208 volts, and the voltage from any line to neutral is 120 volts. Lighting loads and 120-v appliances will be connected between line and neutral. Except as a rare coincidence this will result in an unbalanced wye load. Again line currents will be unbalanced, and due to the unbalance, the neutral wire will also carry some current. Since the voltage between any line and neutral is fixed at $E_L/\sqrt{3}$, it is a simple matter to calculate the individual phase currents. As in any wye system, each line current will be equal to the current in the phase that it feeds. Now with an unbalanced condition, these phase currents (and line currents) are not identical, and their vector sum does not equal zero. This vector sum must be the current flowing in the neutral wire.

EXAMPLE 2

A 208/120-v three-phase, four-wire system has the following loads: Z_1 = 8 ohms resistance and 6 ohms inductive reactance, Z_2 = 12 ohms resistance, and Z_3 = 12 ohms resistance and 16 ohms capacitive reactance. The loads are connected between line and neutral with each load on a separate line. Find line currents and neutral current.

SOLUTION

1. Draw a diagram of the circuit and a vector diagram of the phase voltages (line to neutral) (see Fig. 14-2).

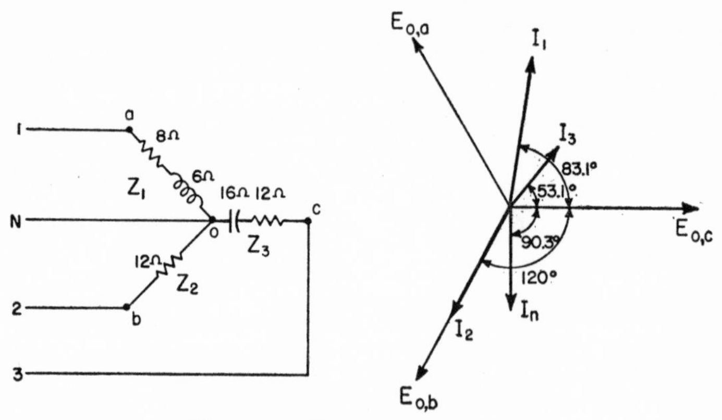

Fig. 14-2. Unbalanced wye load.

2. Express each phase voltage in vector form.

(a) $E_{oa} = 120\underline{/120°}$

(b) $E_{ob} = 120\underline{/-120°}$

(c) $E_{oc} = 120\underline{/0°}$

3. Express each impedance in vector form.

(a) $Z_1 = 8 + j6 = 10\underline{/36.9°}$

(b) $Z_2 = 12 + j0 = 12\underline{/0°}$

(c) $Z_3 = 12 - j16 = 20\underline{/-53.1°}$

4. Solve for each phase (and line) current.

(a) $I_1 = \dfrac{E_{oa}}{Z_1} = \dfrac{120\underline{/120}}{10\underline{/36.9}} = 12\underline{/83.1°}$

(b) $I_2 = \dfrac{E_{ob}}{Z_2} = \dfrac{120\underline{/-120}}{12\underline{/0}} = 10\underline{/-120°}$

(c) $I_3 = \dfrac{E_{oc}}{Z_3} = \dfrac{120\underline{/0}}{20\underline{/-53.1}} = 6\underline{/53.1°}$

5. Draw these currents on the vector diagram.

6. To find the neutral current, we must add the three line currents. The neutral current must then be equal and *opposite* to this sum, so that the total current at the junction will be zero. But first we must express these currents in rectangular form.

(a) $I_1 = -12 \cos 83.1° + j12 \sin 83.1°$
$= 1.44 + j11.9$

(b) $I_2 = -10 \cos 60° - j10 \sin 60°$
$= -5.0 - j8.66$

(c) $I_3 = 6 \cos 53.1° + j6 \sin 53.1°$
$= 3.6 + j4.8$

(d) $I_1 + I_2 + I_3 =$

$$\begin{array}{r} 1.44 + j11.9 \\ -5.00 + j8.66 \\ 3.60 + j4.80 \\ \hline 0.04 + j8.04 \end{array}$$

(e) $I_n = -(0.04 + j8.04)$
$= 8.04\underline{/-90.3°}$

7. Add this current to the vector diagram.

In commercial applications with a three-phase four-wire system the actual loading will consist of a combination of:

(a) balanced three-phase loads, wye or delta.
(b) unbalanced delta loads due to single-phase loads connected across the line.
(c) unbalanced wye loads due to single-phase loads connected from any line to neutral.

Problems of this type are much more tedious, since each type of load must be handled separately and the resulting line currents, for each type of load, must then be added vectorially to get the total line currents. It would be similar to solving four problems: a balanced delta, a balanced wye (covered in Chapter 12), and the unbalanced delta and unbalanced wye as shown above.

Unbalanced wye load, no neutral. To complete the discussion on unbalanced loads, one other type of load must be mentioned. It is the unbalanced wye load, shown above, but without interconnection between the common point of the wye load and the neutral wire of the supply line. Problems of this type are purely academic and have little practical significance. Such a load situation could arise only with a three-phase, four-wire system and single-phase loads connected between line and neutral if the connection between the supply line neutral and the 'local neutral' is broken. This is really a faulty or improper operation and calls for repairs. In fact, the neutral wire in commercial operation is never fused, otherwise a blown fuse could create this situation.

However, let us analyze what would happen if the neutral connection were opened.

If the load were balanced, the vector sum of the three line currents at the common junction of load, or local neutral, would be zero. There is no current in the local neutral wire, and therefore no adverse effect is created by the break between local neutral and supply-line neutral. Meanwhile, since the wye branch impedances are identical, the voltage drops across each wye load are equal, and E_p remains $E_L/\sqrt{3}$. In other words, for a balanced load, operation remains the same with or without the neutral connection.

Now let us consider what would happen with an unbalanced load, if the tie between local neutral and supply line neutral were opened. In Example 2 we saw that since the vector sum of the line currents did not equal zero, an unbalance current flows in the neutral wire. Now the neutral wire is open and current cannot flow in an open line. But neither can current pile up at the local neutral. There is only one possible answer—the individual line currents must change so that their vector sum becomes zero. This does not imply, however, that the currents are identical. A vector sum of zero can be obtained with unequal line currents.

The question now is: What makes the currents change? Since the loads themselves have not changed, the voltage across each load must change. That is exactly what happens. Remember that these loads are connected from one line to neutral, and that the voltage from any line to neutral is fixed at $E_L/\sqrt{3}$ only when the neutral wire is intact. With the neutral wire open, a *floating neutral* is created and the potential of the local neutral will depend on the impedances of the loads. The three phase voltages are unbalanced in magnitude and in phase, and it is quite possible for one phase voltage to exceed the line voltage. Such a condition is definitely undesirable. Some loads will operate inefficiently because of low voltage, while other equipment may be damaged because of overvoltage.

Since loads of this type are not normally encountered in practical applications, the solution of such problems will not be discussed in this text.

Review Problems

1. A three-phase 220-v, 60-cycle supply has the following single-phase loads: Z_1, 80 ohms inductive reactance across lines 1 and 2; Z_2, 60 ohms resistance across lines 2 and 3; Z_3, 100 ohms capacitive reactance across lines 3 and 1. Using a phase sequence of $E_{1,2}$, $E_{2,3}$, $E_{3,1}$, and $E_{1,2}$ as reference, calculate the three line currents (magnitude and phase). Draw the vector diagram.

2. Repeat Problem 1 for a line voltage of 440-v and loads of Z_1 = 20 ohms resistance and 30 ohms inductive reactance, Z_2 = 40 ohms resistance and 50 ohms inductive reactance, Z_3 = 10 ohms resistance and 30 ohms inductive reactance.

3. Repeat Problem 1 for a line voltage of 208 v and loads of Z_1 = 30 ohms resistance and 40 ohms capacitive reactance, Z_2 = 45 ohms resistive, Z_3 = 20 ohms resistance and 15 ohms inductive reactance.

4. Repeat Problem 1 for a line voltage of 208 v and loads of Z_1 = 26 ohms resistance, Z_2 = open circuit, Z_3 = 0.1 henry and 12 ohms resistance.

5. In each of the following cases, the supply is a three-phase, four-wire, 208-v, 60-cycle supply. The phase sequence is $E_{1,2}$, $E_{3,1}$, $E_{2,3}$. The loads are single-phase and connected between line and neutral, with Z_1 from line 1 to neutral, Z_2 from line 2 to neutral, and Z_3 from line 3 to neutral. Find the line currents and draw the vector diagram for

(a) Load values as in Problem 1.
(b) Load values as in Problem 2.
(c) Load values as in Problem 3.
(d) Load values as in Problem 4.

6. A three-phase, four-wire, 208-v, 60-cycle supply is feeding three single-phase line-to-line loads, and three single-phase line-to-neutral loads as follows:

$Z_{1,2}$ = 8 ohms resistance and 10 ohms capacitive reactance.
$Z_{2,3}$ = 4 ohms resistance and 12 ohms inductive reactance.
$Z_{3,1}$ = 6 ohms resistance and 12 ohms inductive reactance.
$Z_{0,1}$ = 16 ohms resistance.
$Z_{0,2}$ = 20 ohms resistance and 16 ohms inductive reactance.
$Z_{0,3}$ = 15 ohms resistance and 25 ohms capacitive reactance.

Using a phase sequence of $E_{1,2}$, $E_{2,3}$, $E_{3,1}$, find the magnitude and phase angle of the current in each of the four lines. Draw the vector diagram.

7. Repeat Problem 6 for

$Z_{1,2}$ = 20 ohms resistance and 16 ohms inductive reactance.
$Z_{2,3}$ = 15 ohms resistance and 25 ohms capacitive reactance.
$Z_{3,1}$ = 16 ohms resistance.
$Z_{0,1}$ = 6 ohms resistance and 12 ohms inductive reactance.
$Z_{0,2}$ = 8 ohms resistance and 10 ohms capacitive reactance.
$Z_{0,3}$ = 4 ohms resistance and 12 ohms inductive reactance.

APPENDIX 1

Trigonometry

ANY THREE SIDED FIGURE is called a *triangle*—because it includes three angles. All the angles of the triangle may be acute angles (less than 90°); or one of the angles may be exactly 90°; or one of the angles may be an obtuse angle (greater than 90°). In all cases, however, the sum of the angles in any triangle is equal to 180°. Three such typical triangles are shown in Fig. A-1.

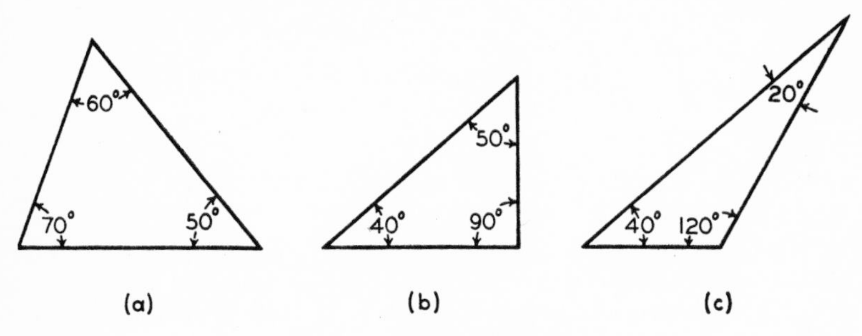

Fig. A-1. Typical triangles.

Solution of problems in technical fields often requires the addition or subtraction of vector quantities—for example, forces or velocities in mechanics; voltages, currents, or impedances in electricity and electronics. These problems can be solved mathematically by the use of trigonometry. Although there are trigonometric formulas and methods for handling acute and obtuse triangles [such as (a) and (c) in Fig. A-1], it is distinctly preferable in electrical problems to use *right-triangle methods* throughout. Any other triangle can be resolved into equivalent right triangles. This discussion and the formulas that follow are based on right-triangle principles.

Lines *A-B-C* and *A-D-E* in Fig. A-2 form an angle at their junction. If you measure this angle with a protractor, you will find that it is 25°. *Regardless of the lengths of these lines* (*A-B-C* and *A-D-E*), *this angle does not change.*

From points *B* and *C* let us drop two perpendicular lines down to the base line to form right angles at *D* and *E* respectively. Now we have formed two right triangles *B-A-D* and *C-A-E*. Remembering that the sum of the angles of any triangle is 180°, and since these triangles have a common angle of 25° and a right angle of 90° (at D and E), the remaining angle (at B and C) must in each case be 65°. These two triangles are said to be *similar triangles*. (Any two triangles whose angles are equal are called similar triangles). This is true regardless of the over-all size of the triangles.

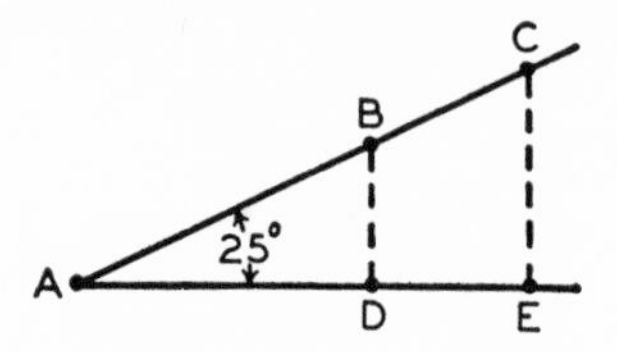

Fig. A-2. Formation of right triangle.

Whenever triangles are similar, the ratio of any two sides of one triangle is equal to the ratio of the corresponding two sides of the other triangle. For example in Fig. A-2:

$$\frac{BD}{AD} = \frac{CE}{AE} = \text{a constant}$$

also

$$\frac{BD}{AB} = \frac{CE}{AC} = \text{another constant}$$

and

$$\frac{AD}{AB} = \frac{AE}{AC} = \text{another constant}$$

The values of these constants depends only on the size of the angle at A. (Of course, it must be realized that if this angle is increased, the angles at B and C must decrease, because the sum of all three angles must remain 180°). In other words, we could also have said that the value of the ratio constant also depends on the size of the angles at B or C.

For any given right triangle we therefore have three different constants depending on which two sides we use for our ratio. Also, the value of these constants varies with the size of the angles—or is a function of the angle. In order to identify which of the three ratios we are referring to at any one time, the ratios are specified by naming the three functions of the angle: the *sine*, the *cosine*, and the *tangent* of the angle.

Figure A-3 shows a typical right triangle. The Greek letter theta (θ) is used to identify the angle under discussion in this triangle. Let us evaluate the constants for this angle. Remember that the actual size of the triangle does not matter as long as angle θ is of fixed value. First let us give appropriate names to the sides of this triangle:

1. The side opposite the 90° angle (A-B) is always called the HYPOTENUSE.

2. Side A-C is called the side ADJACENT. Of course the hypotenuse is also an adjacent side—but it already has its own name. There should be no confusion as to which side we mean by adjacent.

3. Side B-C, since it is opposite to the angle under discussion, is called the side OPPOSITE.

Obviously if we were discussing the angle at B, the hypotenuse would remain the same, but the side adjacent and side opposite would be reversed. Now let us evaluate our functions of angle θ. By definition:

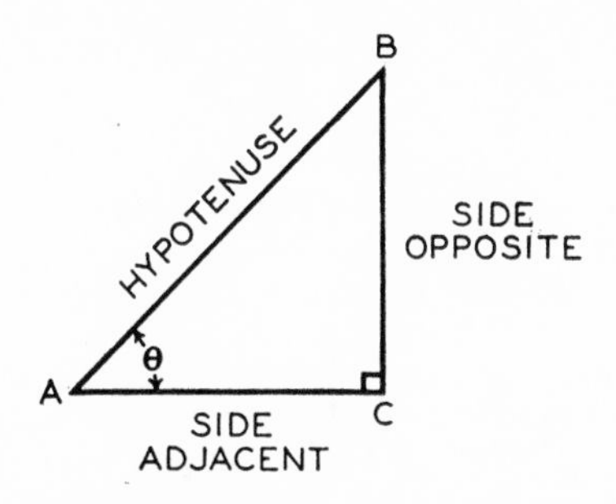

Fig. A-3. Evaluation of trigonometric functions of a right triangle.

(a) The *sine* of an angle is the ratio of the length of the side opposite to the length of the hypotenuse, or

$$\sin\,\theta = \frac{\text{opposite}}{\text{hypotenuse}}$$

(b) The *cosine* of an angle is the ratio of the length of the side adjacent to the length of the hypotenuse, or

$$\cos\,\theta = \frac{\text{adjacent}}{\text{hypotenuse}}$$

(c) The *tangent* of an angle is the ratio of the length of the side opposite to the length of the side adjacent, or

$$\tan\,\theta = \frac{\text{opposite}}{\text{adjacent}}$$

We know that the value of the above ratios depends *not* on the size of the triangle but only on the size of the angles. The question now is in what manner do these functions vary with size of angle? Let us check this relation for angles between zero and 90°. Figure A-4 shows four triangles all with hypotenuses of equal length. Let us make this length 10 units. What's that? You only see two triangles? Well just wait a minute and you will see all four.

1. *For $\theta = 0°$* (θ_1)—The triangle automatically collapses into a straight line. The hypotenuse is O-C; the adjacent side is also O-C; and side opposite is *zero*.

(a) $\sin\,\theta_1 = \dfrac{\text{opposite}}{\text{hypotenuse}} = \dfrac{0}{10} = 0.000$

(b) $\cos\,\theta_1 = \dfrac{\text{adjacent}}{\text{hypotenuse}} = \dfrac{10}{10} = 1.000$

(c) $\tan\,\theta_1 = \dfrac{\text{opposite}}{\text{adjacent}} = \dfrac{0}{10} = 0.000$

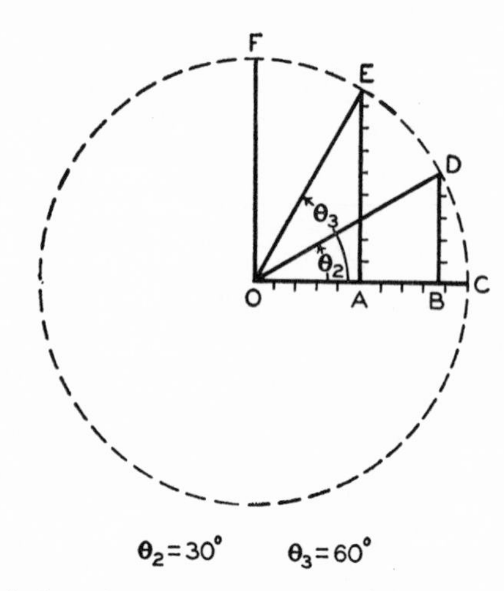

Fig. A-4. Variation of trigonometric functions from zero to 90 degrees.

2. *For* $\theta = 30°$ (θ_2)—The hypotenuse is now *O-D* (still 10 units); the side opposite has increased to *B-D* (5.00 units); the side adjacent has decreased to *O-B* (8.66 units).

(a) $\sin\,\theta_2 = \dfrac{\text{opposite}}{\text{hypotenuse}} = \dfrac{5.00}{10} = 0.500$

(b) $\cos\,\theta_2 = \dfrac{\text{adjacent}}{\text{hypotenuse}} = \dfrac{8.66}{10} = 0.866$

(c) $\tan\,\theta_2 = \dfrac{\text{opposite}}{\text{adjacent}} = \dfrac{5.00}{8.66} = 0.577$

3. *For* $\theta = 60°$ (θ_3)—The hypotenuse *O-E* is 10 units; the side opposite *A-E* is 8.66 units; side adjacent *O-A* is 5.00 units.

(a) $\sin\,\theta_3 = \dfrac{\text{opposite}}{\text{hypotenuse}} = \dfrac{8.66}{10} = 0.866$

(b) $\cos\theta_3 = \dfrac{\text{adjacent}}{\text{hypotenuse}} = \dfrac{5.00}{10} = 0.500$

(c) $\tan\theta_3 = \dfrac{\text{opposite}}{\text{adjacent}} = \dfrac{8.66}{5.00} = 1.732$

4. *For* $\theta = 90°$ (θ_4)—Again the triangle collapses into a straight line (*O-F*). The hypotenuse *O-F* is 10 units; the side opposite is also *O-F* (10 units); the side adjacent is now zero.

(a) $\sin\theta_4 = \dfrac{\text{opposite}}{\text{hypotenuse}} = \dfrac{10}{10} = 1.000$

(b) $\cos\theta_4 = \dfrac{\text{adjacent}}{\text{hypotenuse}} = \dfrac{0}{10} = 0.000$

(c) $\tan\theta_4 = \dfrac{\text{opposite}}{\text{adjacent}} = \dfrac{10}{0} = \text{infinite } (\infty)$

To summarize, as the angle increases from zero to 90 degrees:

1. The sine of the angle *increases* from zero to a maximum of 1.0.
2. The cosine of the angle *decreases* from 1.0 to zero.
3. The tangent of the angle *increases* from zero to infinity.

Notice in the above illustrations, that the sine of 30° is the same as the cosine of 60°. This same coincidence will be found for any other pair of angles whose sum is 90° (complementary angles). For example, the sine of 15° would equal the cosine of 75°.

To find the trigonometric functions or constants for angles of any value, we could of course draw the angle accurately, construct a right triangle, scale each side accurately, and get the ratios of the sides. This is laborious, and the graphical results are not too accurate. Luckily this work has all been done, and these values can be found in published tables of trigonometric function (see Appendix 2).

These are many other triangle relations covered in a complete course in trigonometry. However only one other relation is of importance in electrical or electronic work. It is the relationship between the length of the three sides of a right triangle, or the *theorem of Phythagoras:*

> *The square of the hypotenuse is equal to the sum of the squares of the other two sides.*

Expressing this theorem mathematically, if c is the hypotenuse, and a and b are the other two sides of a right triangle, then

$$c^2 = a^2 + b^2$$

from which

$$c = \sqrt{a^2 + b^2}$$

$$b = \sqrt{c^2 - a^2}$$

$$a = \sqrt{c^2 - b^2}$$

APPENDIX 2

Natural Sines, Cosines and Tangents

0°–14.9°

Degs.	Function	0.0°	0.1°	0.2°	0.3°	0.4°	0.5°	0.6°	0.7°	0.8°	0.9°
0	sin	0.0000	0.0017	0.0035	0.0052	0.0070	0.0087	0.0105	0.0122	0.0140	0.0157
	cos	1.0000	1.0000	1.0000	1.0000	1.0000	1.0000	0.9999	0.9999	0.9999	0.9999
	tan	0.0000	0.0017	0.0035	0.0052	0.0070	0.0087	0.0105	0.0122	0.0140	0.0157
1	sin	0.0175	0.0192	0.0209	0.0227	0.0244	0.0262	0.0279	0.0297	0.0314	0.0332
	cos	0.9998	0.9998	0.9998	0.9997	0.9997	0.9997	0.9996	0.9996	0.9995	0.9995
	tan	0.0175	0.0192	0.0209	0.0227	0.0244	0.0262	0.0279	0.0297	0.0314	0.0332
2	sin	0.0349	0.0366	0.0384	0.0401	0.0419	0.0436	0.0454	0.0471	0.0488	0.0506
	cos	0.9994	0.9993	0.9993	0.9992	0.9991	0.9990	0.9990	0.9989	0.9988	0.9987
	tan	0.0349	0.0367	0.0384	0.0402	0.0419	0.0437	0.0454	0.0472	0.0489	0.0507
3	sin	0.0523	0.0541	0.0558	0.0576	0.0593	0.0610	0.0628	0.0645	0.0663	0.0680
	cos	0.9986	0.9985	0.9984	0.9983	0.9982	0.9981	0.9980	0.9979	0.9978	0.9977
	tan	0.0524	0.0542	0.0559	0.0577	0.0594	0.0612	0.0629	0.0647	0.0664	0.0682
4	sin	0.0698	0.0715	0.0732	0.0750	0.0767	0.0785	0.0802	0.0819	0.0837	0.0854
	cos	0.9976	0.9974	0.9973	0.9972	0.9971	0.9969	0.9968	0.9966	0.9965	0.9963
	tan	0.0699	0.0717	0.0734	0.0752	0.0769	0.0787	0.0805	0.0822	0.0840	0.0857
5	sin	0.0872	0.0889	0.0906	0.0924	0.0941	0.0958	0.0976	0.0993	0.1011	0.1028
	cos	0.9962	0.9960	0.9959	0.9957	0.9956	0.9954	0.9952	0.9951	0.9949	0.9947
	tan	0.0875	0.0892	0.0910	0.0928	0.0945	0.0963	0.0981	0.0998	0.1016	0.1033
6	sin	0.1045	0.1063	0.1080	0.1097	0.1115	0.1132	0.1149	0.1167	0.1184	0.1201
	cos	0.9945	0.9943	0.9942	0.9940	0.9938	0.9936	0.9934	0.9932	0.9930	0.9928
	tan	0.1051	0.1069	0.1086	0.1104	0.1122	0.1139	0.1157	0.1175	0.1192	0.1210
7	sin	0.1219	0.1236	0.1253	0.1271	0.1288	0.1305	0.1323	0.1340	0.1357	0.1374
	cos	0.9925	0.9923	0.9921	0.9919	0.9917	0.9914	0.9912	0.9910	0.9907	0.9905
	tan	0.1228	0.1246	0.1263	0.1281	0.1299	0.1317	0.1334	0.1352	0.1370	0.1388
8	sin	0.1392	0.1409	0.1426	0.1444	0.1461	0.1478	0.1495	0.1513	0.1530	0.1547
	cos	0.9903	0.9900	0.9898	0.9895	0.9893	0.9890	0.9888	0.9885	0.9882	0.9880
	tan	0.1405	0.1423	0.1441	0.1459	0.1477	0.1495	0.1512	0.1530	0.1548	0.1566
9	sin	0.1564	0.1582	0.1599	0.1616	0.1633	0.1650	0.1668	0.1685	0.1702	0.1719
	cos	0.9877	0.9874	0.9871	0.9869	0.9866	0.9863	0.9860	0.9857	0.9854	0.9851
	tan	0.1584	0.1602	0.1620	0.1638	0.1655	0.1673	0.1691	0.1709	0.1727	0.1745
10	sin	0.1736	0.1754	0.1771	0.1788	0.1805	0.1822	0.1840	0.1857	0.1874	0.1891
	cos	0.9848	0.9845	0.9842	0.9839	0.9836	0.9833	0.9829	0.9826	0.9823	0.9820
	tan	0.1763	0.1781	0.1799	0.1817	0.1835	0.1853	0.1871	0.1890	0.1908	0.1926
11	sin	0.1908	0.1925	0.1942	0.1959	0.1977	0.1994	0.2011	0.2028	0.2045	0.2062
	cos	0.9816	0.9813	0.9810	0.9806	0.9803	0.9799	0.9796	0.9792	0.9789	0.9785
	tan	0.1944	0.1962	0.1980	0.1998	0.2016	0.2035	0.2053	0.2071	0.2089	0.2107
12	sin	0.2079	0.2096	0.2113	0.2130	0.2147	0.2164	0.2181	0.2198	0.2215	0.2232
	cos	0.9781	0.9778	0.9774	0.9770	0.9767	0.9763	0.9759	0.9755	0.9751	0.9748
	tan	0.2126	0.2144	0.2162	0.2180	0.2199	0.2217	0.2235	0.2254	0.2272	0.2290
13	sin	0.2250	0.2267	0.2284	0.2300	0.2318	0.2334	0.2351	0.2368	0.2385	0.2402
	cos	0.9744	0.9740	0.9736	0.9732	0.9728	0.9724	0.9720	0.9715	0.9711	0.9707
	tan	0.2309	0.2327	0.2345	0.2364	0.2382	0.2401	0.2419	0.2438	0.2456	0.2475
14	sin	0.2419	0.2436	0.2453	0.2470	0.2487	0.2504	0.2521	0.2538	0.2554	0.2571
	cos	0.9703	0.9699	0.9694	0.9690	0.9686	0.9681	0.9677	0.9673	0.9668	0.9664
	tan	0.2493	0.2512	0.2530	0.2549	0.2568	0.2586	0.2605	0.2623	0.2642	0.2661
Degs.	Function	0′	6′	12′	18′	24′	30′	36′	42′	48′	54′

Degs.	Function	0.0°	0.1°	0.2°	0.3°	0.4°	0.5°	0.6°	0.7°	0.8°	0.9°
15	sin	0.2588	0.2605	0.2622	0.2639	0.2656	0.2672	0.2689	0.2706	0.2723	0.2740
	cos	0.9659	0.9655	0.9650	0.9646	0.9641	0.9636	0.9632	0.9627	0.9622	0.9617
	tan	0.2679	0.2698	0.2717	0.2736	0.2754	0.2773	0.2792	0.2811	0.2830	0.2849
16	sin	0.2756	0.2773	0.2790	0.2807	0.2823	0.2840	0.2857	0.2874	0.2890	0.2907
	cos	0.9613	0.9608	0.9603	0.9598	0.9593	0.9588	0.9583	0.9578	0.9573	0.9568
	tan	0.2867	0.2886	0.2905	0.2924	0.2943	0.2962	0.2981	0.3000	0.3019	0.3038
17	sin	0.2924	0.2940	0.2957	0.2974	0.2990	0.3007	0.3024	0.3040	0.3057	0.3074
	cos	0.9563	0.9558	0.9553	0.9548	0.9542	0.9537	0.9532	0.9527	0.9521	0.9516
	tan	0.3057	0.3076	0.3096	0.3115	0.3134	0.3153	0.3172	0.3191	0.3211	0.3230
18	sin	0.3090	0.3107	0.3123	0.3140	0.3156	0.3173	0.3190	0.3206	0.3223	0.3239
	cos	0.9511	0.9505	0.9500	0.9494	0.9489	0.9483	0.9478	0.9472	0.9466	0.9461
	tan	0.3249	0.3269	0.3288	0.3307	0.3327	0.3346	0.3365	0.3385	0.3404	0.3424
19	sin	0.3256	0.3272	0.3289	0.3305	0.3322	0.3338	0.3355	0.3371	0.3387	0.3404
	cos	0.9455	0.9449	0.9444	0.9438	0.9432	0.9426	0.9421	0.9415	0.9409	0.9403
	tan	0.3443	0.3463	0.3482	0.3502	0.3522	0.3541	0.3561	0.3581	0.3600	0.3620
20	sin	0.3420	0.3437	0.3453	0.3469	0.3486	0.3502	0.3518	0.3535	0.3551	0.3567
	cos	0.9397	0.9391	0.9385	0.9379	0.9373	0.9367	0.9361	0.9354	0.9348	0.9342
	tan	0.3640	0.3659	0.3679	0.3699	0.3719	0.3739	0.3759	0.3779	0.3799	0.3819
21	sin	0.3584	0.3600	0.3616	0.3633	0.3649	0.3665	0.3681	0.3697	0.3714	0.3730
	cos	0.9336	0.9330	0.9323	0.9317	0.9311	0.9304	0.9298	0.9291	0.9285	0.9278
	tan	0.3839	0.3859	0.3879	0.3899	0.3919	0.3939	0.3959	0.3979	0.4000	0.4020
22	sin	0.3746	0.3762	0.3778	0.3795	0.3811	0.3827	0.3843	0.3859	0.3875	0.3891
	cos	0.9272	0.9265	0.9259	0.9252	0.9245	0.9239	0.9232	0.9225	0.9219	0.9212
	tan	0.4040	0.4061	0.4081	0.4101	0.4122	0.4142	0.4163	0.4183	0.4204	0.4224
23	sin	0.3907	0.3923	0.3939	0.3955	0.3971	0.3987	0.4003	0.4019	0.4035	0.4051
	cos	0.9205	0.9198	0.9191	0.9184	0.9178	0.9171	0.9164	0.9157	0.9150	0.9143
	tan	0.4245	0.4265	0.4286	0.4307	0.4327	0.4348	0.4369	0.4390	0.4411	0.4431
24	sin	0.4067	0.4083	0.4099	0.4115	0.4131	0.4147	0.4163	0.4179	0.4195	0.4210
	cos	0.9135	0.9128	0.9121	0.9114	0.9107	0.9100	0.9092	0.9085	0.9078	0.9070
	tan	0.4452	0.4473	0.4494	0.4515	0.4536	0.4557	0.4578	0.4599	0.4621	0.4642
25	sin	0.4226	0.4242	0.4258	0.4274	0.4289	0.4305	0.4321	0.4337	0.4352	0.4368
	cos	0.9063	0.9056	0.9048	0.9041	0.9033	0.9026	0.9018	0.9011	0.9003	0.8996
	tan	0.4663	0.4684	0.4706	0.4727	0.4748	0.4770	0.4791	0.4813	0.4834	0.4856
26	sin	0.4384	0.4399	0.4415	0.4431	0.4446	0.4462	0.4478	0.4493	0.4509	0.4524
	cos	0.8988	0.8980	0.8973	0.8965	0.8957	0.8949	0.8942	0.8934	0.8926	0.8918
	tan	0.4877	0.4899	0.4921	0.4942	0.4964	0.4986	0.5008	0.5029	0.5051	0.5073
27	sin	0.4540	0.4555	0.4571	0.4586	0.4602	0.4617	0.4633	0.4648	0.4664	0.4679
	cos	0.8910	0.8902	0.8894	0.8886	0.8878	0.8870	0.8862	0.8854	0.8846	0.8838
	tan	0.5095	0.5117	0.5139	0.5161	0.5184	0.5206	0.5228	0.5250	0.5272	0.5295
28	sin	0.4695	0.4710	0.4726	0.4741	0.4756	0.4772	0.4787	0.4802	0.4818	0.4833
	cos	0.8829	0.8821	0.8813	0.8805	0.8796	0.8788	0.8780	0.8771	0.8763	0.8755
	tan	0.5317	0.5340	0.5362	0.5384	0.5407	0.5430	0.5452	0.5475	0.5498	0.5520
29	sin	0.4848	0.4863	0.4879	0.4894	0.4909	0.4924	0.4939	0.4955	0.4970	0.4985
	cos	0.8746	0.8738	0.8729	0.8721	0.8712	0.8704	0.8695	0.8686	0.8678	0.8669
	tan	0.5543	0.5566	0.5589	0.5612	0.5635	0.5658	0.5681	0.5704	0.5727	0.5750
Degs.	Function	0′	6′	12′	18′	24′	30′	36′	42′	48′	54′

Degs.	Function	0.0°	0.1°	0.2°	0.3°	0.4°	0.5°	0.6°	0.7°	0.8°	0.9°
30	sin	0.5000	0.5015	0.5030	0.5045	0.5060	0.5075	0.5090	0.5105	0.5120	0.5135
	cos	0.8660	0.8652	0.8643	0.8634	0.8625	0.8616	0.8607	0.8599	0.8590	0.8581
	tan	0.5774	0.5797	0.5820	0.5844	0.5867	0.5890	0.5914	0.5938	0.5961	0.5985
31	sin	0.5150	0.5165	0.5180	0.5195	0.5210	0.5225	0.5240	0.5255	0.5270	0.5284
	cos	0.8572	0.8563	0.8554	0.8545	0.8536	0.8526	0.8517	0.8508	0.8499	0.8490
	tan	0.6009	0.6032	0.6056	0.6080	0.6104	0.6128	0.6152	0.6176	0.6200	0.6224
32	sin	0.5299	0.5314	0.5329	0.5344	0.5358	0.5373	0.5388	0.5402	0.5417	0.5432
	cos	0.8480	0.8471	0.8462	0.8453	0.8443	0.8434	0.8425	0.8415	0.8406	0.8396
	tan	0.6249	0.6273	0.6297	0.6322	0.6346	0.6371	0.6395	0.6420	0.6445	0.6469
33	sin	0.5446	0.5461	0.5476	0.5490	0.5505	0.5519	0.5534	0.5548	0.5563	0.5577
	cos	0.8387	0.8377	0.8368	0.8358	0.8348	0.8339	0.8329	0.8320	0.8310	0.8300
	tan	0.6494	0.6519	0.6544	0.6569	0.6594	0.6619	0.6644	0.6669	0.6694	0.6720
34	sin	0.5592	0.5606	0.5621	0.5635	0.5650	0.5664	0.5678	0.5693	0.5707	0.5721
	cos	0.8290	0.8281	0.8271	0.8261	0.8251	0.8241	0.8231	0.8221	0.8211	0.8202
	tan	0.6745	0.6771	0.6796	0.6822	0.6847	0.6873	0.6899	0.6924	0.6950	0.6976
35	sin	0.5736	0.5750	0.5764	0.5779	0.5793	0.5807	0.5821	0.5835	0.5850	0.5864
	cos	0.8192	0.8181	0.8171	0.8161	0.8151	0.8141	0.8131	0.8121	0.8111	0.8100
	tan	0.7002	0.7028	0.7054	0.7080	0.7107	0.7133	0.7159	0.7186	0.7212	0.7239
36	sin	0.5878	0.5892	0.5906	0.5920	0.5934	0.5948	0.5962	0.5976	0.5990	0.6004
	cos	0.8090	0.8080	0.8070	0.8059	0.8049	0.8039	0.8028	0.8018	0.8007	0.7997
	tan	0.7265	0.7292	0.7319	0.7346	0.7373	0.7400	0.7427	0.7454	0.7481	0.7508
37	sin	0.6018	0.6032	0.6046	0.6060	0.6074	0.6088	0.6101	0.6115	0.6129	0.6143
	cos	0.7986	0.7976	0.7965	0.7955	0.7944	0.7934	0.7923	0.7912	0.7902	0.7891
	tan	0.7536	0.7563	0.7590	0.7618	0.7646	0.7673	0.7701	0.7729	0.7757	0.7785
38	sin	0.6157	0.6170	0.6184	0.6198	0.6211	0.6225	0.6239	0.6252	0.6266	0.6280
	cos	0.7880	0.7869	0.7859	0.7848	0.7837	0.7826	0.7815	0.7804	0.7793	0.7782
	tan	0.7813	0.7841	0.7869	0.7898	0.7926	0.7954	0.7983	0.8012	0.8040	0.8069
39	sin	0.6293	0.6307	0.6320	0.6334	0.6347	0.6361	0.6374	0.6388	0.6401	0.6414
	cos	0.7771	0.7760	0.7749	0.7738	0.7727	0.7716	0.7705	0.7694	0.7683	0.7672
	tan	0.8098	0.8127	0.8156	0.8185	0.8214	0.8243	0.8273	0.8302	0.8332	0.8361
40	sin	0.6428	0.6441	0.6455	0.6468	0.6481	0.6494	0.6508	0.6521	0.6534	0.6547
	cos	0.7660	0.7649	0.7638	0.7627	0.7615	0.7604	0.7593	0.7581	0.7570	0.7559
	tan	0.8391	0.8421	0.8451	0.8481	0.8511	0.8541	0.8571	0.8601	0.8632	0.8662
41	sin	0.6561	0.6574	0.6587	0.6600	0.6613	0.6626	0.6639	0.6652	0.6665	0.6678
	cos	0.7547	0.7536	0.7524	0.7513	0.7501	0.7490	0.7478	0.7466	0.7455	0.7443
	tan	0.8693	0.8724	0.8754	0.8785	0.8816	0.8847	0.8878	0.8910	0.8941	0.8972
42	sin	0.6691	0.6704	0.6717	0.6730	0.6743	0.6756	0.6769	0.6782	0.6794	0.6807
	cos	0.7431	0.7420	0.7408	0.7396	0.7385	0.7373	0.7361	0.7349	0.7337	0.7325
	tan	0.9004	0.9036	0.9067	0.9099	0.9131	0.9163	0.9195	0.9228	0.9260	0.9293
43	sin	0.6820	0.6833	0.6845	0.6858	0.6871	0.6884	0.6896	0.6909	0.6921	0.6934
	cos	0.7314	0.7302	0.7290	0.7278	0.7266	0.7254	0.7242	0.7230	0.7218	0.7206
	tan	0.9325	0.9358	0.9391	0.9424	0.9457	0.9490	0.9523	0.9556	0.9590	0.9623
44	sin	0.6947	0.6959	0.6972	0.6984	0.6997	0.7009	0.7022	0.7034	0.7046	0.7059
	cos	0.7193	0.7181	0.7169	0.7157	0.7145	0.7133	0.7120	0.7108	0.7096	0.7083
	tan	0.9657	0.9691	0.9725	0.9759	0.9793	0.9827	0.9861	0.9896	0.9930	0.9965
Degs.	Function	0′	6′	12′	18′	24′	30′	36′	42′	48′	54′

Degs.	Function	0.0°	0.1°	0.2°	0.3°	0.4°	0.5°	0.6°	0.7°	0.8°	0.9°
45	sin	0.7071	0.7083	0.7096	0.7108	0.7120	0.7133	0.7145	0.7157	0.7169	0.7181
	cos	0.7071	0.7059	0.7046	0.7034	0.7022	0.7009	0.6997	0.6984	0.6972	0.6959
	tan	1.0000	1.0035	1.0070	1.0105	1.0141	1.0176	1.0212	1.0247	1.0283	1.0319
46	sin	0.7193	0.7206	0.7218	0.7230	0.7242	0.7254	0.7266	0.7278	0.7290	0.7302
	cos	0.6947	0.6934	0.6921	0.6909	0.6896	0.6884	0.6871	0.6858	0.6845	0.6833
	tan	1.0355	1.0392	1.0428	1.0464	1.0501	1.0538	1.0575	1.0612	1.0649	1.0686
47	sin	0.7314	0.7325	0.7337	0.7349	0.7361	0.7373	0.7385	0.7396	0.7408	0.7420
	cos	0.6820	0.6807	0.6794	0.6782	0.6769	0.6756	0.6743	0.6730	0.6717	0.6704
	tan	1.0724	1.0761	1.0799	1.0837	1.0875	1.0913	1.0951	1.0990	1.1028	1.1067
48	sin	0.7431	0.7443	0.7455	0.7466	0.7478	0.7490	0.7501	0.7513	0.7524	0.7536
	cos	0.6691	0.6678	0.6665	0.6652	0.6639	0.6626	0.6613	0.6600	0.6587	0.6574
	tan	1.1106	1.1145	1.1184	1.1224	1.1263	1.1303	1.1343	1.1383	1.1423	1.1463
49	sin	0.7547	0.7559	0.7570	0.7581	0.7593	0.7604	0.7615	0.7627	0.7638	0.7649
	cos	0.6561	0.6547	0.6534	0.6521	0.6508	0.6494	0.6481	0.6468	0.6455	0.6441
	tan	1.1504	1.1544	1.1585	1.1626	1.1667	1.1708	1.1750	1.1792	1.1833	1.1875
50	sin	0.7660	0.7672	0.7683	0.7694	0.7705	0.7716	0.7727	0.7738	0.7749	0.7760
	cos	0.6428	0.6414	0.6401	0.6388	0.6374	0.6361	0.6347	0.6334	0.6320	0.6307
	tan	1.1918	1.1960	1.2002	1.2045	1.2088	1.2131	1.2174	1.2218	1.2261	1.2305
51	sin	0.7771	0.7782	0.7793	0.7804	0.7815	0.7826	0.7837	0.7848	0.7859	0.7869
	cos	0.6293	0.6280	0.6266	0.6252	0.6239	0.6225	0.6211	0.6198	0.6184	0.6170
	tan	1.2349	1.2393	1.2437	1.2482	1.2527	1.2572	1.2617	1.2662	1.2708	1.2753
52	sin	0.7880	0.7891	0.7902	0.7912	0.7923	0.7934	0.7944	0.7955	0.7965	0.7976
	cos	0.6157	0.6143	0.6129	0.6115	0.6101	0.6088	0.6074	0.6060	0.6046	0.6032
	tan	1.2799	1.2846	1.2892	1.2938	1.2985	1.3032	1.3079	1.3127	1.3175	1.3222
53	sin	0.7986	0.7997	0.8007	0.8018	0.8028	0.8039	0.8049	0.8059	0.8070	0.8080
	cos	0.6018	0.6004	0.5990	0.5976	0.5962	0.5948	0.5934	0.5920	0.5906	0.5892
	tan	1.3270	1.3319	1.3367	1.3416	1.3465	1.3514	1.3564	1.3613	1.3663	1.3713
54	sin	0.8090	0.8100	0.8111	0.8121	0.8131	0.8141	0.8151	0.8161	0.8171	0.8181
	cos	0.5878	0.5864	0.5850	0.5835	0.5821	0.5807	0.5793	0.5779	0.5764	0.5750
	tan	1.3764	1.3814	1.3865	1.3916	1.3968	1.4019	1.4071	1.4124	1.4176	1.4229
55	sin	0.8192	0.8202	0.8211	0.8221	0.8231	0.8241	0.8251	0.8261	0.8271	0.8281
	cos	0.5736	0.5721	0.5707	0.5693	0.5678	0.5664	0.5650	0.5635	0.5621	0.5606
	tan	1.4281	1.4335	1.4388	1.4442	1.4496	1.4550	1.4605	1.4659	1.4715	1.4770
56	sin	0.8290	0.8300	0.8310	0.8320	0.8329	0.8339	0.8348	0.8358	0.8368	0.8377
	cos	0.5592	0.5577	0.5563	0.5548	0.5534	0.5519	0.5505	0.5490	0.5476	0.5461
	tan	1.4826	1.4882	1.4938	1.4994	1.5051	1.5108	1.5166	1.5224	1.5282	1.5340
57	sin	0.8387	0.8396	0.8406	0.8415	0.8425	0.8434	0.8443	0.8453	0.8462	0.8471
	cos	0.5446	0.5432	0.5417	0.5402	0.5388	0.5373	0.5358	0.5344	0.5329	0.5314
	tan	1.5399	1.5458	1.5517	1.5577	1.5637	1.5697	1.5757	1.5818	1.5880	1.5941
58	sin	0.8480	0.8490	0.8499	0.8508	0.8517	0.8526	0.8536	0.8545	0.8554	0.8563
	cos	0.5299	0.5284	0.5270	0.5255	0.5240	0.5225	0.5210	0.5195	0.5180	0.5165
	tan	1.6003	1.6066	1.6128	1.6191	1.6255	1.6319	1.6383	1.6447	1.6512	1.6577
59	sin	0.8572	0.8581	0.8590	0.8599	0.8607	0.8616	0.8625	0.8634	0.8643	0.8652
	cos	0.5150	0.5135	0.5120	0.5105	0.5090	0.5075	0.5060	0.5045	0.5030	0.5015
	tan	1.6643	1.6709	1.6775	1.6842	1.6909	1.6977	1.7045	1.7113	1.7182	1.7251
Degs.	Function	0′	6′	12′	18′	24′	30′	36′	42′	48′	54′

Degs.	Function	0.0°	0.1°	0.2°	0.3°	0.4°	0.5°	0.6°	0.7°	0.8°	0.9°
60	sin	0.8660	0.8669	0.8678	0.8686	0.8695	0.8704	0.8712	0.8721	0.8729	0.8738
	cos	0.5000	0.4985	0.4970	0.4955	0.4939	0.4924	0.4909	0.4894	0.4879	0.4863
	tan	1.7321	1.7391	1.7461	1.7532	1.7603	1.7675	1.7747	1.7820	1.7893	1.7966
61	sin	0.8746	0.8755	0.8763	0.8771	0.8780	0.8788	0.8796	0.8805	0.8813	0.8821
	cos	0.4848	0.4833	0.4818	0.4802	0.4787	0.4772	0.4756	0.4741	0.4726	0.4710
	tan	1.8040	1.8115	1.8190	1.8265	1.8341	1.8418	1.8495	1.8572	1.8650	1.8728
62	sin	0.8829	0.8838	0.8846	0.8854	0.8862	0.8870	0.8878	0.8886	0.8894	0.8902
	cos	0.4695	0.4679	0.4664	0.4648	0.4633	0.4617	0.4602	0.4586	0.4571	0.4555
	tan	1.8807	1.8887	1.8967	1.9047	1.9128	1.9210	1.9292	1.9375	1.9458	1.9542
63	sin	0.8910	0.8918	0.8926	0.8934	0.8942	0.8949	0.8957	0.8965	0.8973	0.8980
	cos	0.4540	0.4524	0.4509	0.4493	0.4478	0.4462	0.4446	0.4431	0.4415	0.4399
	tan	1.9626	1.9711	1.9797	1.9883	1.9970	2.0057	2.0145	2.0233	2.0323	2.0413
64	sin	0.8988	0.8996	0.9003	0.9011	0.9018	0.9026	0.9033	0.9041	0.9048	0.9056
	cos	0.4384	0.4368	0.4352	0.4337	0.4321	0.4305	0.4289	0.4274	0.4258	0.4242
	tan	2.0503	2.0594	2.0686	2.0778	2.0872	2.0965	2.1060	2.1155	2.1251	2.1348
65	sin	0.9063	0.9070	0.9078	0.9085	0.9092	0.9100	0.9107	0.9114	0.9121	0.9128
	cos	0.4226	0.4210	0.4195	0.4179	0.4163	0.4147	0.4131	0.4115	0.4099	0.4083
	tan	2.1445	2.1543	2.1642	2.1742	2.1842	2.1943	2.2045	2.2148	2.2251	2.2355
66	sin	0.9135	0.9143	0.9150	0.9157	0.9164	0.9171	0.9178	0.9184	0.9191	0.9198
	cos	0.4067	0.4051	0.4035	0.4019	0.4003	0.3987	0.3971	0.3955	0.3939	0.3923
	tan	2.2460	2.2566	2.2673	2.2781	2.2889	2.2998	2.3109	2.3220	2.3332	2.3445
67	sin	0.9205	0.9212	0.9219	0.9225	0.9232	0.9239	0.9245	0.9252	0.9259	0.9265
	cos	0.3907	0.3891	0.3875	0.3859	0.3843	0.3827	0.3811	0.3795	0.3778	0.3762
	tan	2.3559	2.3673	2.3789	2.3906	2.4023	2.4142	2.4262	2.4383	2.4504	2.4627
68	sin	0.9272	0.9278	0.9285	0.9291	0.9298	0.9304	0.9311	0.9317	0.9323	0.9330
	cos	0.3746	0.3730	0.3714	0.3697	0.3681	0.3665	0.3649	0.3633	0.3616	0.3600
	tan	2.4751	2.4876	2.5002	2.5129	2.5257	2.5386	2.5517	2.5649	2.5782	2.5916
69	sin	0.9336	0.9342	0.9348	0.9354	0.9361	0.9367	0.9373	0.9379	0.9385	0.9391
	cos	0.3584	0.3567	0.3551	0.3535	0.3518	0.3502	0.3486	0.3469	0.3453	0.3437
	tan	2.6051	2.6187	2.6325	2.6464	2.6605	2.6746	2.6889	2.7034	2.7179	2.7326
70	sin	0.9397	0.9403	0.9409	0.9415	0.9421	0.9426	0.9432	0.9438	0.9444	0.9449
	cos	0.3420	0.3404	0.3387	0.3371	0.3355	0.3338	0.3322	0.3305	0.3289	0.3272
	tan	2.7475	2.7625	2.7776	2.7929	2.8083	2.8239	2.8397	2.8556	2.8716	2.8878
71	sin	0.9455	0.9461	0.9466	0.9472	0.9478	0.9483	0.9489	0.9494	0.9500	0.9505
	cos	0.3256	0.3239	0.3223	0.3206	0.3190	0.3173	0.3156	0.3140	0.3123	0.3107
	tan	2.9042	2.9208	2.9375	2.9544	2.9714	2.9887	3.0061	3.0237	3.0415	3.0595
72	sin	0.9511	0.9516	0.9521	0.9527	0.9532	0.9537	0.9542	0.9548	0.9553	0.9558
	cos	0.3090	0.3074	0.3057	0.3040	0.3024	0.3007	0.2990	0.2974	0.2957	0.2940
	tan	3.0777	3.0961	3.1146	3.1334	3.1524	3.1716	3.1910	3.2106	3.2305	3.2506
73	sin	0.9563	0.9568	0.9573	0.9578	0.9583	0.9588	0.9593	0.9598	0.9603	0.9608
	cos	0.2924	0.2907	0.2890	0.2874	0.2857	0.2840	0.2823	0.2807	0.2790	0.2773
	tan	3.2709	3.2914	3.3122	3.3332	3.3544	3.3759	3.3977	3.4197	3.4420	3.4646
74	sin	0.9613	0.9617	0.9622	0.9627	0.9632	0.9636	0.9641	0.9646	0.9650	0.9655
	cos	0.2756	0.2740	0.2723	0.2706	0.2689	0.2672	0.2656	0.2639	0.2622	0.2605
	tan	3.4874	3.5105	3.5339	3.5576	3.5816	3.6059	3.6305	3.6554	3.6806	3.7062
Degs.	Function	0′	6′	12′	18′	24′	30′	36′	42′	48′	54′

Natural Sines, Cosines and Tangents

Degs.	Function	0.0°	0.1°	0.2°	0.3°	0.4°	0.5°	0.6°	0.7°	0.8°	0.9°
75	sin	0.9659	0.9664	0.9668	0.9673	0.9677	0.9681	0.9686	0.9690	0.9694	0.9699
	cos	0.2588	0.2571	0.2554	0.2538	0.2521	0.2504	0.2487	0.2470	0.2453	0.2436
	tan	3.7321	3.7583	3.7848	3.8118	3.8391	3.8667	3.8947	3.9232	3.9520	3.9812
76	sin	0.9703	0.9707	0.9711	0.9715	0.9720	0.9724	0.9728	0.9732	0.9736	0.9740
	cos	0.2419	0.2402	0.2385	0.2368	0.2351	0.2334	0.2317	0.2300	0.2284	0.2267
	tan	4.0108	4.0408	4.0713	4.1022	4.1335	4.1653	4.1976	4.2303	4.2635	4.2972
77	sin	0.9744	0.9748	0.9751	0.9755	0.9759	0.9763	0.9767	0.9770	0.9774	0.9778
	cos	0.2250	0.2232	0.2215	0.2198	0.2181	0.2164	0.2147	0.2130	0.2113	0.2096
	tan	4.3315	4.3662	4.4015	4.4374	4.4737	4.5107	4.5483	4.5864	4.6252	4.6646
78	sin	0.9781	0.9785	0.9789	0.9792	0.9796	0.9799	0.9803	0.9806	0.9810	0.9813
	cos	0.2079	0.2062	0.2045	0.2028	0.2011	0.1994	0.1977	0.1959	0.1942	0.1925
	tan	4.7046	4.7453	4.7867	4.8288	4.8716	4.9152	4.9594	5.0045	5.0504	5.0970
79	sin	0.9816	0.9820	0.9823	0.9826	0.9829	0.9833	0.9836	0.9839	0.9842	0.9845
	cos	0.1908	0.1891	0.1874	0.1857	0.1840	0.1822	0.1805	0.1788	0.1771	0.1754
	tan	5.1446	5.1929	5.2422	5.2924	5.3435	5.3955	5.4486	5.5026	5.5578	5.6140
80	sin	0.9848	0.9851	0.9854	0.9857	0.9860	0.9863	0.9866	0.9869	0.9871	0.9874
	cos	0.1736	0.1719	0.1702	0.1685	0.1668	0.1650	0.1633	0.1616	0.1599	0.1582
	tan	5.6713	5.7297	5.7894	5.8502	5.9124	5.9758	6.0405	6.1066	6.1742	6.2432
81	sin	0.9877	0.9880	0.9882	0.9885	0.9888	0.9890	0.9893	0.9895	0.9898	0.9900
	cos	0.1564	0.1547	0.1530	0.1513	0.1495	0.1478	0.1461	0.1444	0.1426	0.1409
	tan	6.3138	6.3859	6.4596	6.5350	6.6122	6.6912	6.7720	6.8548	6.9395	7.0264
82	sin	0.9903	0.9905	0.9907	0.9910	0.9912	0.9914	0.9917	0.9919	0.9921	0.9923
	cos	0.1392	0.1374	0.1357	0.1340	0.1323	0.1305	0.1288	0.1271	0.1253	0.1236
	tan	7.1154	7.2066	7.3002	7.3962	7.4947	7.5958	7.6996	7.8062	7.9158	8.0285
83	sin	0.9925	0.9928	0.9930	0.9932	0.9934	0.9936	0.9938	0.9940	0.9942	0.9943
	cos	0.1219	0.1201	0.1184	0.1167	0.1149	0.1132	0.1115	0.1097	0.1080	0.1063
	tan	8.1443	8.2636	8.3863	8.5126	8.6427	8.7769	8.9152	9.0579	9.2052	9.3572
84	sin	0.9945	0.9947	0.9949	0.9951	0.9952	0.9954	0.9956	0.9957	0.9959	0.9960
	cos	0.1045	0.1028	0.1011	0.0993	0.0976	0.0958	0.0941	0.0924	0.0906	0.0889
	tan	9.5144	9.6768	9.8448	10.02	10.20	10.39	10.58	10.78	10.99	11.20
85	sin	0.9962	0.9963	0.9965	0.9966	0.9968	0.9969	0.9971	0.9972	0.9973	0.9974
	cos	0.0872	0.0854	0.0837	0.0819	0.0802	0.0785	0.0767	0.0750	0.0732	0.0715
	tan	11.43	11.66	11.91	12.16	12.43	12.71	13.00	13.30	13.62	13.95
86	sin	0.9976	0.9977	0.9978	0.9979	0.9980	0.9981	0.9982	0.9983	0.9984	0.9985
	cos	0.0698	0.0680	0.0663	0.0645	0.0628	0.0610	0.0593	0.0576	0.0558	0.0541
	tan	14.30	14.67	15.06	15.46	15.89	16.35	16.83	17.34	17.89	18.46
87	sin	0.9986	0.9987	0.9988	0.9989	0.9990	0.9990	0.9991	0.9992	0.9993	0.9993
	cos	0.0523	0.0506	0.0488	0.0471	0.0454	0.0436	0.0419	0.0401	0.0384	0.0366
	tan	19.08	19.74	20.45	21.20	22.02	22.90	23.86	24.90	26.03	27.27
88	sin	0.9994	0.9995	0.9995	0.9996	0.9996	0.9997	0.9997	0.9997	0.9998	0.9998
	cos	0.0349	0.0332	0.0314	0.0297	0.0279	0.0262	0.0244	0.0227	0.0209	0.0192
	tan	28.64	30.14	31.82	33.69	35.80	38.19	40.92	44.07	47.74	52.08
89	sin	0.9998	0.9999	0.9999	0.9999	0.9999	1.000	1.000	1.000	1.000	1.000
	cos	0.0175	0.0157	0.0140	0.0122	0.0105	0.0087	0.0070	0.0052	0.0035	0.0017
	tan	57.29	63.66	71.62	81.85	95.49	114.6	143.2	191.0	286.5	573.0
Degs.	Function	0′	6′	12′	18′	24′	30′	36′	42′	48′	54′

APPENDIX 3

Functions of Angles Greater than 90 Degrees

THE USUAL PROBLEMS ENCOUNTERED in electrical and electronic work are with angles of 90° or less. Occasionally, however, it may be necessary to deal with angles greater than 90°. Functions for angles over 90° are not included in Appendix 2. Since these functions are periodic—that is the values are repeated—extension of the tables is not necessary. The values of such functions can be found as shown below.

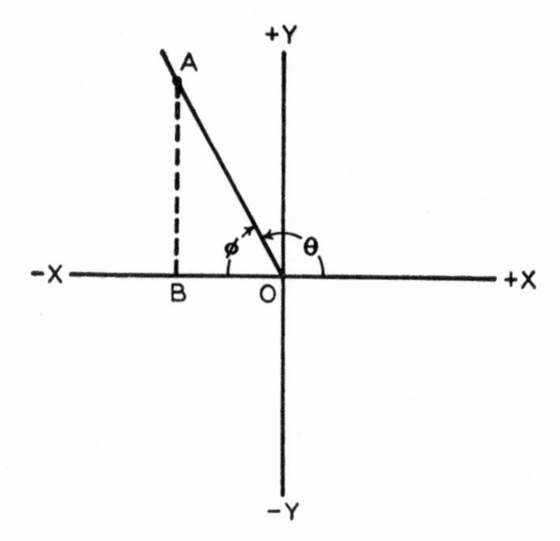

Fig. A-5. Function of angles in the second quadrant.

Angles in the second quadrant (90°–180°). Figure A-5 shows an angle, θ, greater than 90°. From point A, let us drop a perpendicular to the X-axis, forming a right triangle O-A-B. (Just a word about quadrant measurements. Horizontal lines measured from point O to the right are positive, while to the left they are negative. Similarly, vertical lines measured from point O upward are positive, while downward they are negative.) From this right triangle,

$$\sin \theta = \frac{\text{opposite}}{\text{hypotenuse}} = \frac{B\text{-}A}{O\text{-}A}$$

But this is the same as the sine of the new angle ϕ (phi). Since $\theta + \phi = 180°$ (straight line), we can then say:

1. $\sin \theta$ (between 90° and 180°) $= \sin (180° - \theta)$

Similarly

2. $\cos \theta$ (between 90° and 180°) $= -\cos (180° - \theta)$

and

3. $\tan \theta$ (between 90° and 180°) $= -\tan (180° - \theta)$

The reason for the negative values for cosines and tangents is that line *O-B*, is in the negative direction.

Angles in the third quadrant (180°–270°). In Fig. A-6, angle θ represents some angle greater than 180°, but less than 270°. Again let us drop a perpendicular from *A* to the horizontal, forming right triangle *O-A-B*. The new angle ϕ just formed is equal to $(\theta - 180°)$ degrees. By definition,

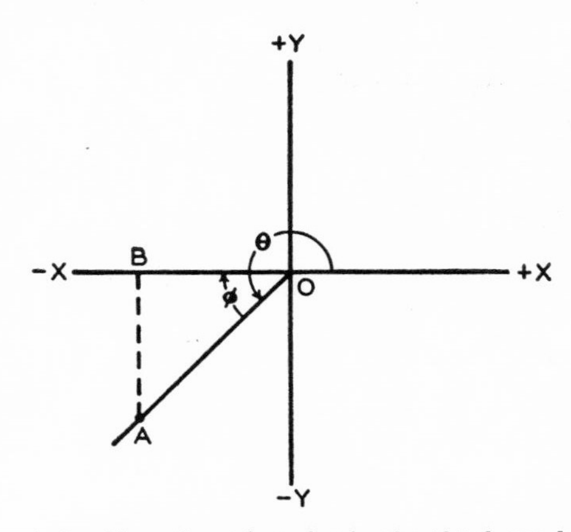

Fig. A-6. Function of angles in the third quadrant.

$\sin \theta = \dfrac{\text{opposite}}{\text{hypotenuse}} = \dfrac{B\text{-}A}{O\text{-}A}$. Again this is the same as $\sin \phi$. Since *B-A* is in the negative direction, and since $\phi = (\theta - 180°)$ degrees, we have:

1. $\sin \theta$ (between 180° and 270°) $= -\sin (\theta - 180°)$

Similarly

2. $\cos \theta$ (between 180° and 270°) $= -\cos (\theta - 180°)$

and

3. $\tan \theta$ (between 180° and 270°) $= \tan (\theta - 180°)$

Notice that the cosine is also negative since *O-B*, the adjacent side, is negative in direction, while the tangent is positive because the numerator (*B-A*) and the denominator (*O-B*) of its ratio are both negative.

Angles in the fourth quadrant (270°–360°). Angle θ, Fig. A-7, represents any angle in the fourth quadrant (between 270° and 360°). Angle ϕ is equal to $(360° - \theta)$. If we drop a perpendicular from point A to the horizontal, then from the right triangle O-A-B, by definition

$$\sin \theta = \frac{\text{opposite}}{\text{hypotenuse}} = \frac{B\text{-}A}{O\text{-}A}$$

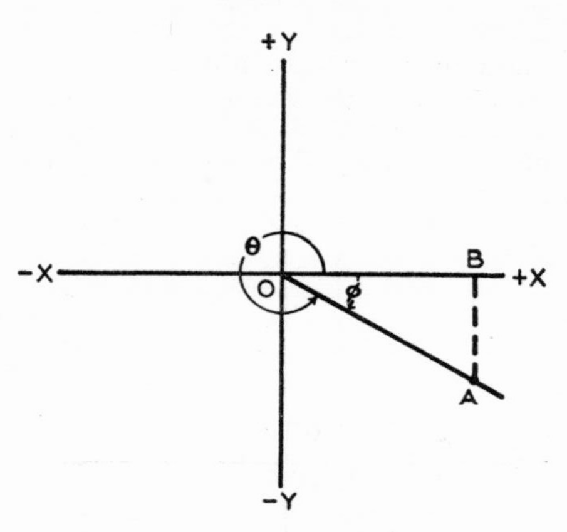

Fig. A-7. Function of angles in the fourth quadrant.

This is the same as sin ϕ. Since B-A is in the negative direction, and $\sin \phi = (360° - \theta)$ degrees we have:

1. $\sin \theta$ (between 270° and 360°) $= -\sin (360° - \theta)$

Similarly

2. $\cos \theta$ (between 270° and 360°) $= \cos (360° - \theta)$

and

3. $\tan \theta$ (between 270° and 360°) $= -\tan (360° - \theta)$

APPENDIX 4

RMA Standard Color Coding for Resistors

To facilitate servicing, a color coding scheme is used to designate the resistance value of any resistor. Such a color coding method gives the resistance value to two significant figures only. Offhand, such a designation seems too inaccurate. But remember that the accuracy of the average resistor is at best only within $\pm 5\%$ of the nominal value. Two significant figures is sufficient to express any resistance value to better than 5% tolerance. The color coding system is not used for precision resistors.

There are two methods used for designating resistance values. Each method involves the use of three identifying colors. The older method uses body, tip, and dot. The newer method uses three bands reading from end to center. The first color (body or first band) designates the first digit of the resistance value. The second color (tip or second band) designates the second digit. The third color (dot or third band) designates the *number* of zeros to be added to the above digits.

Each color is assigned a definite value as shown below:

Color	Value	Color	Value
Black	0	Green	5
Brown	1	Blue	6
Red	2	Violet (purple)	7
Orange	3	Gray	8
Yellow	4	White	9

Figure A-8 shows the color code scheme applied to the old (a) and new (b) method.

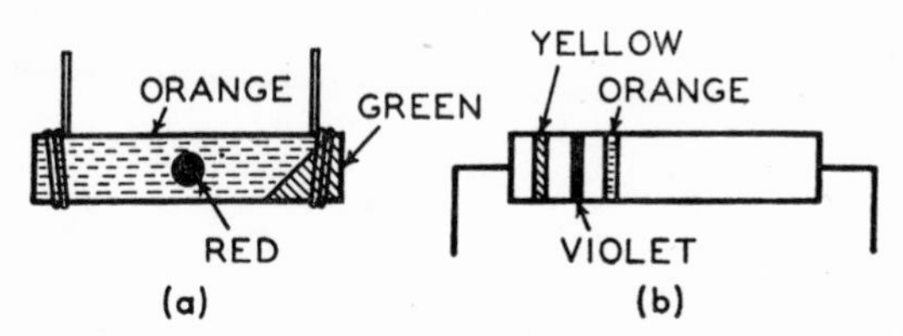

Fig. A-8. Methods of color coding for resistors:

(a) $R = 3 - 5 - 00 = 3500\Omega$.
(b) $R = 4 - 7 - 000 = 47{,}500\Omega$.

When the resistance value is less than 10 ohms, the color coding system described above is inadequate. To remedy this situation decimal multipliers are used in place of the third color designators (body, dot, or third band). The multipliers used are:

Gold.. 0.1
Silver...................................... 0.01

For example, a resistor of 2.7 ohms would have a first band (or body) color of red; a second band (or tip) color of purple; and a third band (or dot) color of gold:

$$2 - 7 \times 0.1 = 2.7 \text{ ohms}$$

The tolerance (or accuracy) of a resistor is indicated by another dot (old method) or a fourth band (new method) placed usually at the other end of the resistor. If no tolerance designator is used, the resistor may deviate as much as ±20% from its nominal value. The tolerance designators are:

Gold.. ± 5%
Silver...................................... ±10%

APPENDIX 5

Color Coding Systems for Capacitors

ORIGINALLY, CONDENSER RATINGS were stamped directly on the unit, or on a paper wrapper around the unit. But when the color coding scheme proved so successful for resistors, manufacturers decided to try a similar system for capacitors. Unfortunately, the entire color coding system was not planned at this time—only one type of capacitor was coded, and only for capacitance (expressed in $\mu\mu$f) to two significant figures. This required a simple three-dot system—the first two for the significant figures and the third for the number of zeros to be added. This system is identical to the RMA Resistor Code.

As the coding system was expanded to include more data, a certain degree of confusion has resulted. The color designators vary from as few as three to as many as six. Even worse, the location and meaning of each designator varies, depending on the number of markers used and the type of capacitors. Under such conditions, the only method of approach is to treat each system individually.

RMA 3-dot system (adopted in 1936). The 3-dot system is used for postage-stamp type mica condensers when the voltage rating is 500 volts and the tolerance is $\pm 20\%$ (see Fig. A-9a). The significance of the color dots is the same as for resistors. Capacitance is expessed to two significant figures, by the first two dots, while the third dot (the decimal multiplier, M) indicates the number of zeros to be added. Capacitance values are in micromicrofarads. A molded arrow (or arrowheads) is used to indicate the order in which these colors are to be taken. Capacitors with this type of marking are still in use.

4-dot system. This scheme is the same as the previous one—with the addition of a fourth dot to express percent tolerance, T (see Fig. A-9b). The significance of the tolerance dot colors is shown in a table on page 208. Capacitance values are again denoted in micromicrofarads to two significant figures. This type of marking is seldom seen.

5-dot system. In this system, the smaller physical-size capacitors have the first two dots on the front face and the other three dots on the rear face (see Fig 8-9c). Capacitors of larger physical size have all five dots on the one face. This type is shown in Fig. A-9d). The extra dot (compared to the 4-dot system) is used to denote capacitance values to three significant figures.

RMA 6-dot system (adopted in 1938). By this system, capacitance values are expressed (in $\mu\mu$f) to three significant figures, using four of the designators. The fifth and sixth designators are used to indicate tolerance (T) and voltage rating (V). This type is shown in Fig. A-9e.

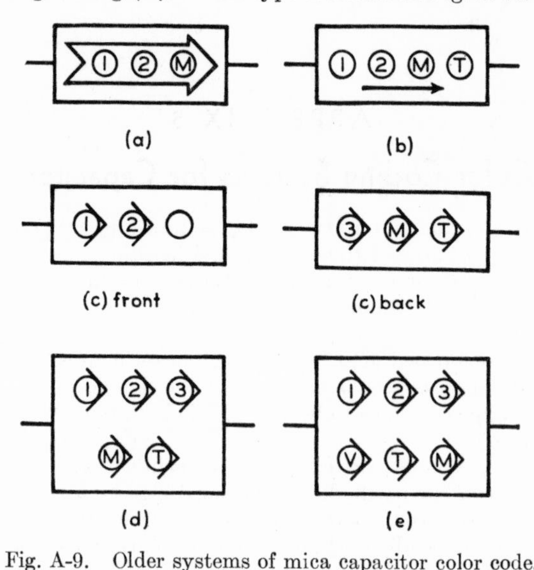

Fig. A-9. Older systems of mica capacitor color code.

The significance of the color designators is shown in the table below.

SIGNIFICANCE OF COLOR DESIGNATORS

Color	Significant figure 1, 2, or 3	Decimal Multiplier, M		Per cent tolerance, T	Voltage rating, V
		Power of 10	Number of zeros added		
Black	0	10^0	None	....	....
Brown	1	10^1	1 zero added	±1	100
Red	2	10^2	2 " "	±2	200
Orange	3	10^3	3 " "	±3	300
Yellow	4	10^4	4 " "	±4	400
Green	5	10^5	5 " "	±5	500
Blue	6	10^6	6 " "	±6	600
Violet	7	10^7	7 " "	±7	700
Gray	8	10^8	8 " "	±8	800
White	9	10^9	9 " "	±9	900
Gold	..	10^{-1}	X.1	±5	1,000
Silver	..	10^{-2}	X.01	±10	2,000
No color	..	....	....	±20	500

Joint Army-Navy (JAN) and RMA 1948. The JAN system and the 1948 RMA system look identical to the 6-dot system described above. However the significance of the dots is somewhat altered. This system is clearly shown in Fig. A-10. Four of the dots have the same meaning as before (1, 2, *M*, *T*), capacitance values being denoted to two significant figures. Standard tolerance values are ±2, ±3, ±5, ±10, and ±20%. The capacitor may use either mica or paper dielectric. This is indicated by the upper right dot. The lower left dot (d) designates the "class" or 'characteristics' of the capacitor and deals with *Q* factor, insulation resistance, capacitance drift with change in temperature, and methods of testing. For this purpose capacitors are divided into seven classifications (*A*, *B*, *C*, *I*, *D*, *J* and *E*). For details of the characteristics of each class refer to *RMA STANDARD REC*-115, September 1948.

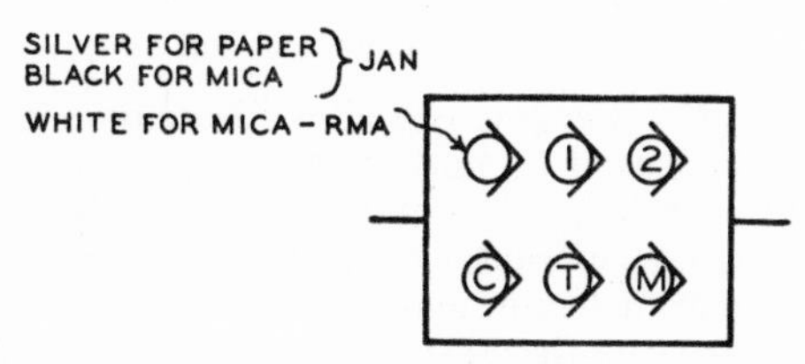

Fig. A-10. JAN and RMA (1948) capacitor color code.

A 6-dot color code may therefore refer to the 1938 RMA, 1948 RMA or JAN standards. This should not cause confusion if you note the color of the upper left dot. Black or silver could only mean JAN system, whereas a white dot would indicate the 1948 RMA system. Any other color in this location would definitely imply use of the 1938 RMA standard.

Tubular paper capacitors. This type of capacitor is coded with narrow bands, reading from left toward center. The first three bands indicate capacitance value to two significant figures—the third band being the multiplier. In this respect the coding and color values are similar to the 3-dot RMA system. The fourth band designates tolerance as follows:

Green	±5%	Black	±20%
White	±10%	Orange	±30%
Yellow	±40%		

Voltage ratings up to 900 volts are denoted by the fifth color band in accordance to the RMA color code. Ratings above 900 volts are designated by two bands (5th and 6th) using the RMA significant figure values (× 100). For example:

(a) 1000 volts:

brown band (1) and black band (0) = 1 − 0 × 100 = 1000.

(b) 1600 volts:

brown band (1) and blue band (6) $= 1 - 6 \times 100 = 1600$.

This system is shown in Fig. A-11a.

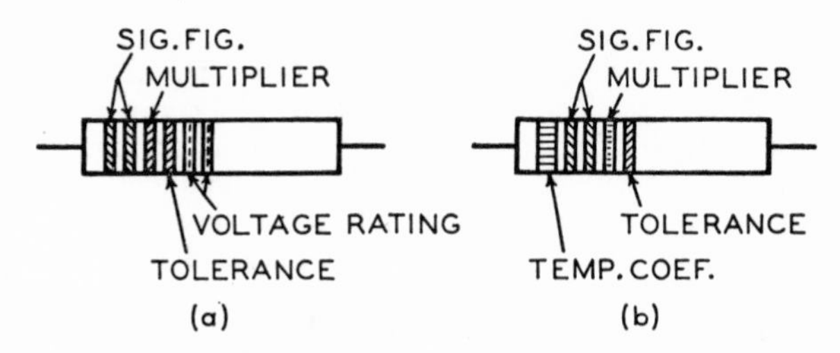

Fig. A-11. Color coding for tubular paper and ceramic capacitors.

Ceramic capacitors. Ceramic capacitors use either dots or bands as designators. The first band (or dot) at the left is made wider. Reading from left to right, the designators are: temperature coefficient, first significant figure, second significant figure, multiplier, and tolerance. The colors used for significant figures and multiplier have the same values as shown in the table above for the other type of capacitors. The temperature coefficient and tolerance coding is shown below.

Color	Temp. Coef.*	Tolerance, Per Cent	
		10 $\mu\mu$f and over	Under 10 $\mu\mu$f
Black	0	±20	±2.0
Brown	− 30	± 1	±0.1
Red	− 80	± 2	±0.2
Orange	−150		
Yellow	−220		
Green	−330	± 5	±0.5
Blue	−470		
Violet	−750		
Gray	+ 30		±0.25
White	+500	±10	±1.0

* Temperature coefficients are expressed in 10^{-6} $\mu\mu$f per $\mu\mu$f per degree centigrade, or parts per million per degree centigrade.

Index

D

E

F

G

H

I